WORKBOOK TO ACCOMPANY

logic

WORKBOOK TO ACCOMPANY

logic

ROBERT BAUM
RENSSELAER POLYTECHNIC INSTITUTE

HOLT, RINEHART AND WINSTON

NEW YORK   CHICAGO SAN FRANCISCO ATLANTA DALLAS MONTREAL TORONTO LONDON SYDNEY

Project Editors: Nicholas L. Falletta
William F. Briel
Design and composition: Allen Wayne Technical Corporation
Copyright © 1975 by Holt, Rinehart and Winston
All rights reserved
Printed in the United States of America
ISBN: 0-03-013381-5
 678 008 9876543

CONTENTS

160
B347l
workbook
c.2

PREFACE

The purpose of this workbook is to help the student master the key concepts of logic and gain practice in working out problems therein. It is designed principally as a supplement to the textbook *Logic*, by Robert Baum, but is complete enough to be used independently as a text-workbook if so desired.

Organization of the Workbook
Like the textbook, the workbook contains twelve chapters grouped in four main sections, dealing respectively with syllogistic logic, symbolic logic, induction, and the uses of logic in ordinary language. A preliminary introduction reviews the concepts of 'argument,' the sentence/statement distinction, and deductive versus inductive reasoning. For each chapter there is a comprehensive summary, reviewing all major concepts in greater detail than in the end-of-chapter summaries in the textbook. New examples are brought in to illustrate the concepts, in order to shed light on the material from as many different angles as possible.

Extensive exercises are also provided—frequently of the same types as in the textbook, but in some cases quite different. As in the text, the exercises are drawn from a variety of sources as wide and challenging as the uses of logic in real life. Answers are given for all exercises except the few discussion questions for which specific answers are impossible.

How to Use the Workbook
Each student will no doubt find his or her own way to make best use of this material. In general, it is suggested that you read the text assignments first, think about them, and then work out all the exercise problems in the textbook. By the time you have checked your answers to these latter, you will know what areas need additional work. You can then concentrate on these areas, in both reading and exercises, in the workbook.

In addition, you may find the workbook useful for review before exams. For this purpose, it will probably be most helpful to reread the workbook summaries first, for a general overview, and then return to the textbook to check any details about which you are uncertain. However you elect to use the workbook, you should remember that it is an aid, not an end in itself, and you are free to treat it accordingly.

intro-
duc-
tion

Defining Logic

Defining logic is not a simple task. Some people have maintained that logic is the study of the laws of thought. This definition is problematic since it includes many mental activities such as daydreaming and imagining which are outside the domain of logic; logicians are only concerned with the one type of thinking known as reasoning. Other people have maintained that logic is the study of the laws of reasoning. However, this definition might cause one to confuse logic with the discipline of psychology, because of the different meanings of the word 'law.' Psychology is concerned with **descriptive laws** of reasoning; that is, it seeks to describe the way people reason. Logic is concerned with **prescriptive laws** of reasoning; that is, it seeks to set standards for the ways in which people *ought* to reason if they wish to reason well. As a prescriptive discipline, logic attempts to provide criteria for evaluating the processes of reasoning which are used to make inferences and reach conclusions as well as techniques for applying these criteria to concrete arguments.

Recognizing an Argument

As used in logic, the term **'argument'** refers to a set of statements, one of which is designated as a conclusion and the remainder of which are asserted as being true and as offering evidence that supports or implies the conclusion. This definition assumes a distinction between statements and sentences. A **sentence** is a physical and linguistic entity which can be used to convey meaning and perform a variety of tasks in different contexts. A **statement** is not a sentence; it is an assertion, description, or piece of information about which it can properly be said that it is true or false. The following points about the sentence/statement distinction are important.

1. The context in which a sentence is uttered rather than its grammatical structure is the best clue to determining whether or not it is being used to express a statement. The function which a sentence performs—for example, conveying information, asking a question, issuing a command, making an exclamation—is not invariably related to its grammatical structure. Statements are most obviously expressed by declarative sentences, but not all declarative sentences express statements, and imperative, interrogative, and exclamatory sentences may be used to express statements in certain contexts.
2. Different statements can be expressed by the same sentence. For example, "This is a lovely city" might be used to express a statement about San Francisco, Chicago, New York, London, or Paris, depending on where the speaker is at the time the sentence is uttered.
3. Different sentences may be used to express the same statement. For example, the sentences, "My aunt's pen is on my uncle's table," "The pen of my aunt is on the table of my uncle," and "La plume de ma tante est sur la table de mon oncle," all express the same statement, if uttered by the same person in the same context.

Exercise 1

In most ordinary contexts, would each of the following sentences be more likely to express a statement, a question, a command, or an exclamation? Check the boxes under **S** for statements, **Q** for questions, **C** for commands, and **E** for exclamations.

	S	Q	C	E
1. Be sure to sign your tax return before mailing it.	☐	☐	☐	☐
2. Are you going to go to the basketball game tonight?	☐	☐	☐	☐
3. Lorenzo de Medici lived in the fifteenth century.	☐	☐	☐	☐
4. Get out of here!	☐	☐	☐	☐
5. Aha!	☐	☐	☐	☐
6. Gather ye rosebuds while ye may.	☐	☐	☐	☐
7. Who was the twenty-third president of the United States?	☐	☐	☐	☐
8. Why did this have to happen to me?	☐	☐	☐	☐
9. Who says I'm not a good poker player?	☐	☐	☐	☐
10. It's Greek to me.	☐	☐	☐	☐
11. More than half a million human beings speak Mandarin Chinese.	☐	☐	☐	☐
12. Do you mean to tell me that you still haven't taken out the garbage?	☐	☐	☐	☐
13. What time is it?	☐	☐	☐	☐
14. If you touch my little brother again, you're going to end up with a mouth full of loose teeth!	☐	☐	☐	☐
15. The best laid plans of mice and men will oft times go astray.	☐	☐	☐	☐

Exercise 2

Each of the following is a nondeclarative sentence. (a) Does each sentence probably express a statement in the context indicated? (b) If so, formulate a declarative sentence which could be used to express the same statement.

1. *Context:* One student to another student in the hallway. The student speaking has been trying to avoid Professor Brown, because she owes him a term paper. She has just seen Professor Brown walking down the hall towards her.
   Sentence: Oh, no!
2. *Context:* Spoken by a student in an algebra class to the teacher.
   Sentence: How did you get "$3x = -7$" from "$3x + 10 = 3$"?
3. *Context:* Prosecutor to jury at a treason trial.
   Sentence: What penalty can be too great for a man who would dare to betray his native land to its avowed enemies?

4. *Context:* Two college students to another college student.
   Sentence: Come on along and see some Charlie Chaplin films with us.
5. *Context:* One friend talking on the phone to another.
   Sentence: John and Joan make a nice couple, don't they?

Premises and Conclusions
The first step in evaluating an argument is to identify the premise(s) and conclusion which comprise it. Identification of the premise(s) and conclusion may be facilitated by the presence of indicator words. Common ones include:

> *Conclusion Indicators:* thus, accordingly, it follows that, implies that, therefore, hence
> *Premise Indicators:* since, because, for, given that, due to, insofar as, inasmuch as, in view of, as shown by, can be inferred from

Premise(s) and conclusion do not occur in any particular order within arguments, nor do they always contain indicator words. In such cases, the identification of a particular statement as a conclusion or premise is dependent upon the context and the relationship of the sentences in the argument to each other.

Exercise 3
Identify (a) the conclusion and (b) the premise(s) of each of the following arguments.

1. The defendant is insane. Therefore, he is not guilty.
2. Some mammals can fly, since bats can fly.
3. That is not a good French dictionary, because it does not show how each word should be pronounced.
4. The flu is caused by a virus, consequently it can't be cured with antibiotics.
5. This figure is a pentagon, so the sum of its interior angles is 540 degrees.
6. It will take two seconds for that rock to fall, since it is going to fall a distance of sixty-four feet.
7. Coffee keeps people awake, hence it must contain a stimulant.
8. Since Mr. Scott is a judge, it follows that he is a lawyer.
9. The housing bill will never come to a vote on the floor of Congress, since the opposition has enough votes to kill it in committee.
10. That this solution is an acid can be inferred from the fact that it turns litmus paper red.
11. Tom will not be able to go to the New Year's Eve party at the club, due to the fact that he is not a member.
12. Composers do not have to be able to hear music in order to write it, as can be shown by the fact that Beethoven was deaf.

13. Starvation will inevitably occur somewhere in the world, inasmuch as the expanding world population will eventually increase beyond the capacity of the total world agricultural resources to feed it.
14. Oil is becoming more expensive and plastics are made from oil, therefore plastics are becoming more expensive.
15. As a body approaches the speed of light, its mass becomes infinite. Therefore, it cannot travel faster than the speed of light, since an infinite force would be needed to accelerate it.

Problems in Recognizing an Argument

Arguments may be difficult to identify for several reasons. Among the most common problems in recognizing an argument are:

1. A series of statements may be asserted as true (one of the prerequisites of an argument) but may not offer a conclusion or provide support for one. In other words, a series of sentences expressing statements may simply constitute exposition.
2. A type of statement which is especially apt to be mistaken for an argument is the **conditional**. A conditional (If . . . then . . .) statement is a single complex proposition which is not an argument but which may be used as part of an argument.

   Example:
   If you drink milk, you will have healthy teeth.

   The error people often make in interpreting a conditional statement as an argument is to divide the sentence into what seems to be a premise statement ("you drink milk") and a conclusion statement ("you will have healthy teeth"). However, the only thing which is being asserted by a conditional statement is that a particular relationship holds between the two components of the sentence: if the first component is true, then the second component also will be true. It is *not* being asserted that the antecedent is, in fact, true.

3. There may be no indicator words present in an argument, thereby making it difficult to recognize. Then, too, indicator words are sometimes present when no argument exists. Also, some indicator words have more than one meaning and do not always function to identify premises or conclusions. For example, 'because' sometimes indicates a causal relation between events described by two statements rather than indicating that the second is a premise.
4. Many arguments are not fully stated; the conclusion and/or one or more of the premises may be left out. Such arguments are called *enthymemes.*

   Example:
   All dogs are mammals.
   Therefore, Fido is a mammal.

The missing premise in this example is 'Fido is a dog.' A general rule of thumb for supplying missing premises is to add whatever premises are needed to make the argument as good as possible. The rule is sometimes referred to as the **principle of charity**.

5. Whenever attempting to identify an argument, particular care should always be paid to the context in which the sentences are uttered. This is especially crucial when supplying missing premise(s) and/or conclusion in an argument.

One other important distinction relating to identifying arguments is that between arguments and inferences. **Inference** is the psychological process of moving from one thought to another presumably related thought.

Example:
A person looks up at the sky, observes that it is cloudy, and makes the assertion, 'It probably will rain today.'

An inference is not an argument, but an argument can be constructed that corresponds to any inference. The argument corresponding to this inference is:

In most instances in the past, if it was cloudy, then it rained.
It is cloudy today.
Therefore, it will probably rain today.

Exercise 4
Examine each sentence or group of sentences given below. (a) Assuming ordinary context, would each sentence or group normally be used to express an argument? (b) If not, why not? If so, identify the conclusion and premise(s).

1. If a television set is completely transistorized, then a picture will appear immediately after the switch is turned on.
2. If you want a ride to Chicago for Thanksgiving, give Joan a call.
3. Logic is distinct from psychology for logic deals with prescriptive laws whereas psychology deals with descriptive laws.
4. Of course, you are an idealist. All Sagittarians are idealists.
5. French is called a romance language because it is derived from Latin.
6. Don't use that book when you write your paper because Professor Brown doesn't agree with the person who wrote it.
7. President Nixon was impeachable because he was involved in obstruction of justice.
8. Your car was losing power because one of the spark plug wires had come loose.
9. That dime is dated 1947. And all dimes dated 1964 or earlier are made of silver.
10. The United States has always been governed by a president, Congress, and Supreme Court since it first came into existence as a nation.

11. The United States has always been governed by a president, Congress, and Supreme Court, inasmuch as that is the form of government specified in the Constitution.
12. That could not have been Helen you met last night. Helen has short brown hair.
13. If a rock is quartz, it will scratch glass.
14. If a rock is quartz, it will scratch glass. This rock is made of quartz. Therefore, it will scratch glass.
15. If a rock is quartz, it will scratch glass. This rock will not scratch glass, so it can't be quartz.
16. Since the turn of the century, commencement exercises were held on Wednesday afternoons. In the late sixties, administrators changed that date to Saturday, possibly because of a desire for better attendance.

Deductive Arguments

There are two types of argument: deductive and inductive. **A valid deductive argument** can be defined as one in which:

> *if* the premises are true, then the conclusion *must* be true; that is, it is *impossible* for all of the premises to be true and the conclusion false; or,
> the conclusion is *contained* in the premises.

The following are examples of valid deductive arguments:

Examples:
1. The Leaning Tower of Pisa is in Spain.
   Spain is in Africa.
   Africa is in the Northern Hemisphere.
   Therefore, the Leaning Tower of Pisa is in the Northern Hemisphere.
2. If Mickey Rooney is 8 feet tall, he is the tallest man in the world.
   Mickey Rooney is 8 feet tall.
   Therefore, he is the tallest man in the world.
3. Plato was a Greek.
   Plato was a philosopher.
   Therefore, some Greeks were philosophers.

All of these arguments are valid, although one contains false premises and a true conclusion, one contains false premises and a false conclusion, and one contains true premises and a true conclusion. The only situation ruled out by the definition of validity is one in which a false conclusion is asserted to follow from true premises. In short, if an argument is deductively valid, then if its premises are true, its conclusion must also be true. One significant additional characteristic of a valid deductive argument is that its premises provide *absolute* support for the conclusion. In other words, for any valid deductive argument, given that the original premises are true, the addition of any information whatsoever to this set of premises will not affect the truth of the conclusion.

The validity of a deductive argument is determined by its logical *form*, rather than its content. It is possible to demonstrate the invalidity of an argument or argument form by means of a counterexample. In constructing a **counterexample**, one keeps the same argument form but changes the factual content in such a way as to make all of the premises of the argument true and the conclusion false.

Example:
Some women are redheads.
Lucille Ball is a woman.
Therefore, Lucille Ball is a redhead.

Counterexample:
Some foreign automobiles cost more than $20,000.
The Volkswagen bug is a foreign made automobile.
Therefore, the Volkswagen bug costs more than $20,000.

Exercise 5
Each of the following deductive arguments is invalid. Provide a counterexample for each.

1. No sculptures are paintings.
   No tapestries are paintings.
   Therefore, no tapestries are sculptures.
2. All marigolds are plants.
   All flowers are plants.
   Therefore, all marigolds are flowers.
3. If you studied hard, then you got an A in logic.
   You got an A in logic.
   Therefore, you studied hard.
4. If you studied hard, then you got an A in logic.
   You did not study hard.
   Therefore, you did not get an A in logic.
5. Some Greeks are philosophers.
   Socrates was a Greek.
   Therefore, Socrates was a philosopher.
6. All industrialists are rich.
   Henry Ford was rich.
   Therefore, Henry Ford was an industrialist.
7. Some foods are sweet.
   Some berries are foods.
   Therefore, some berries are sweet.

8. Some businessmen are not Americans.
   Therefore, some Americans are not businessmen.
9. Bronze is a metal.
   Bronze is made of copper and tin.
   Therefore, copper is a metal and tin is a metal.
10. Orange juice is a delicious drink.
    Pineapple juice is a delicious drink.
    Therefore, orange-pineapple juice is a delicious drink.

Inductive Arguments

An inductive argument is any argument which is not deductively valid; that is, the premises of an inductive argument do not provide absolute support for its conclusion. This obviously includes a wide range of arguments—from those whose premises provide very strong but not absolute support for the conclusion to those whose premises provide no support at all for the conclusion. All inductive arguments are such that the addition of new premises to the original set of premises can affect the support given to the truth of the conclusion.

It has been said frequently that in deductive arguments a person reasons from general to particular, whereas in inductive arguments one reasons from particular to general. Such a distinction is fallacious. It is quite possible to have an inductive argument with general premises and a particular conclusion, or particular premises and a particular conclusion in addition to one which has particular premises and a general conclusion. The following are examples of inductive arguments.

Examples:
1. Rufus is a dog and has a tail.
   Fido is a dog and has a tail.
   Sydney is a dog and has a tail.
   Elizabeth is a dog and has a tail.
   Therefore, probably all dogs have tails.
2. Animal A is a fiddler crab and burrows a hole in the sand.
   Animal B is a fiddler crab and burrows a hole in the sand.
   Animal C is a fiddler crab and burrows a hole in the sand.
   Animal D is a fiddler crab.
   Therefore, Animal D probably burrows a hole in the sand.
3. All life in earth is carbon-based.
   Therefore, probably all life everywhere in the universe is carbon-based.

Exercise 6

Examine each argument below, assuming that each premise is true. (a) Is the argument inductive or deductive. (b) Explain your answer.

1. John's birthday is exactly one week after Marsha's birthday. Marsha's birthday is March 11th. Therefore, John's birthday is March 18.
2. $3x + y = 10$ and $y = 4$, therefore $x = 2$.

3. Bob and Kay both have blue eyes. Therefore, the child they are expecting will have blue eyes.

4. John must have a toothache again. He is not looking very cheerful.

5. The electric company says that if the demand for electricity continues to grow at the present rate, a new power station must be operational by 1980. Therefore, construction must start immediately.

6. No Vulcans are Cligons. Mr. Spock is a Vulcan. Therefore, he is not a Cligon.

7. Since three-fifths of the state's registered voters are three-fifths Republican, state senator Elfon, who is the Republican candidate for governor, will most likely be elected.

8. One of these statements must be false, because if two statements contradict each other, they both cannot be true, and these two statements do contradict each other.

9. Bill is a Sagittarian, so his birthday is in December.

10. Bill is a Sagittarian, therefore, he is impulsive.

11. The average college educated person has a higher yearly income than the national average. Helen has a college education, so her yearly income is above the national average.

12. No species of animal observed to date except man is capable of rational thought. Therefore, man is the only rational animal.

Criteria for Good Deductive Arguments

A good deductive argument, one whose conclusion can be trusted to be true, is said to be sound. To be **sound**, a deductive argument must satisfy three conditions: it must be valid; the truth of all its premises must be reasonably well established; and it must not be circular.

Example:
The Fountain of Trevi is in Rome.
Rome is in Italy.
Therefore, the Fountain of Trevi is in Italy.

Ordinarily, the logician has no special qualifications to decide if the proposition expressed by a particular statement is true or false. In any case, our primary concern when examining a deductive argument is determining whether or not it is valid. However, it is sometimes necessary to consider the question of truth or falsity when supplying a missing premise or premises in an enthymeme. The **principal of charity** stipulates that one should supply premises which make the argument as good as possible; that is, premises which make the argument sound. However, in some situations it is difficult to adhere to the principal of charity, since we are sometimes confronted with a choice of adding well established true premises that will make an argument valid or adding questionable premises that will make an argument invalid. As logicians it is more appropriate that we add those premises that will make the argument valid, since our expertise is with determining validity rather than establishing truth. However, there are some situations in which adding a premise whose truth is well established does not result in a deductively valid argument but rather a strong inductive argument. In such cases, it is probably better to choose the interpretation that results in the strong inductive argument with premises whose truth are quite well established rather than the validly deductive argument with false or highly questionable premises.

Exercise 7
Each of the following arguments is an enthymeme. Identify (a) the conclusion and (b) the premise(s) of the argument (c) Supply a missing premise that would make the argument *deductively valid.*

1. That is not a rose bush because it doesn't have thorns.
2. *Rhoda* is a television series, so naturally it is childish.
3. That is a conifer because it is a pine tree.
4. All metaphysicians are eccentric, so Karl is eccentric.
5. Gregory is not a Turkish Cypriot, there he is a Greek Cypriot.
6. If the demand for sugar exceeds the supply, the price of sugar will go up. Therefore, the price of sugar will go up.
7. Senator Brandt is a major party candidate and he is not a Republican. Therefore, he is a Democrat.
8. All trees are plants and all oaks are trees. Therefore, all oaks are living things.

Criteria for Good Inductive Arguments
Neither the term 'sound' nor the term 'valid' is appropriately applied to inductive arguments. By their nature inductive arguments are more difficult to evaluate than deductive ones, since the premises do not provide absolute support for their conclusions. Of course, the truth of the premises of a good inductive argument must be reasonably well established. Other than that, we must consider the relative strength of support which the set of premises provides for the truth of the conclusion. Unlike a deductive argument, an inductive argument can be strengthened or weakened by the addition of further premises.

Example:
All swans I have observed are white.
Therefore, all swans are white.

Stronger:
All swans I have observed have been white.
All swans observed by all of my friends have been white.
Therefore, all swans are white.

Weaker:
All swans I have observed are white.
I have observed only one swan.
Therefore, all swans are white.

Exercise 8
Assuming ordinary context, evaluate each of the following inductive arguments. Identify (a) the conclusion and (b) the premise(s). (c) Add a premise that will make the argument stronger. (d) Add a premise that would make the argument weaker.

1. I liked the 1969 Beaujolais wine that I drank.
   I liked the 1970 Beaujolais wine that I drank.
   I liked the 1971 Beaujolais wine that I drank.
   Therefore, I will like the 1972 Beaujolais wine that I am going to drink.
2. Sluggo Jones has hit more home runs this season than any other player on the team. Therefore, he is likely to hit a home run today.
3. There has been an outbreak of the Asian flu in the U.S. this month. You are more likely to catch the flu than I am because I have had a flu vaccination but you have not.
4. The guests our family has to dinner always like my mother's pot roasts. The Karlans are coming to dinner and my mother is serving pot roast. Therefore, the Karlans will like her pot roast.
5. Most east coast newspaper editors are liberals. Mr. Harrison is an east coast newspaper editor. Therefore, Mr. Harrison is probably liberal.
6. The automobile as we know it will eventually have to be replaced with other means of transportation, since at the present rate of consumption, the known world petroleum reserves will be exhausted by 2005.

1. categorical statements

Categorical Statements
Categorical statements are propositions which assert that part or all of the class of things named by the subject term is included in or excluded from the class of things named by the predicate term. According to the Aristotelian interpretation, the class of things referred to by the subject term must contain at least one member in order for a statement to qualify as categorical.

A categorical statement can be described in terms of quality and quantity. The **quality** of a categorical statement is determined by the inclusion or exclusion of the members of the subject class in the predicate class. A statement which asserts that all or part of the subject class is included in the predicate class is said to be **affirmative** in quality; whereas a statement which asserts that all or part of the subject class is excluded from the predicate is said to be **negative** in quality. The **quantity** of a categorical statement is determined by whether *all* or some of the members of the subject class are referred to by the subject term. A statement which refers to all the members of the subject class is said to be **universal** in quantity; whereas a statement which explicitly refers to at least one of the members of the subject class is **particular** in quality. There are four types of categorical statement:

1. **Universal affirmative statements**, also called **A** statements, affirm that all members of the subject class are included in the predicate class.

   Example:
   All dogs are animals.

2. **Particular affirmative statements**, also known as **I** statements, affirm that at least one member of the subject class is included in the predicate class.

   Example:
   Some animals are dogs.

3. **Universal negative statements**, or **E** statements, affirm that all members of the subject class are excluded from the predicate class.

   Example:
   No reptiles are dogs.

4. **Particular negative statements**, or **O** statements, affirm that at least one member of the subject class is excluded from the predicate class.

   Example:
   Some animals are not reptiles.

Exercise 1-1

Check the appropriate box, indicating whether each of the following sentences expresses an **A, E, I, O** statement.

	A	E	I	O
1. All typewriters are noisy.	☐	☐	☐	☐
2. Some days are not sunny.	☐	☐	☐	☐
3. No man is an island.	☐	☐	☐	☐
4. Some Frenchmen are Parisians.	☐	☐	☐	☐
5. Dolphins are all cetaceans.	☐	☐	☐	☐
6. Some dolphins are not cetaceans.	☐	☐	☐	☐
7. All seals have a smooth coat of fur.	☐	☐	☐	☐
8. No seals have a smooth coat of fur.	☐	☐	☐	☐
9. Some books are heavy.	☐	☐	☐	☐
10. Nobody waved goodby.	☐	☐	☐	☐

Standard Form Sentences

Categorical statements may be expressed in a variety of different ways. For the sake of convenience, logicians use a standard form sentence to express each of the four types of categorical statement. A **standard form sentence** contains a quantifier (either 'all' or 'some'), a noun, modified noun, or noun clause as its subject term; a present tense form of the verb 'to be' called the **copula**; and a noun, modified noun, or noun clause as its predicate term. Standard form sentences can be referred to as **A, E, I** or **O** sentences, depending on the type of categorical statement normally expressed by sentences with that form.

Examples:

All men are mammals.	(Standard form **A** sentence)
Some animals are men.	(Standard form **I** sentence)
No men are animals.	(Standard form **E** sentence)
Some animals are not men.	(Standard form **O** sentence)

Standard form sentences can be abbreviated by replacing the subject and predicate terms with capital letters, usually taken from the principal words in each term. The **abbreviation** of a standard form sentence expresses a statement that is true or false, just as the original sentence does. Whenever abbreviating a standard form sentence, one should provide a dictionary, indicating the term which a particular letter represents. This can be done by underlining the appropriate letters in the original sentence.

Example:

| All dogs are animals. | (Standard form **A** sentence) |
| All D are A. | (Abbreviation) |

Each type of categorical statement has its own schema which is used to exhibit the logical form of the statement. The **schema** of each type of categorical statement is formed by removing both the subject and predicate terms and retaining only the quantifier and copula. Then the letters S and P, underscored to indicate that each represents a blank for which a noun or noun clause may be substituted, are appropriately inserted. The schema of a categorical statement does not express a statement which is true or false. The following are the schemata for the four different types of categorical statement:

All S are P.	(A statement schema)
Some S are P.	(I statement schema)
No S are P.	(E statement schema)
Some S are not P	(O statement schema)

Translating into Standard Form
Particular care must be taken when translating ordinary language sentences into standard form. The following are examples for study.

Examples:
Original: Every student in the class passed the examination.
Standard form: All students in the class are persons who passed the examination.

Original: All the flowers near the window are growing nicely.
Standard form: All flowers that are near the window are things that are growing nicely.

Original: Many voters in the district are liberals.
Standard form: Some voters in the district are persons who are liberal.

Original: Anyone who can't read should be ineligible to vote.
Standard form: All persons who cannot read are persons who should be ineligible to vote.

When translating sentences into standard form, it is worthwhile to keep the four types of statement schemata in mind in addition to the following rules of thumb.

1. Make certain that both the subject and predicate term contain a noun or noun clause.
2. Make certain that a present tense form of the verb 'to be' appears.
3. Statements expressed by sentences with terms such as 'only,' or 'none but' are **exclusive** statements. Sentences expressing exclusive statements should be translated into standard form **A** sentences, by reversing the subject and predicate terms.

Example:
Original: None but a madman is capable of doing that.
Standard form: All persons capable of doing that are madmen.

(Note: Statements expressed by sentences beginning with the term 'the only' are not exclusive.)

4. Sentences expressing either singular affirmative statements or singular negative statements should be translated into standard form **A** or **E** sentences respectively.

Examples:
Original: John is a college graduate.
Standard form: All persons who are members of the class of which John is the only person are college graduates.

Original: Mary is not a member of the club.
Standard form: No persons that are members of the class of which Mary is the only member are members of the club.

5. **Exceptive sentences** are complex sentences which in ordinary contexts usually express two statements. Sentences which contain quantifiers such as 'almost all' and 'not quite all' express exceptive statements, and should be translated into standard form **I** and **O** sentences.

Example:
Original: Almost all of the ticketholders demanded their money back.
Standard form: 'Some ticketholders are persons who demanded their money back' *and* 'Some ticketholders are not persons who demanded their money back.'

Sentences which begin with quantifiers such as 'all but,' 'all except,' or '_____ alone' express exceptive statements and should be translated into standard form **A** and **E** statements.

Example:
Original: All except the teachers knew cheating had taken place.
Standard form: 'All nonteachers are persons that knew cheating had taken place' and 'No teachers are persons who knew that cheating had taken place.'

6. When translating ordinary language sentences into standard form, careful attention should be paid to the context in which the sentence is being used. If the context does not provide enough information to clearly indicate which type of statement is being expressed, then the sentence should be translated in its weakest sentence. For example, if a sentence seems to express either

an **E** or an **O** statement, and the context does not clearly indicate which, the sentence should be translated into a standard form O sentence.

Example:
Original: All instructors are not geniuses.
Standard form: Some instructors are not geniuses.

One must be particularly careful when translating sentences that contain quantifiers such as 'Not all,' 'Almost all,' 'Not quite everyone,' and 'All but a few.' Such sentences generally express two statements.

Exercise 1-2
(a) If necessary, translate the following sentences into standard form. (b) Indicate whether each expresses an **A, E, I** or **O** statement. (c) Write an abbreviation for each sentence. (Be sure to underline letters in the subject and the predicate of the sentence to show what the letters used in the abbreviation represent.) (d) Write the schema for each statement.

1. All Frenchmen are Europeans.
2. No ponderosas are shrubs.
3. Some sailors are swarthy.
4. Some hives do not have bees.
5. Kraters are Greek vases.
6. Panama hats are made in Equador.
7. Many fans are not machines.
8. Almost all paperbacks are inexpensive.
9. Only members of the club are invited.
10. All but automotive unions have settled

Venn Diagrams and Categorical Statements
The logical form of each of the four types of categorical statement can be displayed by means of Venn diagrams. When constructing Venn diagrams, the following principles apply:

1. Two overlapping circles are used to represent the classes of things referred to by the subject and predicate terms of the categorical statement.
2. If an area of a circle is shaded, this indicates that it is empty; that is, the class that it represents contains no members.
3. If an 'X' appears in an area of a circle, then the designated class contains at least one member.
4. If an 'X' appears on a line between two circles, one or the other of the designated classes contains at least one member, but it is undetermined which class it is. An 'X' on a line does *not* mean that *both* classes contain members, although it does not rule out this possibility.

5. The circles representing the subject and predicate classes of a categorical statement are placed within a rectangle which represents the universe of discourse. It is possible and sometimes desirable to limit the universe of discourse to a specific class such as the class of all physical objects or the class of all human beings, but we stipulate in this book that the universe of discourse is everything that exists—both physical and nonphysical. The area inside the rectangle and outside of both circles represents the class of all things which are not contained in either or both of the two classes referred to by the subject and predicate terms of the categorical statement.

On the Aristotelian interpretation (which stipulates that the class of things referred to by the subject term must contain at least one member), the Venn diagrams for the different types of categorical statement are:

Universal Affirmative Statement: All S are P.

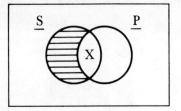

A: All S are P.

Universal Negative Statement: No S are P.

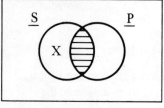

E: No S is P.

Particular Affirmative Statement: Some S are P.

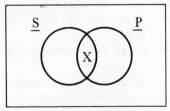

I: Some S are P.

Particular Negative Statement: Some S̲ are not P̲.

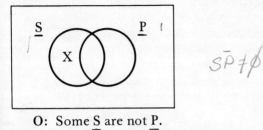

$S\bar{P} \neq \emptyset$

O: Some S̲ are not P̲.

Exercise 1-3
(a) If necessary, translate each of the following sentences into standard form.
(b) Write an abbreviation for each sentence. (Be sure to provide a dictionary, indicating what each letter represents.) (c) Write the schema for each. (d) Fill in the Venn diagram for each.

1. Some dogs are pets.

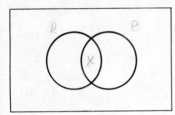

2. All oaks are hardwoods.

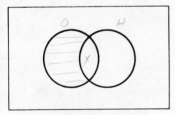

3. No termites are ants.

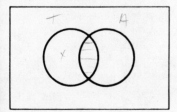

4. Some nebulae are not galaxies.

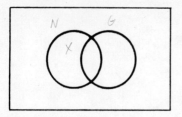

5. All harpies are mythological.

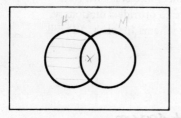

6. Some dancers can charleston.

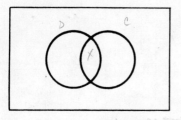

7. No behaviorists tolerate idle speculation.

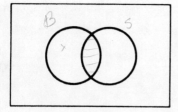

8. Only citizens can vote.

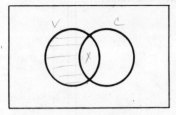

All people who can vote are citizens (handwritten)

9. Almost all art collectors are rich.

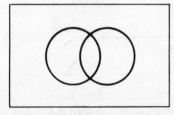

Two ideas (handwritten)
Some are rich ... *Some are not* (handwritten)

10. All except exceptive statements are easy to translate into standard form.

all nonexceptive statements are easy to translate ... *No exceptive statements are easy to translate* (handwritten)

All non S are P ... *No S are P* (handwritten)

Immediate Inferences and the Traditional Square of Opposition

An **immediate inference** occurs when a conclusion is drawn from exactly one premise.

Example:
All men are mammals. (Premise)
Therefore, some men are mammals. (Conclusion)

Assuming that each of the four types of categorical statement have the same subject and predicate terms, certain truth relationships exist among these different statements. On the Aristotelian interpretation which assumes that the class of things referred to by the subject term contains at least one member, a variety of kinds of valid immediate inference can be exhibited by means of what is called the traditional square of opposition.

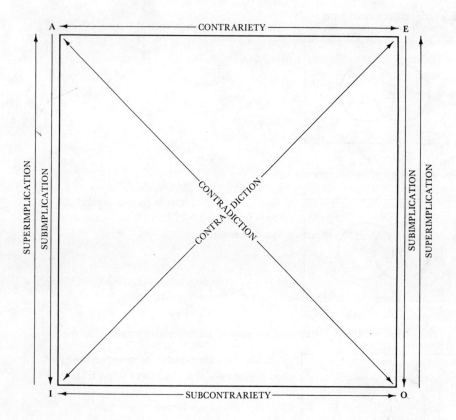

Contradictory propositions are categorical statements with the same subject and predicate term which are related in such a way that if one is true then the other must be false, and if one is false then the other must be true. On the Aristotelian interpretation, **A** and **O** propositions and **E** and **I** propositions are contradictories.

Examples:

All men are mammals. **(A)**   No soft drinks are ales. **(E)**
Some men are not mammals. **(O)**   Some soft drinks are ales. **(I)**

Contrary propositions are categorical statements with the same subject and predicate terms which are related in such a way that both cannot be true at the same time, but both may be false. On the Aristotelian interpretation, **A** and **E** statements are contraries.

Example:

All men are rational animals. **(A)**
No men are rational animals. **(E)**

Subcontrary propositions are categorical statements with the same subject and predicate terms which are related in such a way that both cannot be false, but both may be true. On the Aristotelian interpretation, **I** and **O** propositions are subcontraries.

Example:
Some men are rational animals. (**I**)
Some men are not rational animals. (**O**)

Subimplication, sometimes called **subalternation**, is the process by which the truth of a particular statement is inferred from the truth of its corresponding universal statement. From the truth of **A** and **E** statements (called **superimplicants** or **superalterns**), it is possible to infer the truth of **I** and **O** statements respectively (called **subimplicants** or **subalterns**).

Examples:

All men are rational animals (**A**)	No dogs are reptiles. (**E**)
Some men are rational animals. (**I**)	Some dogs are not reptiles. (**O**)

Superimplication, or **superalternation**, is the process by which the falsity of a universal statement is inferred from the falsity of its corresponding particular statement. On the Aristotelian interpretation, it is possible to infer the falsity of an **A** statement from the falsity of an **I** statement and the falsity of an **E** statement from the falsity of an **O** statement.

The following table presents a summary of the immediate inferences that can be made from each type of categorical statement on the basis of the traditional square of opposition.

If **A** *is true*	*If* **E** *is true*	*If* **I** *is true*	*If* **O** *is true*
E is false	A is false	E is false	A is false
I is true	I is false	A is undetermined	E is undetermined
O is false	O is true	O is determined	I is undetermined

If **A** *is false*	*If* **E** *is false*	*If* **I** *is false*	*If* **O** *is false*
O is true	I is true	A is false	E is false
E is undetermined	A is undetermined	E is true	A is true
I is undetermined	O is undetermined	O is true	I is true

Exercise 1-4
Below you will find pairs of categorical statements. (a) Identify the relationship that exists between each pair. Is the relationship one of contradiction, contrariety, subcontrariety, subimplication or superimplication or none of these? (b) Assuming that the first statement of each pair is true, what can be inferred about the truth value of the second statement? (c) Assuming that the first state-

ment is false, what can be inferred about the truth value of the second statement?

1. All judges are lawyers.
   No judges are lawyers.
2. Some judges are lawyers.
   Some judges are not lawyers.
3. No wagons are motor vehicles.
   Some wagons are not motor vehicles.
4. Some books are not dictionaries.
   No books are dictionaries.
5. Some wagons are not motor vehicles.
   All wagons are motor vehicles.
6. No shrews are rodents.
   Some shrews are rodents.
7. No shrews are rodents.
   All shrews are rodents.
8. Some books are dictionaries.
   All books are dictionaries.
9. Some books are not dictionaries.
   Some books are dictionaries.
10. Some judges are not lawyers.
    All judges are lawyers.

Consistency and Independence

Two statements are said to be logically **consistent** if it is logically possible for both to be true at the same time. All A and I statements with the same subject and predicate terms, E and O statements with the same subject and predicate terms, and I and O statements with the same subject and predicate terms are logically consistent.

Examples:
All Russians are Communists. **(A)**
Some Russians are Communists. **(I)**

No cats are dogs. **(E)**
Some cats are not dogs. **(O)**

Some plants are trees. **(I)**
Some plants are not trees. **(O)**

Two statements are said to be logically **independent** if knowledge of the truth value of one (either true or false) tells us logically nothing about the truth value of the other and vice versa.

Examples:
Some cats are tabbies.
Some cats are Persians.

Some cats are not tabbies.
Some cats are Persian.

(Note: It is impossible for the four types of categorical statement with the same subject and predicate terms to be logically independent.)

Exercise 1-5
Examine each pair of sentences below. By placing an X in the appropriate box, indicate whether the statements are logically consistent or inconsistent and logically dependent or independent.

	Con-sistent	Incon-sistent	Depen-dent	Inde-pendent
1. Some devices are machines. Some devices are not machines.	☒	☐	☐	☐
2. All thoroughbreds can run fast. Some thoroughbreds have broken legs.	☐	☐	☐	☐
3. Jim is happy. Donna is unhappy.	☐	☐	☐	☐
4. All devices are machines. No devices are machines.	☐	☐	☐	☐
5. Some devices are machines. No devices are machines.	☐	☒	☐	☐
6. All devices are machines. Some devices are machines.	☒	☐	☐	☐
7. Some devices are machines. Some devices are clever.	☐	☐	☐	☐
8. Leap years have 366 days. Stonehenge is in England.	☐	☒	☐	☐

Existential Import and the Boolean Square of Opposition

On the Aristotelian system which we have been discussing, it has been stipulated that the class of things referred to by the subject term must contain at least one member. Such statements are said to carry **existential import**; that is, they presuppose the existence of at least one thing which is contained in the class referred to by at least one term. Because of the restriction of existential import, certain statements such as 'Mermaids are good swimmers' and 'The present queen of the United States is thirty-five years of age' cannot be dealt with on the Aristotelian interpretation, since the subject term of both statements refer to an empty class. Similarly, a statement such as 'All students who use illicit drugs are persons who will be suspended' cannot be dealt with according to the Aristotelian interpretation, if no students use illicit drugs, and thus the subject term refers to an empty class.

Because of the restriction which existential import places on the Aristotelian system of logic, the requirement that the subject class of a proposition must contain at least one member has been dropped by more and more logicians. This results in what is known as the **Boolean interpretation**, after its proponent George Boole, a nineteenth century English logician.

Since the Boolean interpretation does not presuppose the existence of any member in the class referred to by any terms of a universal categorical statement, Venn diagrams for A and E statements on the Boolean interpretation are different from those on the Aristotelian interpretation, as shown below:

On the Aristotelian Interpretation   *On the Boolean Interpretation*

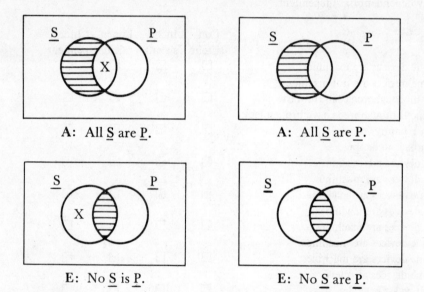

A: All <u>S</u> are <u>P</u>.   A: All <u>S</u> are <u>P</u>.

E: No <u>S</u> is <u>P</u>.   E: No <u>S</u> are <u>P</u>.

Venn diagrams for **I** and **O** propositions are identical on both the Aristotelian and Boolean interpretations, since particular statements are always interpreted as asserting that the class referred to by the subject term contains at least one member.

If the requirement that the subject class of a categorical statement must contain at least one member is dropped, then only the logical relationship of contradiction holds, as shown on the next page in the Boolean square of opposition:

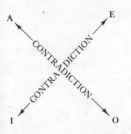

The chart below presents a summary of the immediate inferences that can be made on the Boolean square of opposition.

If A is true	If E is true	If I is true	If O is true
E is undetermined	A is undetermined	A is undetermined	E is undetermined
I is undetermined	I is false	E is false	A is false
O is false	O is undetermined	O is undetermined	I is undetermined

If A is false	If E is false	If I is false	If O is false
E is undetermined	A is undetermined	A is undetermined	E is undetermined
I is undetermined	I is true	E is true	A is true
O is true	O is undetermined	O is undetermined	I is undetermined

Exercise 1-6

(a) Write an abbreviation for each of the following standard form sentences.
(b) Provide the schema for each. (c) Fill in the Venn diagrams on the left according to the Aristotelian interpretation. (d) Fill in the Venn diagram on the right according to the Boolean interpretation.

1. All dogs are four-legged creatures.

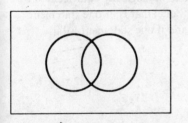

2. No dilemmas are unsolvable problems.

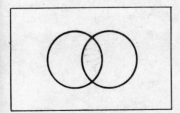

3.   Some planets are things which have moons.

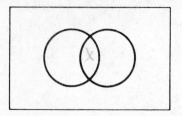

4.   Some cats are not animals that can jump well.

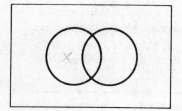

Exercise 1-7
Repeat Exercise 1-4 using the Boolean interpretation.

Immediate Inferences Between Equivalent Statements
The immediate inferences discussed so far have been concerned only with
propositions which contain the same subject and predicate terms and which
vary in quantity, quality or both. There are other kinds of immediate inference
which can be made from categorical propositions which have different subject
and predicate terms. These inferences involve categorical propositions which
are logically equivalent. Two categorical propositions are **logically equivalent**
if and only if they necessarily have the same truth value; that is, if one statement
is true, it follows that the other statement is true, and if one statement is false,
it follows that the other is false.

   Example:
   Some creative persons are poets.
   Some poets are creative persons.

Venn diagrams of logically equivalent statements are always exactly the same, as
shown in this example:

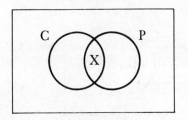

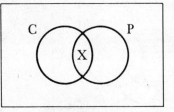

Some C are P.   Some P are C.

Immediate Inferences between Equivalent Statements and the Boolean Interpretation

We are concerned with three types of immediate inference involving logically equivalent statements: obversion, conversion, and contraposition. We shall consider these first on the Boolean interpretation.

Obversion is the mechanical process of changing the quality of a categorical proposition and replacing the predicate term with its complement. The **complement of a class** is the class of all things or beings in the universe of discourse that do not belong to the class. The complement of the class of cars is the class of all those things that are not cars. The complement of any class is expressed by joining the prefix 'non' to the name of the class. For instance, in the example above, the complement of the class of cars is expressed by the term 'noncars'. The following are some examples of statements (called obvertends) and their respective obverses.

Examples:

All animals are mammals.	(Obvertend)
No animals are nonmammals.	(Obverse)
Some animals are mammals.	(Obvertend)
Some animals are not nonmammals.	(Obverse)

Our concern, of course, is whether or not the original statement and its obverse are logically equivalent statements. These can be tested by means of Venn diagrams. The Venn diagrams below represent the pairs of statements in the examples above. The Venn diagrams for the statements in each pair are identical, indicating that the original statement and its obverse are logically equivalent on the Boolean interpretation.

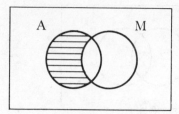

A: All A are M.

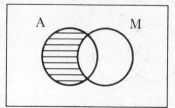

E: No A are nonM.

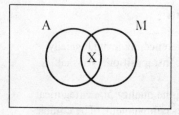

I: Some A are M.

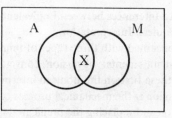

O: Some A are not nonM.

The obverses of all four types of categorical proposition are logically equivalent to their original statements on the Boolean interpretation.

Conversion is the mechanical process of interchanging the subject and predicate terms of a categorical proposition.

Examples:

Some buildings are skyscrapers.   (Convertend)
Some skyscrapers are buildings.   (Converse)

No humans are one-celled organisms.   (Convertend)
No one-celled organisms are humans.   (Converse)

On the Boolean interpretation, all **E** and **I** propositions are logically equivalent to their converses, but no **A** and **O** propositions are logically equivalent to their converses.

Contraposition is the mechanical process of interchanging the subject and predicate terms of a categorical statement and then replacing each with its complement.

Examples:

All men are mammals.   (Original)
All nonmammals are nonmen.   (Contrapositive)

On the Boolean interpretation, all **A** and **O** statements, but no **E** or **I** statements, are logically equivalent to their contrapositives.

A summary of obversion, conversion and contraposition on the Boolean interpretation appears below.

OBVERSION

Original Statement		Obverse
A: All S are P	equivalent	E: No S are nonP
E: No S are P	equivalent	A: All S are nonP
I: Some S are P	equivalent	O: Some S are not nonP
O: Some S are not P	equivalent	I: Some S are nonP

CONVERSION

Original Statement		Converse
A: All S are P	not equivalent	A: All P are S
E: No S are P	equivalent	E: No P are S
I: Some S are P	equivalent	I: Some P are S
O: Some S are not P	not equivalent	O: Some P are not S

CONTRAPOSITION

Original Statement		Contrapositive
A: All S are P	equivalent	A: All nonP are nonS
E: No S are P	not equivalent	E: No nonP are nonS
I: Some S are P	not equivalent	I: Some nonP are nonS
O: Some S are not P	equivalent	O: Some nonP are not nonS

Exercise 1-8

(a) In the space provided, write the obverse of each of the following statements.
(b) Determine whether or not the original statement and its obverse are logically equivalent on the Boolean interpretation, using the Venn diagrams provided.

1. All sonnets are poems
   a. _No sonnets are nonpoems_
   b.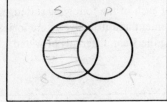

2. No butterflies are moths.
   a. <u> *all B $\overline{m}$* </u>
   b.

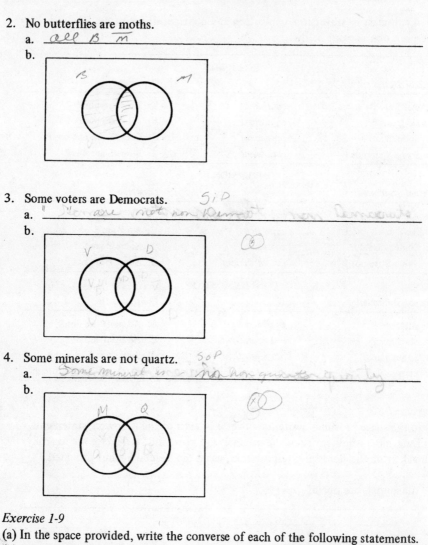

3. Some voters are Democrats.   *SiP*
   a. <u>*There are not non Democrat*   *non Democrats*</u>
   b.

4. Some minerals are not quartz.   *SoP*
   a. <u>*Some mineral is a non non quartz quality*</u>
   b.

Exercise 1-9
(a) In the space provided, write the converse of each of the following statements.
(b) Determine whether or not the original statement and its converse are logically equivalent on the Boolean interpretation, using the Venn diagrams provided.

1. All amphoras are vases.
   a.
   b.

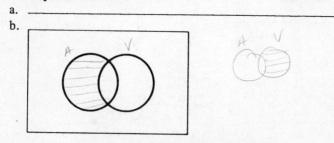

2. No wineskins are bottles.

a. _____

b.

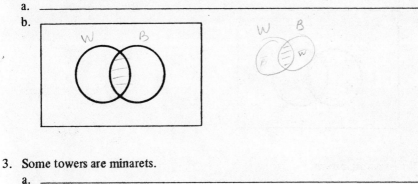

3. Some towers are minarets.

a. _____

b.

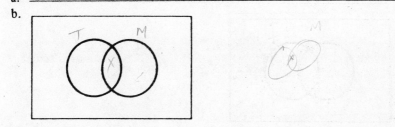

4. Some rulers are not emperors.

a. _____

b.

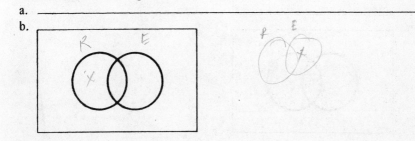

Exercise 1-10

(a) In the space provided, write the contrapositive of each of the following statements. (b) Determine whether or not the original statement and its contrapositive tive are logically equivalent on the Boolean interpretation, using the Venn diagrams provided.

1. All togas are garments.
   a. _All non garments are non togas_
   b.

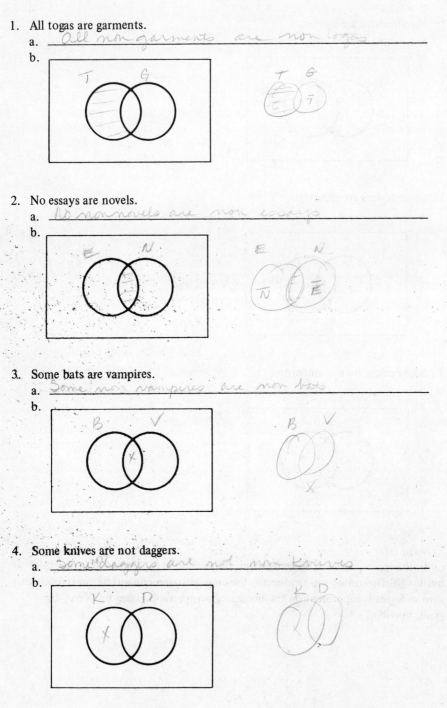

2. No essays are novels.
   a. _No nonnovels are non essays_
   b.

3. Some bats are vampires.
   a. _Some non vampires are non bats_
   b.

4. Some knives are not daggers.
   a. _Some daggers are not non knives_
   b.

S — 1 member

Immediate Inferences on the Aristotelian Interpretation

On the Aristotelian interpretation which stipulates that the class of things referred to by the subject term must contain at least one member, the obverses of all four types of categorical proposition are logically equivalent to their original statements.

On the Aristotelian interpretation, no **A** or **O** statements are logically equivalent to their converses; and **E** and **I** statements are logically equivalent *only if* the additional requirement that the class referred to by the predicate term must contain at least one member is satisfied. **Conversion by limitation**, which holds only on the Aristotelian interpretation, refers to the process of interchanging the subject and predicate terms and changing the quantity of an original **A** statement. It is possible to validly dervive a converse by limitation from an **A** statement. However, the converse by limitation is only implied by the original **A** statement, it is not equivalent to it.

$S_a\ M$

$M_i\ S$

Example:

All sheep are mammals.   (Original)
Some mammals are sheep.   (Converse by limitation)

On the Aristotelian interpretation, any **O** statement is logically equivalent to its contrapositive; any **A** statement is logically equivalent to its contrapositive *only if* the additional requirements that the predicate *and* complementary classes must each contain at least one member are satisfied; and no **I** or **E** statements are logically equivalent to their contrapositives. **Contraposition by limitation** is the process of interchanging the subject and predicate terms of a categorical statement, replacing each with its complement, and then changing the quantity of the statement. The contrapositive by limitation of an **E** statement can be validly derived from its original only on the Aristotelian interpretation. The contrapositive by limitation is only implied by, it is not logically equivalent to, the original **E** statement.

A summary of obversion, conversion, and contraposition on the Aristotelian interpretation—with the necessary added restriction—appears below.

$S_e\ P$

$P_o\ \overline{S}$

OBVERSION		
Original Statement		*Obverse*
A: All S are P	*equivalent*	E: No S are nonP
P: No S are P	*equivalent*	A: All S are nonP
I: Some S are P	*equivalent*	O: Some S are not nonP
O: Some S are not P	*equivalent*	I: Some S are nonP

CONVERSION

Original Statement		*Converse*
A: All S are P	*not equivalent*	**A:** All P are S
A: All S are P	*implies*	**I:** Some P are S
		(by limitation)
E: No S are P	*not equivalent**	**E:** No P are S
I: Some S are P	*not equivalent**	**I:** Some P are S
O: Some S are not P	*not equivalent*	**O:** Some P are not S

CONTRAPOSITION

Original Statement		*Contrapositive*
A: All S are P	*not equivalent***	**A:** All nonP are nonS
E: No S are P	*not equivalent*	**E:** No nonP are nonS
E: No S are P	*implies*	**O:** Some nonP are not nonS
		(by limitation)
I: Some S are P	*not equivalent*	**I:** Some nonP are nonS
O: Some S are not P	*equivalent*	**O:** Some nonP are not nonS

* These statements become equivalent if the additional requirement that the predicate class must contain at least one member is satisfied.

**These statements become equivalent if the additional requirements that the predicate class and the complementary classes of every term of the original statement must contain at least one member are satisfied.

Exercise 1-11

(a) In the space provided, write the obverse of each of the following statements. (b) Determine whether or not the original statement and its obverse are logically equivalent on the Aristotelian interpretation. (c) Write any additional requirement(s) which may be necessary to make the original statement and its obverse logically equivalent.

1. All senators are politicians.

    a. _____

    b.

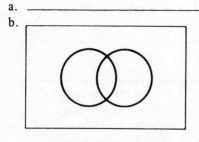

    c. _____

2. No biscuits are muffins.
   a. _____
   b.

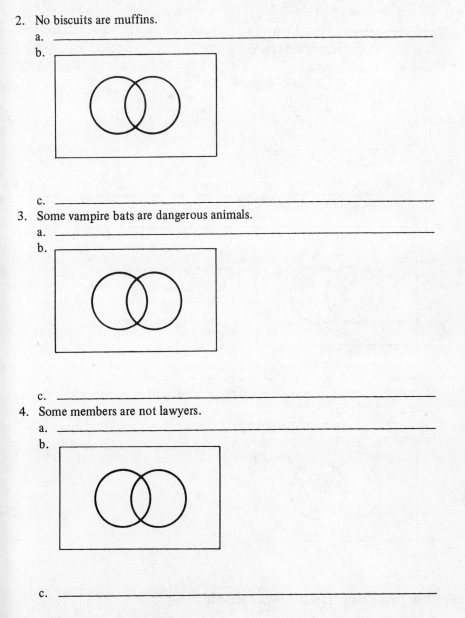

   c. _____
3. Some vampire bats are dangerous animals.
   a. _____
   b.

   c. _____
4. Some members are not lawyers.
   a. _____
   b.

   c. _____

Exercise 1-12
(a) In the space provided, write the converse of each of the following statements.
(b) Determine whether or not the original statement and its converse are logically equivalent on the Aristotelian interpretation, using the Venn diagrams provided.
(c) Write any additional requirement(s) which may be necessary to make the original statement and its converse logically equivalent.

1. All asps are vipers.
   a. _All vipers are asps_
   b.

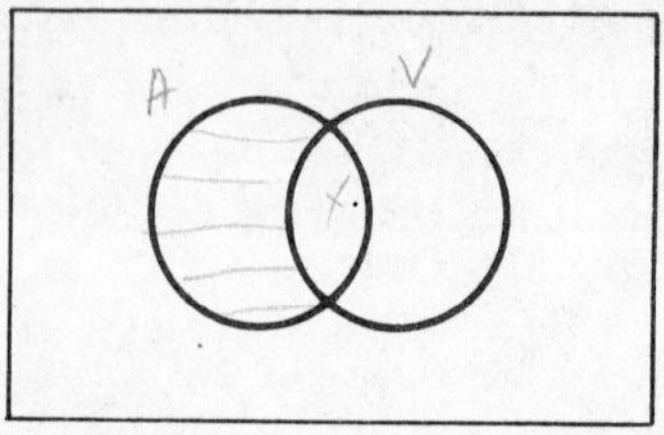

   c. _____

2. No women are four-star generals.
   a. _No 4★ generals are women_
   b.

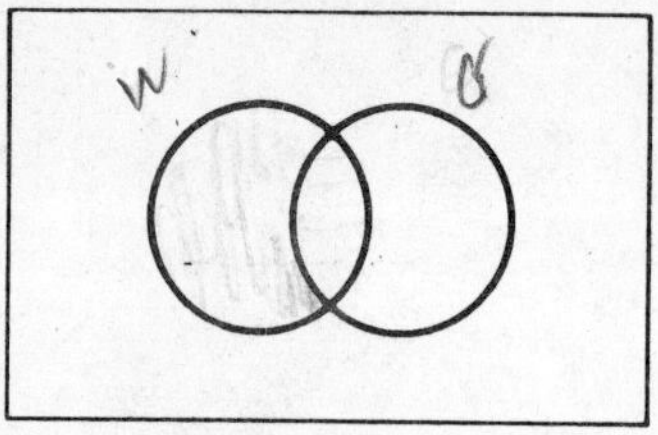

   c. _____

3. Some tables are marble things.
   a. _Some marble things are tables_
   b.

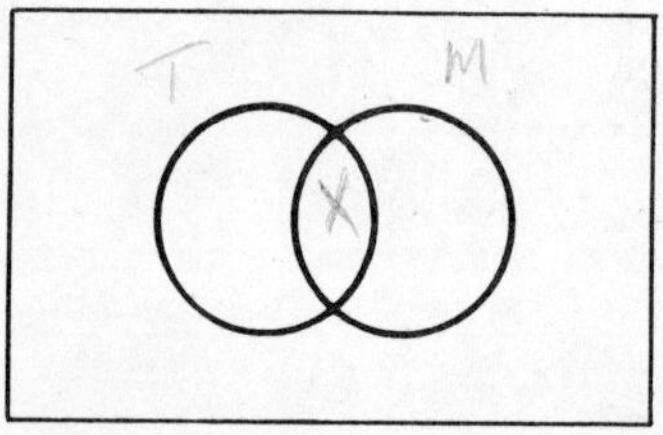

   c. _____

4. Some representatives are not elected persons.
   a. _Some elected persons are not representative_
   b.

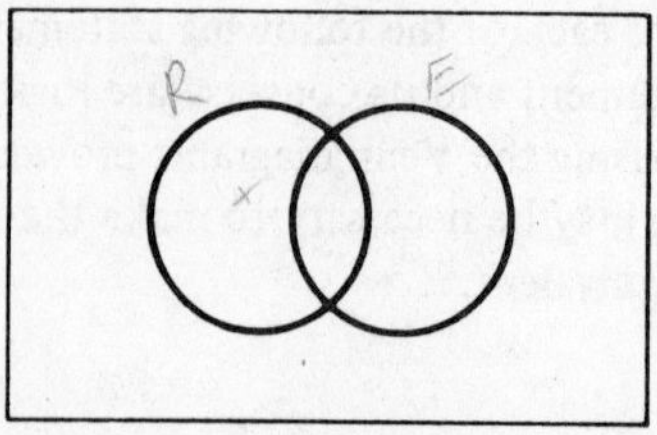

   c. _____

Exercise 1-13
(a) In the space provided, write the contrapositive of each of the following statements. (b) Determine whether or not the original statement and its contrapositive are logically equivalent on the Aristotelian interpretation, using the Venn diagrams provided. (c) Write any additional requirement(s) which may be necessary to make the original statement and its contrapositive logically equivalent.

1. All members are graduates of Harvard.
   a. <u>All non graduates of Harvard are non members</u>
   b.

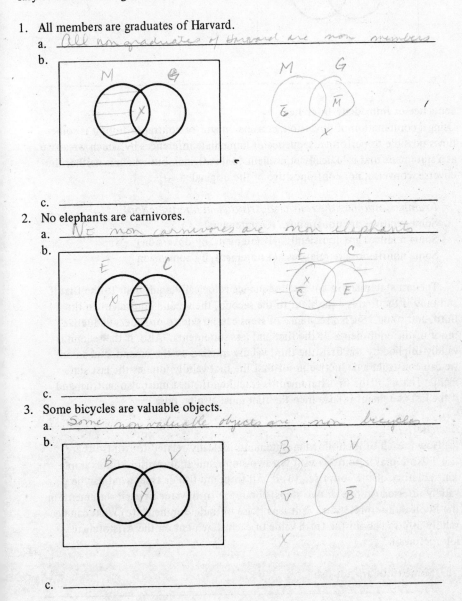

   c. _____
2. No elephants are carnivores.
   a. <u>No non carnivores are non elephants</u>
   b.

   c. _____
3. Some bicycles are valuable objects.
   a. <u>Some non valuable objects are non bicycles</u>
   b.

   c. _____

4. Some kettles are not deep things.

a. ___Some nondeep things are not non kettles___

b.

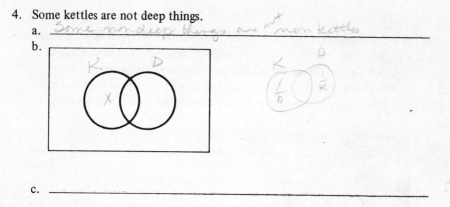

c. _____

Sequence of Immediate Inferences

Using a combination of obversion, conversion and/or contraposition, it is sometimes possible to perform a sequence of immediate inferences by which we arrive
at a statement that is logically equivalent to its original, but which is neither the
obverse, converse, nor contrapositive of the original.

> *Example (assuming the restricted Aristotelian interpretation):*
> Some relatives are not friends. (**O** statement)
> Some relatives are nonfriends. (**I** statement, by obversion)
> Some nonfriends are relatives. (**I** statement, by conversion)

The last statement in any such sequence is logically equivalent to the first if
and only if the first is equivalent to the second, the second equivalent to the
third, and so on. Such a sequence of steps can be said to provide a deductive
proof of the equivalence of the first and last statements. Also, if the second is
validly implied by the first, the third validly implied by the second, and so on,
we can construct a deductive proof that the first validly implies the last statement. That is, if the first statement is true then the last must also be true, and
if the last statement is false then the first must also be false.

Exercise 1-14
(a) How is each of the following statements logically related to '<u>All trout are
fish</u>'? Note that in some cases it is a two-step sequential relation, for example,
contradictory of the converse. (b) If 'All trout are fish' is true, what can be
validly inferred (in one or two steps) about the truth value of each statement on
the Boolean interpretation? Is it true, false or undetermined? (c) What can be
validly inferred about the truth value of each statement on the Aristotelian
interpretation?

T a F (T)

1. Some trout are not fish.
   (a) ___T o F   contradictory___
   (b) ___F___
   (c) ___F___

2. No trout are fish.
   (a) _T e F_   contrary
   (b) _u_   (F)   Boolean
   (c) _F_

3. Some trout are fish.
   (a) _T i F_   subimplicate
   (b) _u_   (T)
   (c) _T_

4. No trout are nonfish.
   (a) _N T are nonF_
   (b) ____
   (c) _T_

5. All fish are trout.
   (a) _F a T_   converse
   (b) _u_   Boolean
   (c) _u_   _T if limitation_

6. No fish are trout.
   (a) _F e T_   contrary of converse   _TaF / FaT_
   (b) _u_
   (c) _F_

7. Some fish are trout.
   (a) _F i T_   subimplicate of converse
   (b) _u_
   (c) _T_

8. Some fish are not trout.
   (a) _F o T_   contradiction of converse
   (b) _u_
   (c) _u_

9. All nonfish are nontrout.
   (a) _F a T_   contrapositive
   (b) _T_
   (c) _T_   by limitation

10. No nonfish are nontrout.
    (a) _F e T_   contrary of contrapositive
    (b) _u_
    (c) _F_   (by contrary of contrapositive (lim.))

11. Some nonfish are nontrout.
    (a) _F i T_   subimplicate of contrapositive
    (b) _u_
    (c) _T_

12. Some nonfish are not nontrout.
    (a) _F o T_   contradiction of contrapositive
    (b) _F_
    (c) _F_

Exercise 1-15

(a) How is each of the following statements logically related to 'Some officials are not umpires'? Note that in some cases it is a two-step sequential relation, for example, contradictory of the converse. (b) If 'Some officials are not umpires' is true, what can be validly inferred (in one or two steps) about the truth value of each statement on the Boolean interpretation? (c) If 'Some officials are not umpires' is true, what can be validly inferred about the truth value of each statement on the Aristotelian interpretation with all the special restrictions?

1. All officials are umpires.
   (a) _O a U   contradiction_
   (b) _F_
   (c) _F_
2. Some officials are umpires.
   (a) _O i U   sub contrary_
   (b) _U_
   (c) _U_
3. No officials are umpires.
   (a) _O e U   super implication_
   (b) _U_
   (c) _U_
4. Some officials are nonumpires.
   (a) _O i Ū   obverse_
   (b) _T_
   (c) _T_
5. No officials are nonumpires.
   (a) _O e Ū   contradiction of obverse_
   (b) _F_
   (c) _F_
6. All officials are nonumpires.
   (a) _O a Ū   superimplicant of obverse_
   (b) _U_
   (c) _U_
7. Some umpires are not officials.
   (a) _U o O   converse_
   (b) _U_
   (c) _U_
8. Some nonumpires are not nonofficials.
   (a) _Ū o Ō   contrapositive_
   (b) _T_
   (c) _T_
9. Some nonumpires are nonofficials.
   (a) _Ū i Ō   subcontrary of contrapositive_
   (b) _U_
   (c) _U_

10. All nonumpires are nonofficials.
    (a) ___ Π a Ō ___ contradictory contrapositive ___
    (b) ___ E ___
    (c) ___ E ___

2. categorical syllogisms

Mediate and Immediate Inferences
The arguments discussed in Chapter 1 involved immediate inferences, arguments in which the conclusion is derived from exactly one premise. When the conclusion of an argument is drawn from more than one premise, we are dealing with mediate inferences.

Examples:
Immediate Inference:
All dogs are four-legged animals.
Therefore, some dogs are four-legged animals.

Mediate Inference:
All dogs are four-legged animals.
Fido is a dog.
Therefore, Fido is a four-legged animal.

Categorical Syllogisms
A **categorical syllogism** is an argument composed of exactly three categorical statements (a conclusion and two premises) containing three terms, each of which appears twice in the argument, but only once in any one statement.

Example:
All welfare recipients are people who want to work.
Some Americans are welfare recipients.
Therefore, some Americans are people who want to work.

When a syllogism is composed of three categorical statements expressed by standard form sentences and when these statements are presented in a given order, then the syllogism is said to be in standard form. To understand the concept of a standard form syllogism, it is necessary to understand the concepts of major and minor premises.

The predicate term of the conclusion of a syllogism is called the **major term**, and the subject term of the conclusion is called the **minor term**. The remaining term is called the **middle term** of the syllogism. The premise containing the major term is called the **major premise**; the premise containing the minor term is called the **minor premise**.

Example:
All welfare recipients are people who want to work.
Some Americans are fat people.
Therefore, some Americans are people who overeat.

Major term: People who want to work
Minor term: Americans
Middle term: Welfare recipients

A **syllogism** is in **standard form** when its three propositions, expressed by standard form sentences, follow the order of major premise, minor premise, and conclusion.

Exercise 2-1
Examine each of the following arguments. (a) Determine if it is a categorical syllogism. (b) If it is a categorical syllogism, determine whether or not it is in standard form. (c) If it is not, put it in standard form.

1. All ostriches are birds, therefore some ostriches are birds.
2. No sloops are motorboats.
   All hydroplanes are motorboats.
   Therefore, no hydroplanes are sloops.
3. All cats are mammals.
   All mammals are vertebrates.
   All vertebrates are animals.
   Therefore, all cats are animals.
4. No hyperbolas are squares, since all hyperbolas are conic sections, but no squares are conic sections.
5. Some drinkers are drunkards.
   All drunkards are alcoholics.
   Therefore, some drinkers are alcoholics.
6. All documentaries are educational.
   Some films are documentaries.
   Therefore, some films are educational.
7. No fluorescent lights are incandescent lights.
   Some electric lights are incandescent lights.
   Therefore, some electric lights are not incandescent lights.
8. If this painting is a Rembrandt, then it must be an expensive thing.
   This painting is a Rembrandt.
   Therefore, this painting must be an expensive thing.
9. Some coaches are teachers, so some teachers are coaches.
10. Some men do not have the use of reason; therefore, some rational animals do not have the use of reason, since all men are rational animals.

Syllogistic Abbreviations and Schemata
Syllogisms can be abbreviated using the methods of the previous chapter. However, two more procedures are required: 1) placing a line between the premises and the conclusion and 2) using the symbol '∴' to represent the word 'therefore'.

Example:

Syllogism:	
No rats are primates.	*Abbreviation:*
	No R are P.
Some animals are rats.	Some A are R.
Therefore, some animals are not primates.	Some A are not P.

Just as each type of categorical proposition has a logical form which can be represented by a schema, the logical form of a categorical syllogism may also be represented by a schema. If we remove the three terms of a categorical syllogism and fill the remaining blanks with different symbols for each term, the result is an argument schema. Thus, the argument schema for the example presented above would be:

Example:
No ********** are . . . .
Some ---------- are **********.
Therefore, some ---------- are not . . . .

A more convenient method for representing an argument schema involves using the symbols S, P, and M. The symbol S is used to represent the blanks to be filled by the subject term of the conclusion (i.e. the minor term) of any syllogism. The symbol P is used to represent the blanks to be filled by the predicate term of the conclusion (i.e. the major term) of any syllogism. And the symbol M is used to represent the blanks to be filled by the middle term of any syllogism. Using our example above, we can schematize this argument in the following way:

Example:
No M are P.
Some S are M.
∴Some S are not P.

The result of substituting nouns or noun clauses for the symbols or blanks in an argument schema to produce an argument is called an **interpretation** of the argument schema.

Mood and Figure
The **mood** of a standard form syllogism is the particular combination of categorical statements of which the syllogism is comprised, expressed in terms of the statement names **A, E, I** and **O**. The first letter in the mood description indicates the form of the major premise, the second that of the minor premise, and the third that of the conclusion.

Example:
All cats are felines. (**A**)
Some tabbies are cats. (**I**)
Therefore, some tabbies are felines. (**I**)

This syllogism has the mood **AII**. The **figure** of a standard form categorical syllogism is determined by the placement of the middle term in the two premises of the syllogism. There are four possible arrangements, traditionally numbered as follows:

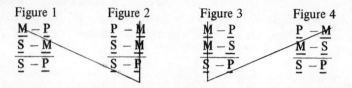

Figure 1   Figure 2   Figure 3   Figure 4

The **form** of a syllogism is determined by the combination of its mood and figures It is conventional to express the form of a syllogism by placing the number of its figure after the letters that state its mood. For example, the syllogism above has the form **AII**-1.

Exercise 2-2

For each of the following standard form categorical syllogisms: (a) Write an abbreviation. (Underline letters in the subject and predicate of each of the three sentences in the syllogism to show what the capital letters used in the abbreviation represent.) (b) Write the argument schema. (c) Give.the form (mood and figure).

1. No Frenchmen are Germans.
   Some composers are Frenchmen.
   Therefore, some composers are not Germans.
2. No Frenchmen are Germans.
   Some Frenchmen are composers.
   Therefore, some composers are not Germans.
3. No rulers are paupers.
   All kings are rulers.
   Therefore, no kings are paupers.
4. All kings are rulers.
   No rulers are paupers.
   Therefore, no paupers are kings.
5. All novels are works of fiction.
   No autobiographies are works of fiction.
   Therefore, no autobiographies are novels.
6. All novels are works of fiction.
   Some autobiographies are not works of fiction.
   Therefore, some autobiographies are not novels.
7. All college professors are well-educated persons.
   No well-educated persons are persons easily fooled.
   Therefore, some persons easily fooled are not college professors.
8. All writers are creative persons.
   All creative persons are intelligent persons.
   Therefore, some intelligent persons are writers.

9. No friends are enemies.
   No relatives are enemies.
   Therefore, some relatives are not friends.
10. All interesting things to read are detective stories.
    No interesting things to read are boring things.
    Therefore, no boring things are detective stories.

Testing for Validity and Invalidity

The validity or invalidity of a syllogism does not depend on its meaning or on the truth or falsity of its statements, but solely on its logical form. A **valid argument schema** is one for which there is no possible interpretation or substitution of terms that would create an argument with true premises and a false conclusion. Accordingly a **valid argument** is one whose schema is valid. There are several methods for testing the validity and invalidity of syllogisms; these include the use of counterexamples, Venn diagrams, and rules.

Testing by Counterexample

A **counterexample** is an interpretation of an argument schema that makes all the premises true and the conclusion false. This method of testing syllogisms involves constructing a syllogism with a particular logical form which is clearly invalid—that is, one which has obviously true premises and a clearly false conclusion. For example, suppose the following syllogism is to be tested by the method of counterexample:

Example:
All flowers are plants.
All roses are plants.
Therefore, all roses are flowers.

Using the method of counterexample, we would seek to construct an argument with the same logical form—that is, an interpretation of the same argument schema—which makes both premises true and the conclusion false. If we are successful, then we know that the argument schema and all arguments with this form are invalid. The following argument has the same form as the last example (**AAA**-2), and both premises are obviously true while the conclusion is obviously false.

Counterexample:
All Americans are human beings.
All Chinese are human beings.
Therefore, all Chinese are Americans.

Counterexamples can be used only to prove the *invalidity* of an argument schema. The failure to produce a counterexample is not sufficient to prove an argument valid. Also, counterexamples are problematic since the truth or falsity of any particular statement can be challenged in one way or another. What is needed is a **decision procedure**, a mechanical procedure that can be used to prove the validity or invalidity of any particular argument schema or argument in a finite number of steps. An ideal decision procedure would also avoid the problem of determining the truth or falsity of specific statements, as is necessary in the method of counterexamples. Two other methods, one using Venn diagrams and one using syllogistic rules, provide such decision procedures.

Exercise 2-3
Write counterexamples for each of the following invalid syllogisms, all of which are in standard form.

1. Some conservatives are Republicans.
    No Republicans are Democrats.
    Therefore, some Democrats are not conservatives.
2. No lions are tigers.
    No tigers are cheetahs.
    Therefore, no lions are cheetahs.
3. Some humans are not musicians.
    All Americans are humans.
    Therefore, some Americans are not musicians.
4. No sergeants are generals.
    All sergeants are officers.
    Therefore, no officers are generals.
5. All falcons are hawks.
    Some birds are hawks.
    Therefore, some birds are falcons.
6. All basketball players are athletes.
    Some men are not basketball players.
    Therefore, some men are not athletes.
7. All primates are mammals.
    No primates are egg-bearing animals.
    Therefore, no egg-bearing animals are mammals.
8. All Frenchwomen are Europeans.
    Some Europeans are college-educated persons.
    Therefore, some college-educated persons are Frenchwomen.

Testing With Venn Diagrams on the Boolean Interpretation
Venn diagrams can be used to represent categorical syllogisms and provide a decision procedure for testing for their validity or invalidity. Since the standard form syllogism has three terms, each of which designates a different class of things, three circles are required to represent the classes to which these three terms refer. When representing the schema of a categorical syllogism with Venn diagrams, the symbols $\underline{S}$, $\underline{P}$, and $\underline{M}$ are used to label the circles. $\underline{S}$ represents the minor term; $\underline{P}$ represents the major term; and $\underline{M}$ represents the middle term.

When diagramming a specific argument, one can use a form of abbreviation, picking a particular letter to represent each of the actual terms of the syllogism under consideration.

Example:
All dogs are carnivores.
All Cairn terriers are dogs.
Therefore, all Cairn terriers are carnivores.

Abbreviation:	*Schema:*
All D are C.	All M are P.
All T are D.	All S are M.
All T are C.	All S are P.

The rules for diagramming a categorical syllogism are an extension of those for diagramming categorical statements. Assuming the Boolean interpretation in which it is not required that the class of things referred to by either term of universal **A** and **E** statements contain at least one member, the rules are:

1. If a statement asserts that a particular class is empty, the area of the diagram representing that class is shaded.
2. An area of the diagram representing a class that is asserted to contain at least one member is marked with an 'X'.
3. When a proposition does not specify in which of two adjacent areas a thing exists, the 'X' is placed on the line between the sections.
4. An area that has been shaded cannot have an 'X' placed in it.
5. Universal statements are always diagrammed first, before any particular statements.
6. Only the major and minor premises of the syllogism are diagrammed. If the argument is valid, the diagram of the conclusion will already be contained in the diagram of the premises. If the argument is invalid, the diagram of the conclusion will not be contained in the diagram of the premises.

Examples:
All dogs are carnivores.
All Cairn terriers are dogs.
Therefore, all Cairn terriers are carnivores.

T   C

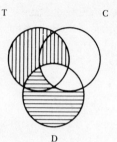

D

Valid, because the area outside of C and inside T is shaded, indicating that the area is empty.

All flowers are plants.
All roses are plants.
Therefore, all roses are flowers.

R   F

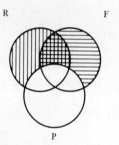

P

Invalid, because there is a section inside of R outside of F which is not shaded, indicating that it is not necessarily empty. The conclusion requires that this area be shaded.

Exercise 2-4
Test the validity of the following categorical syllogisms on the Boolean interpretation with Venn diagrams. (a) Where the syllogism is not in standard form, put it in standard form first. (b) Fill in the Venn diagram. Underline letters in the subject and predicate terms of each sentence and use them to label the appropriate circles of the Venn diagram. (c) Is the syllogism valid or invalid? Explain why.

1.   No butterflies are moths.
    All moths are insects.
    Therefore, no insects are butterflies.
    (b)

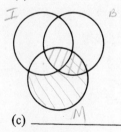

(c) _____

2. No butterflies are moths.
   All swallowtails are butterflies.
   Therefore, no swallowtails are moths.

   (b)

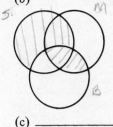

   (c) _____

3. Some dictators are reactionaries.
   All dictators are powerful men.
   Therefore, some powerful men are reactionaries.

   (b)

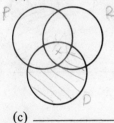

   (c) _____

4. Some reactionaries are powerful men.
   All dictators are powerful men.
   Therefore, some dictators are reactionaries.

   (b)

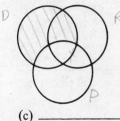

   (c) _____

5. All American Beauties are roses; therefore, all American Beauties are flowers,
   since all roses are flowers.

   (b)

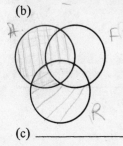

   (c) _____

6. All zinnias are roses, since all zinnias are flowers, and all roses are flowers.

(b)

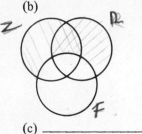

All zinnias are flowers
all roses are flowers

Z are R.

(c) —————————————————————————

7. No cats are canines; therefore, some wolves are canines, since no cats are wolves.

(b)

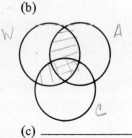

No cats are canines.
No cats are wolves

Some wolves are canines

(c) —————————————————————————

8. Some actors are rich persons.
Some actors are egoists.
Therefore, some rich persons are egoists.

(b)

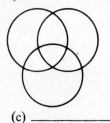

(c) —————————————————————————

9. No oak trees are pine trees, so no conifers are oak trees, since all pine trees are conifers.

(b)

(c) —————————————————————————

10. All lawyers are boring persons.
    All boring persons are persons to be avoided.
    Therefore, some lawyers are persons to be avoided.
    (b)

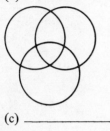

    (c) _____

Exercise 2-5
Using Venn diagrams, test the validity on the Boolean interpretation of the
syllogistic schemata having the following forms. (a) Write out the correct syllogistic schema. (b) Fill in the Venn diagram. (c) Is the schema valid or
invalid? Explain why.

1. **EIO-3**
   (a) ___ M e P _____
          M i S
          S o P
   (b)

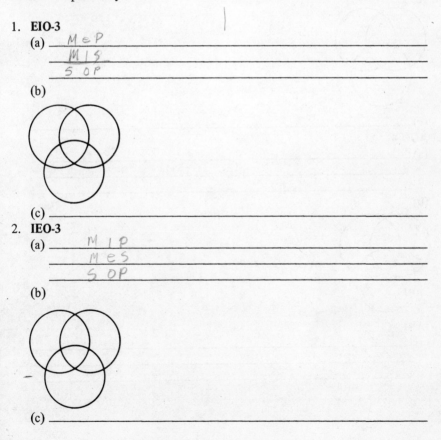

   (c) _____

2. **IEO-3**
   (a) ___ M i P _____
          M e S
          S o P
   (b)

   (c) _____

3. **EAO-2**
   (a) _____ P e M _____
       _____ S A M _____
       _____ S O P _____

   (b)

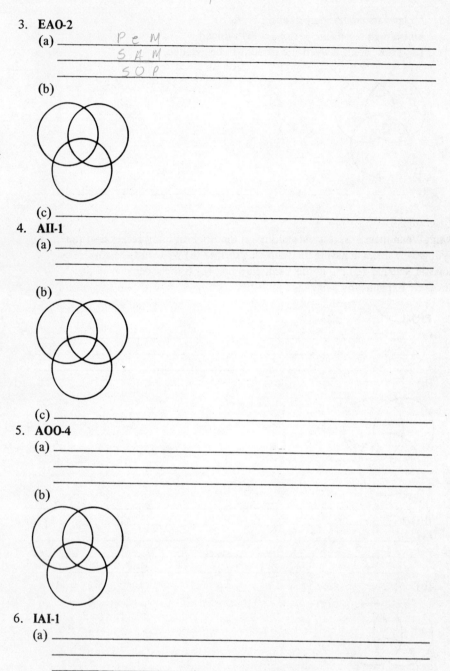

   (c) _____

4. **AII-1**
   (a) _____
       _____
       _____

   (b)

   (c) _____

5. **AOO-4**
   (a) _____
       _____
       _____

   (b)

6. **IAI-1**
   (a) _____
       _____
       _____

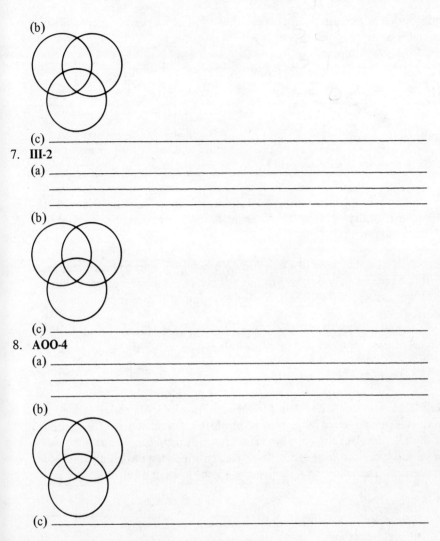

(b)

(c) _____

7. **III-2**

(a) _____

_____

_____

(b)

(c) _____

8. **AOO-4**

(a) _____

_____

(b)

(c) _____

Testing with Rules on the Booleans Interpretation

Of the possible 256 valid syllogisms, only fifteen of these are valid on the
Boolean interpretation. An examination of the valid forms shows that they have
five characteristics in common which distinguish them from the invalid forms.
These characteristics comprise the five syllogistic rules. Any syllogism that
satisfies all five rules is valid, and any syllogism that fails to satisfy one or more
of these five rules is invalid. Two of these rules are dependent on an understanding of the concept of the distribution of terms.

The terms of a categorical proposition are not distributed in and of themselves; rather, terms are distributed *by* the propositions in which they occur.
A term is **distributed** if it occurs in a position in a categorical statement such
that every term which appears in that position in every statement of that form
refers to all members of the class named by the term. A summary of the

distribution of terms in the four types of categorical proposition is presented in the table below:

Types of statement	Terms of statement	Subject term	Predicate Term
A	All S are P.	distributed	undistributed
E	No S are P.	distributed	distributed
I	Some S are P.	undistributed	undistributed
O	Some S are not P.	undistributed	distributed

Having explained the concept of distribution, we can state the five rules for testing the validity or invalidity of a standard form categorical syllogism on the Boolean interpretation.

Rule 1: The middle term of a standard form syllogism must be distributed in at least one premise. The breaking of this rule is referred to by logicians as the *fallacy of the undistributed middle*. The following syllogism violates this rule.

Example:
All cats are creatures that love tuna fish.
Susan is a creature that loves tuna fish.
Therefore, Susan is a cat.

Rule 2: A term that is distributed in the conclusion of a categorical syllogism must also be distributed in the premise in which the term occurs. The breaking of this rules involves committing what is known as the *fallacy of the illicit major* or *the fallacy of the illicit minor*, depending on which term is not distributed in its premise. The following are syllogisms which violate this rule.

Example:
Illicit Major:
All doctors are college graduates.
No nurses are doctors.
Therefore, no nurses are college graduates.

Illicit Minor:
All doctors are humanitarians.
All doctors are college graduates.
Therefore, all college graduates are humanitarians.

Rule 3: A standard form syllogism cannot have two negative premises. Breaking this rule involves committing what is called the *fallacy of negative premises*. An example appears on the next page.

Example:
No movies with Barbra Streisand are boring things.
No movies with Barbra Streisand are inexpensively made movies.
Therefore, no inexpensively made movies are boring things.

Rule 4: A standard form categorical syllogism that contains one negative premise must have a negative conclusion. A syllogism that breaks this rule commits the *fallacy of affirmative conclusion from negative premise.* The following syllogism violates this rule.

Example:
Some cats are not good pets.
All dogs are good pets.
Therefore, some dogs are cats.

Rule 5: A standard form categorical syllogism with two universal premises cannot have a particular conclusion. *This rule is applicable only on the Boolean interpretation.* The breaking of this rule results in what is called the *existential fallacy.* The following syllogism violates this rule.

Example:
All cats are carnivores.
All tigers are cats.
Therefore, some tigers are carnivores.

These five rules are sufficient for providing a decision procedure for testing categorical syllogisms *on the Boolean interpretation.* Although it is possible to add other rules, any such additional rules would be redundant and unnecessary.

Exercise 2-6
Test the validity of each of the following categorical syllogisms on the Boolean interpretation by determining which rule(s), if any, it breaks. (a) Where the syllogism is not in standard form, put it in standard form. (b) Which rule(s), if any, does it break? (c) Is the syllogism valid or invalid?

1. No butterflies are moths.
   All moths are insects.
   Therefore, no insects are butterflies.

   (b) ___ E A | F _____
   (c) _____
2. No butterflies are moths.
   All swallowtails are butterflies.
   Therefore, no swallowtails are moths.
   (b) _____
   (c) _____

3. Some reactionaries are powerful men.
   All dictators are powerful men.
   Therefore, some dictators are reactionaries.
   (b) _____
   (c) _____

4. All liqueurs are alcoholic beverages.
   All brandies are liqueurs.
   Therefore, some brandies are alcoholic beverages.
   (b) _____
   (c) _____

5. Some conservatives are Republicans.
   No Republicans are Democrats.
   Therefore, some Democrats are not conservatives.
   (b) _____
   (c) _____

6. No butterflies are kings.
   Some butterflies are kings.
   Therefore, some monarchs are not kings.
   (b) _____
   (c) _____

7. No lions are tigers; therefore, no lions are cheetahs, since no tigers are
   cheetahs.
   (b) _____
   (c) _____

8. All mayors are politicians.
   Some politicians are not gangsters.
   Therefore, some mayors are gangsters.
   (b) _____
   (c) _____

9. No fish are animals with lungs.
   All guppies are fish.
   Therefore, some guppies are not animals with lungs.

10. All interpreters are bilingual persons.
    Some bilingual persons are persons with good memories.
    Therefore, all persons with good memories are interpreters.
    (b) _____
    (c) _____

Exercise 2-7

Test the validity of the syllogistic schemata having the forms listed below, on the Boolean interpretation. Determine which rule(s), if any, it violates. (a) Write out the correct syllogistic schema. (b) Which rule(s), if any, does the syllogism violate? (c) Is the schema valid or invalid?

1. **EII-1**
   (a) _____
   _____
   _____
   (b) _____
   (c) _____

2. **AEE-2**
   (a) _____
   _____
   _____
   (b) _____
   (c) _____

3. **AEO-3**
   (a) _____
   _____
   _____
   (b) _____
   (c) _____

4. **AII-4**
   (a) _____
   _____
   _____
   (b) _____
   (c) _____

5. **EIO-3**
   (a) _____
   _____
   _____
   (b) _____
   (c) _____

6. **OOO-2**
   (a) _____
   _____
   _____
   (b) _____
   (c) _____

Testing With Rules on the Aristotelian Interpretation

Just as there are differences between the types of immediate inference possible on the Boolean and Aristotelian interpretations, so too there are differences between the two interpretations with regard to categorical syllogisms. We will stipulate that when dealing with categorical syllogisms on the Aristotelian interpretations, we will actually be using a **restricted Aristotelian interpretation**, one which requires that the class referred to by each term of a syllogism must contain at least one member. When dealing with categorical syllogisms on the restricted Aristotelian interpretation, Rule 5 discussed earlier must be discarded. However, it is necessary to substitute a new rule (which we shall refer to as Rule 5-A and *which is applicable only to the restricted Aristotelian interpretation*).

Rule 5-A: A valid categorical syllogism with a negative conclusion must have a negative premise. This rule is actually the converse of Rule 4. The following syllogism violates this new rule.

Example:
All automobiles are vehicles.
All vehicles are man-made objects.
Therefore, some man-made objects are not automobiles.

Rules 1, 2, 3 and 4 on the restricted Aristotelian interpretation are the same as those on the Boolean interpretation. Nine additional syllogistic schemata in addition to those valid on the Boolean interpretation are valid on the restricted Aristotelian interpretation. A summary of this information is presented in the chart below.

Syllogistic Forms Valid on both Boolean and Restricted Aristotelian* Interpretations			
Figure 1	Figure 2	Figure 3	Figure 4
AAA	AEE	AII	AEE
EAE	EAE	IAI	IAI
AII	AOO	EIO	EIO
EIO	EIO	OAO	

Additional Forms Valid on Restricted Aristotelian* Interpretation Only			
Figure 1	Figure 2	Figure 3	Figure 4
AAI	AEO	AAI	AEO
EAO	EAO	EAO	EAO

*Each class referred to by the syllogism must contain at least one member.

Exercise 2-8
Test the validity of each of the following categorical syllogisms on the restricted Aristotelian interpretation by determining which rule(s), if any, it violates.
(a) Where the syllogism is not in standard form, put it in standard form.
(b) Which rule(s), if any, does it violate? (c) Is the syllogism valid or invalid?

1. All basketball players are athletes.
    Some men are not basketball players.
    Therefore, some men are not athletes.
    (b) _____
    (c) _____

2. All drunkards are alcoholics.
   Some drinkers are drunkards.
   Therefore, some drinkers are alcoholics.
   (b) _____
   (c) _____
3. All falcons are hawks.
   All hawks are birds.
   Therefore, some birds are not falcons.
   (b) _____
   (c) _____
4. All falcons are hawks.
   All hawks are birds.
   Therefore, some birds are falcons.
   (b) _____
   (c) _____
5. Some reactionaries are powerful men.
   All dictators are powerful men.
   Therefore, some dictators are reactionaries.
   (b) _____
   (c) _____
6. No maples have gangrenous limbs, because all maples are trees and no trees
   have gangrenous limbs.
   (b) _____
   (c) _____
7. All amoebae are unicellular organisms, so some ameobae are not primates,
   since no primates are unicellular organisms.
   (b) _____
   (c) _____
8. All mushrooms are fungi.
   No mushrooms are animals.
   Therefore, no animals are fungi.
   (b) _____
   (c) _____

Arguments in Ordinary Language

The way in which the statements of a syllogistic argument are translated from
ordinary language into standard form can affect the validity or invalidity of the
argument. When translating ordinary language syllogistic arguments, it is
important to examine the context in which the statements are uttered in order
to clarify any ambiguous terms.

An **enthymeme** is an argument with one or more missing premises and/or a
missing conclusion. When supplying missing premises or conclusions in enthy-
mematical syllogisms, one should adhere to the principle of charity; that is, the
supplied statements would make the argument valid if possible on either or
both the Aristotelian and Boolean interpretations, and the truth of any supplied
premises should be reasonably well established.

When dealing with an enthymematically expressed syllogism, one should determine first which statement, if any, is the conclusion. Then one should determine whether or not the remaining statement is the major or minor premise. If both statements comprising the syllogistic enthymeme are premises, then determining which is the major and which is the minor premise is dependent on supplying the missing conclusion. The missing premise or conclusion is then supplied according to the principle of charity.

Example:
Soybeans are nutritious, since they contain a lot of protein.

Standard Form Syllogism with Missing Premise Supplied:
[All things containing a lot of protein are nutritious things.]
All soybeans are things containing a lot of protein.
Therefore, all soybeans are nutritious things.

Exercise 2-9
Each of the arguments below is an enthymeme. Supply the missing premise or conclusion that would make the enthymeme a *valid* categorical syllogism on the restricted Aristotelian interpretation. Put the syllogism into standard form.

1. All mushrooms are fungi, therefore all toadstools are fungi.
2. Some judges are not elected officials, because some judges are appointed.
3. Some mushrooms are not edible; some are poisonous.
4. Some people jog five miles every day, and all people who jog five miles every day are in good physical condition.
5. No soaps are cleansing agents, because all detergents are cleansing agents.
6. No operas are understandable because they're all written in foreign languages.
7. All foreign language dictionaries are reference books, and no reference books can be taken out of the library.
8. All whiskeys are liquors, therefore some whiskeys are bourbons.
9. Jack cannot practice law; he never passed the bar examination.
10. Mary is a very intelligent person, after all, she is a member of Phi Beta Kappa.

An argument consisting of more than three categorical statements, one of which is designated as the conclusion, is known as a *sorites*.

Example:
No kiwis are reptiles.
All apteryxes are kiwis.
Some vertebrates are reptiles.
Therefore, some vertebrates are not apteryxes.

Although this argument is not a single syllogism, it can be treated as a chain of interlocking syllogisms. If we combine two of the premises and derive a conclusion from this, then combine this with the remaining premise, and make certain to put them in standard order, we can validly derive the final conclusion.

Example:
All apteryxes are kiwis.
No kiwis are reptiles.
[Therefore, no reptiles are apteryxes.]
Some vertebrates are reptiles.
Therefore, some vertibrates are not apteryxes.

One can test sorites for validity by applying the rules or by constructing separate three-circle diagrams for each of the component syllogisms. The sorites is invalid if any one component syllogism is invalid, and valid if all component syllogisms are valid. The sorites above is valid, assuming the Boolean interpretation as shown in the Venn diagrams below:

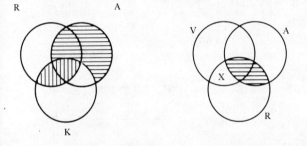

Exercise 2-10
The following groups of sentences are sorites. (a) Put the statements in standard form, supplying all intermediate conclusions. (b) Assuming the Boolean interpretation, determine the validity or invalidity of each component syllogism using Venn diagrams. (c) If invalid, which rule is violated at which step.

1. Some drums are not musical instruments.   D o M   D M W C O
   All woodwinds are musical instruments.   W a M   need O a W
   All drums are cylindrical objects.   D a C
   Therefore, some cylindrical objects are not oboes.   C o O
   (a) _____ W a M _____
   _____ O a W _____
   Therefore, _____ O a M _____ all obos are musical instrument
   _____ D o M _____
   Therefore, _____ D o O _____
   _____ D a C _____
   Therefore, _____ C o O _____

2. All entomologists are zoologists. $E\ a\ Z$
   All zoologists are biologists. $Z\ a\ Bi$
   No biologists are butterflies. $Bi\ e\ B$
   All swallowtails are butterflies. $S\ a\ B$
   All lepidopterists are entomologists. $L\ a\ E$
   Therefore, no swallowtails are lepidopterists. $Se L$

   (a) _____

   Therefore, _____

   Therefore, _____

   Therefore, $L\ a\ E$ _____

   Therefore, $Se L$ _____

3. Some Americans are Westerners.
   All New Yorkers are Americans.
   Some New Yorkers are pretzel vendors.
   No Tibetans are Westerners.
   Therefore, some pretzel vendors are not Tibetans.

   (a) _____ $A\ i\ W$ _____

   Therefore, $N\alpha\ A$ _____

   Therefore, _____

   Therefore, $P_o T$ _____

4. Some things that can be had for a song are rubbish.
   All rubbish is material sold in the street.
   No material sold in the street is valuable material.
   All eggs of the Great Auk are valuable material.
   Therefore, no eggs of the Great Auk are things that can be had for a song.

   (a) _____

   Therefore, _____

   Therefore, _____

   Therefore, _____

5. Paul is always talking.
   No intelligent persons are always talking.
   All college graduates are intelligent persons.
   Therefore, Paula is not college graduate.

   (a) _____

   _____

   Therefore, _____

   _____

   Therefore, _____

3.
truth functional propositions

Compound Propositions and Logical Operators

A proposition is that about which it makes sense to say that it is true or false. This is equivalent to saying that every proposition has a truth value. A compound proposition consists of a logical operator joined to a proposition, or two or more propositions joined together with a logical operator or operators. A **truth-functional proposition** is a compound statement which is such that if we know (1) the truth value of each of its component statements and (2) the meanings of the logical terms in the sentence expressing the compound statement, we can determine precisely the truth or falsity of the compound statement. In other words, the truth value of a truth-functional proposition is a *function* of the truth values of the component statements.

> *Example:*
> It is not the case that Bob is 6 feet tall. (*Sentence expressing a truth-functional proposition*)

A **logical operator** is an expression such that if it is correctly used with the appropriate number of propositions, a new proposition is produced with a different logical structure. No logical operator by itself is or expresses a proposition. A **truth-functional operator** is a logical operator such that when it is correctly used with the appropriate number of propositions, a truth-functional proposition is produced. Some logical operators are not truth-functional operators because knowing the meaning of the logical operator and the truth value of the component proposition(s) is not sufficient for determining the truth value of the compound statement. Sometimes sentences which do not express propositions (for example, those which express commands and questions) are joined together by (or to) logical operators. None of the following examples in which the logical operators are italicized would qualify as truth-functional propositions.

> *Examples:*
> *I don't think* sodium is a metal.
> Open the window *and* let in some fresh air.
> John went on a diet *because* his clothing no longer fit him.

Exercise 3-1
For each of the following sentences, indicate whether (a) it expresses a compound proposition. If so (b) identify all component propositions and (c) logical operators. (d) Indicate whether the compound proposition is truth-functional.

1. Pines are evergreens and oaks are hardwoods.
2. Oaks are evergreens and pines are hardwoods.
3. It is not true that the earth is flat.
4. You ought to know that the earth is not flat.
5. The Flanagans did not come because their car broke down.

6. The Flanagans did not come and their car broke down.
7. Come on out and help me shovel snow.
8. Joseph came out and he helped me shovel snow.
9. Is Maureen coming to dinner or does she have to stay home and study?
10. Maureen is not coming to dinner because she has to stay home and study.

Propositional Abbreviations and Schemata

A **symbol** is a sign which can be used to abbreviate or schematize any of the components in a given system. A **propositional constant** is an abbreviation for a sentence expressing a proposition; the meaning of the symbol remains constant throughout a given context. By convention, capital letters are used as propositional constants. Whenever the component propositions of a compound proposition are different, a different propositional constant should be used for each. If any proposition is repeated in a compound proposition or group of compound propositions, it should be represented by the same letter each time it occurs.

Example:
If Karl Marx is alive then Gerald Ford is alive.
It is not the case that Karl Marx is alive.
Therefore, it is not the case that Gerald Ford is alive.

Abbreviation:
If M then F.
It is not the case that M.
Therefore, it is not the case that F.

A **propositional variable** is a symbol which functions as a blank into which we can insert a sentence expressing any proposition whatever. By convention, the small letters of the alphabet starting with 'p' are used as propositional variables. A formula containing only propositional variables and logical operators is called a **propositional schema**, which displays the form or logical structure of a proposition. Abbreviations of truth functional propositions have truth values, whereas propositional schemata do not.

Example:
Truth-functional proposition: John is eight years old and Mary is ten years old.

Abbreviation: J and M

Schema: p and q

Conjunction

A truth functional proposition whose component propositions are connected by the truth-functional operator 'and' is called a **conjunction**. The component propositions of a conjunction are called **conjuncts**. By convention the truth-functional operator 'and' of a conjunction is abbreviated by the dot symbol '·'. A conjunction is true if and only if both component propositions are true. A conjunction is false if either one or both of its conjuncts are false.

'And' is often used in ordinary English in ways that are not adequately translated by the dot symbol.

Example:
Tom and Mary have been married for three years.

Using the conjunction operator, this sentence would have to be reformulated as:

Tom has been married for three years and Mary has been married for three years.

We can then symbolize this as:

T · M

However, this translation misses the point that Tom and Mary are married *to each other*, hence the symbolization is inadequate and should not be used. The dot symbol can be used to symbolize sentences where 'and' is used to express temporal sequence, but it must be recognized that the temporal meaning is not carried over into the symbolization.

Many words such as 'but', 'although', 'yet,' and 'moreover' operate truth-functionally in the same way as 'and' in some contexts. Insofar as they do, they can be symbolized by the dot symbol. However, such words are often used in a way that carries more meaning than that expressed by our definition of conjunction, so that some meaning is lost in the translation.

Exercise 3-2
(a) Can the dot symbol be used to translate the following sentences? (b) If so, symbolize the sentence, using the appropriate propositional constants. (c) Indicate what sentence each constant represents. (d) Is any significant meaning lost by translating the 'and' (or other operator) as a dot?

1. The Oakland Athletics and the Los Angeles Dodgers played in the world series.
2. The Oakland Athletics and the Los Angeles Dodger are baseball teams.
3. The gunmen robbed the bank and made their getaway.
4. The gunmen covered their faces with masks and wore gloves.
5. The band played rock and roll.
6. The band played *Stardust* and *Moon River*.
7. Kareem Abdul-Jabber scored 20 points although he played only half the game.
8. Each prisoner wore a ball and chain.

Truth Tables

A **truth table** is an illustrative device which is used to display all of the possible combinations of truth values of propositions which could be substituted for the propositional variables in a given propositional schema. Truth tables can be used to define truth-functional operators in terms of an exhaustive list of the possible combinations of truth values in compound statements using a given truth-functional operation.

Let us consider the truth table for any conjunction which can be displayed by the propositional schema

p · q

If we adopt the convention of using the capital letter 'T' to stand for the truth value 'true' and the capital letter 'F' to stand for the truth value 'false,' we can assign the values 'T' or 'F' to any of the four possible instances of 'p · q', as shown below.

p	q	p · q
T	T	T
F	T	F
T	F	F
F	F	F

Thus, if the proposition substituted for 'p' is true and the one substituted for 'q' is also true, then the compound 'p · q' is true; if the proposition substituted for 'p' is true and the one substituted for 'q' is false, the compound 'p · q' is false; and so on. The truth table defines the dot symbol for conjunction in such a way that a conjunction is true if and only if both conjuncts are true; otherwise it is false. This corresponds with the informal definition of conjunction provided earlier.

It has become conventional to display the various possible combinations of truth values of propositions that could be substituted for the variables on a truth table in terms of four rows forming a column under each variable. The order of the T's and F's used is also a standard one. The T's and F's are alternated under the first variable, and pairs of T's and F's are alternated under the second variable. A little thought will make clear that this arrangement is bound to result in a table showing all possible combinations of T and F for a proposition containing only two variables. (Tables for propositions containing three or more variables will be discussed later.

Negation

Negation is the logical operator which operates on a given proposition to form a new compound statement which has the opposite truth value from the original proposition. The standard abbreviation for the negation operator is the *curl* or *tilde* symbol '~'. The truth table definition of the negation operator is shown below.

p	$\sim p$
T	F
F	T

Sometimes it is possible to symbolize a given proposition as either an affirmative or a negative. For example, the statement 'Karl Marx is dead' may be symbolize as 'p' or '~p'. The later symbolization may be taken to mean 'It is not the case that Karl Marx is alive'. Both symbolizations of this proposition are theoretically correct. However, once a particular symbol has been assigned to a proposition in a given argument, the same symbol must be used for every other occurrence of the same proposition in that argument. Thus, if in an argument the statement 'Karl Marx is dead' was symbolized as 'p', then the statement 'It is not the case that Karl Marx is alive' also must be symbolized as 'p'. On the other hand, if the statement 'Karl Marx is dead' was symbolized as '~p', then the statement 'It is not the case that Karl Marx is alive' also must be symbolized as '~p'.

Disjunction

Disjunction or **alternation** is the logical operation which most closely corresponds to the connecting of two sentence by the word 'or' in ordinary English. The two sentences being connected are called **disjuncts** or **alternatives**. 'Or' in English may have an inclusive or exclusive sense. In the **inclusive sense**, 'or' asserts that either the first disjunct or the second *or both* may be true. An inclusive disjunction is true under all circumstances except when both disjuncts are false. In the **exclusive sense**, a disjunction asserts that the first or the second disjuncts, *but not both*, may be true. An exclusive disjunction is true if and only if one disjunct is true and one is false. Since exclusive disjunction is stronger than inclusive disjunction, logicians always assume that 'or' in ordinary English is being used inclusively, unless there is strong evidence otherwise. The logical operator for inclusive disjunction is the *wedge* or 'vee' symbol 'V'. The truth table for disjunction appears below.

p	q	$p \lor q$
T	T	T
F	T	T
T	F	T
F	F	F

Material Implication

The logical operator for **material implication** is symbolized by the *horseshoe* symbol '⊃'. Any proposition of the form 'p⊃q' is false if and only if the proposition substituted for 'p' is true and the proposition substituted for 'q' is false. In all other instances, 'p⊃q' is true, as shown in the truth table definition below.

p	q	p⊃q
T	T	T
F	T	T
T	F	F
F	F	T

The schema 'p⊃q' corresponds most closely in ordinary English to 'If p, then q' or 'p implies q', but the correspondence is not exact. Sentences of the form 'If . . . then . . .' are called **conditionals**, and in ordinary English they often suggest a causal relation which is absent from the truth table definition of material implication. The meaning of the horseshoe is given entirely in its truth table, and it asserts no relationship between the components other than that specified in the truth table.

Propositions of the form 'p if q' are symbolized as 'q⊃p'. Propositions of the form 'p only if q' are symbolized as 'p⊃q'. And propositions of the form 'p even if q' are symbolized simply as 'p'.

Material Equivalence

Material equivalence is the logical operation which joins two propositions into a compound statement that is true if and only if the two components have the same truth value. The logical operator for material equivalence is the symbol '≡', which is best translated as 'if and only if'. The truth table definition of material equivalence is given below.

p	q	p≡q
T	T	T
F	T	F
T	F	F
F	F	T

Exercise 3-3

(a) Symbolize the truth-functional proposition expressed by each of the following sentences using propositional constants and the symbols for conjunction, negation, disjunction, material implication, and material equivalence. (b) Indicate precisely what part of the original sentence each constant symbolizes.

(c) Indicate what significant meaning, if any, is lost in replacing the English word with the logical operator symbol.

1. It is snowing in Detroit or else the weather report is inaccurate. ∨
2. Joyce needs a kitchen table and some chairs for her apartment. ᛌ
3. If an American president's last name was Johnson, then he was vice presi- ⊃ dent before he was president.
4. It is not the case that sugar is a protein. ~
5. A geometrical figure is an equilateral if and only if all its sides have the ≡ same length.
6. Athens and Sparta fought in the Peloponnesian war. ⦁ ~
7. Athens and Sparta were city states in ancient Greece. ᛌ
8. His battery went dead and his car wouldn't start. ᛌ ~
9. Carl drinks bourbon or scotch. ∨
10. I will take the job if it pays well.
11. I will take the job only if it pays well.
12. I will take the job if and only if it pays well.
13. It is not true that all triangles are right triangles.
14. Candles can be made of tallow or beeswax.
15. Oil and water will mix if and only if they are emulsified.
16. Most swans are white, although some are gray.
17. If a total eclipse of the sun occurs, then the sky darkens.
18. If a total eclipse of the sun occurs, then the moon is positioned directly between the earth and the sun.

Grouping

In propositions or arguments containing more than one logical operator, it is important that the different variables be grouped together correctly if we are to represent the meaning of the original proposition accurately. For instance, the following proposition contains more than one logical operator and its meaning is ambiguous.

Example:
It is not true that the John is six feet tall or that I am stupid.

This statement can be taken to mean the following:

Either it is not true that John is six feet tall or I am stupid.
It is not true that either John is six feet tall or I am stupid.

These two sentences express quite different propositions. Such confusion can be avoided by properly grouping the variables and logical operators of a compound proposition with more than one logical operator. **Grouping** is the setting off of compound propositions within a larger compound proposition in such a way that it is made clear to which variable or variables a particular operator applies.

If the original sentence 'It is not true that John is six feet tall or I am stupid' expresses the proposition 'Either it is not true that John is six feet tall or I am stupid', it would be symbolized as:

(~J) ∨ I

If the original sentence expresses the proposition 'It is not true that either John is six feet tall or I am stupid', it would be symbolized as:

~ (J ∨ I)

The **main operator** is that operator in a compound proposition which operates on all the component propositions. In the first translation, the main operator is a disjunction; in the second translation, the main operator is a negation.

Exercise 3-4
(a) Symbolize each of the following sentences. In all cases this requires using more than one logical operator. Use the underlined letters as propositional constants, and use parentheses where necessary to indicate correct grouping of propositional constants and logical operators. (b) Identify the main operator in each formula by underlining it.

1. I am both going to San Francisco and I will stay with my relatives in Oakland, or else I will visit Don.

2. I am going to San Francisco, and either I will stay with my relatives in Oakland or I will visit Don.

3. Either I am going to San Francisco, or I will both stay with my relatives in Oakland and I will visit Don.

4. Either I am going to San Francisco or I will stay with my relatives in Oakland, and in either case I will visit Don.

5. I am going to San Francisco, and I will both stay with my relatives in Oakland and I will visit Don.

6. I am going to San Francisco and will stay with my relatives in Oakland, and I will visit Don.

7. I am going to San Francisco and I will stay with my relatives in Oakland and I will visit Don.

8. It is not the case that both Lassie is a collie and Spot is a mongrel.

9. Lassie is a collie and Spot is not a mongrel.

10. Lassie is not a collie and Spot is a mongrel.

11. Lassie is not a collie and Spot is not a mongrel.

12. It is not the case that both Lassie is not a collie and Spot is not a mongrel.

13. It is not the case that both Lassie is a collie and Spot is not a mongrel.

14. It is not the case that both Lassie is not a collie and Spot is a mongrel.

15. If it snows and driving will be hazardous, then the Bakers will not come.

16. If it snows then both the driving will be hazardous and the Bakers will not come.

17. If it snows then either the driving will not be hazardous or the Bakers will not come.

18. If it snows then either the driving will be hazardous or the Bakers will come.

19. If it snows then if the driving will be hazadrous the Bakers will not come.

20. If it either snows or the driving will be hazardous then the Bakers will not come.

Truth Tables and Propositions with More Than One Logical Operator

There are three basic rules for constructing truth tables for schemata with more than one operator. First, the truth table for a propositional schema should contain 2^n rows, where 'n' is the number of propositional variables in the schema. Second, under the variables, T's and F's should be alternated in the column under the first variable, pairs of T's and F's in the column under the second variable and sets of four T's and four F's in the column under the third, and so on. Third, the part of the truth table under the operators in the schema should be filled in with the appropriate truth values, beginning with any and all negations directly attached to operators, then any and all operators connecting two components neither of which is inside parentheses, then any and all negations outside of single parentheses, etc. The last operator under which the column is filled in is the main operator, and this column provides the truth table definition of the schema. For example, the truth table for the proposition '$((p \lor q) \supset \sim r)$' would be constructed in the following way.

3-10

Example:

p	q	r	~ ((p ∨ q) ⊃ ~ r)
T	T	T	F
F	T	T	F
T	F	T	F
F	F	T	F
T	T	F	T
F	T	F	T
T	F	F	T
F	F	F	T
			(1)

p	q	r	~ ((p ∨ q)	⊃ ~r)
T	T	T	T	F
F	T	T	T	F
T	F	T	T	F
F	F	T	F	F
T	T	F	T	T
F	T	F	T	T
T	F	F	T	T
F	F	F	F	T
			(2)	(1)

p	q	r	~ ((p ∨ q)	⊃	~r)
T	T	T	T	F	F
F	T	T	T	F	F
T	F	T	T	F	F
F	F	T	F	T	F
T	T	F	T	T	T
F	T	F	T	T	T
T	F	F	T	T	T
F	F	F	F	T	T
			(2)	(3)	(1)

p	q	r		~ ((p ∨ q) ⊃ ~r)			
T	T	T		T	T	F	F
F	T	T		T	T	F	F
T	F	T		T	T	F	F
F	F	T		F	F	T	F
T	T	F		F	T	T	T
F	T	F		F	T	T	T
T	F	F		F	T	T	T
F	F	F		F	F	T	T
				(4)	*(2)*	*(3)*	*(1)*

Exercise 3-5
Construct truth tables for each of the following propositional schemata.

1. p ⊃ ~ q
2. p ∨ ~ q
3. p · ~ q
4. ~ p · ~ q
5. ~ (p · q)
6. ~ (p · ~q)
7. (p · q) ⊃ p
8. (p · q) ⊃ q
9. (p · q) ⊃ r
10. (p ∨ q) ⊃ r
11. (p ⊃ q) ⊃ r
12. ((p ⊃ q) · p) ⊃ q
13. ((p ⊃ q) · ~ q) ⊃ ~ p
14. (p ⊃ q) ≡ (~ q ⊃ ~ p)
15. ~ (p · q) ≡ (~ p ∨ ~ q)
16. ~ (p · q) ≡ (~ p · q)

Logically Equivalent Statements
Once a procedure for constructing truth tables for any truth-functional propositional schema has been devised, it is possible to compare the propositional schemata of statements with different logical structures. Any two schemata with the same truth-table columns under their main operators are said to be logically equivalent.

According to the **law of double negation**, whenever a negative sentence is itself negated the resulting statement is logically equivalent to the proposition with both negations removed. Thus, the statements 'p' and '~~p' are logically equivalent. This is shown by the truth table below.

p	$\sim\ \sim p$
T	T F
F	F T
	(2) (1)

According to **De Morgan's Theorems**, 1) the negation of the *disjunction* of two statements is logically equivalent to the *conjunction* of the negations of the statements and 2) the negation of the *conjunction* of two statements is logically equivalent to the *disjunction* of the negations of the two statements. Thus, the schemata '$\sim(p \lor q)$' and '$(\sim p \cdot \sim q)$' are logically equivalent, and the schemata '$\sim(p \cdot q)$' and '$(\sim p \lor \sim q)$' are logically equivalent. These equivalences can be demonstrated by means of truth tables.

An alternative definition is that two statements are logically equivalent if and only if, when they are connected by the symbol '$\equiv$', the column under that symbol contains only T's. A sentence expressing a material equivalence is sometimes called a **biconditional**, in that its first component materially implies the second *and* the second materially implies the first. The truth table below demonstrates that the proposition '$(p \supset q) \equiv \sim(p \cdot \sim q)$' is a biconditional.

Example:

p	q	$(p$	$\supset$	$q)$	$\equiv$	$\sim$	$(p$	$\cdot$	$\sim q)$
T	T		T		T	T		F	F
F	T		T		T	T		F	F
T	F		F		T	F		T	T
F	F		T		T	T		F	T
			(2)		*(4)*	*(3)*		*(2)*	*(1)*

Exercise 3-6
(a) Are each of the following pairs of propositional schemata logically equivalent?
(b) Construct a truth table to determine your answer in each case.

1. $p \cdot q$ $\sim(\sim p \lor \sim q)$
2. $p \cdot \sim q$ $\sim(\sim p \lor q)$
3. $\sim p \cdot q$ $\sim(p \lor \sim q)$
4. $\sim(p \lor q)$ $\sim p \lor q$
5. $p \supset q$ $\sim p \lor q$
6. $\sim(p \supset q)$ $p \lor \sim q$
7. $p \cdot q$ $p \equiv q$
8. $\sim(p \cdot \sim q) \cdot \sim(q \cdot \sim p)$ $p \equiv q$

Tautologies, Contradictions and Contingent Statements

A proposition is a **tautology** if and only if its schema has only T's under the main operator in its truth table; that is, its logical form makes it *impossible* for it to be false. Two tautologies are the schema 'p $\vee \sim$ p' which expresses the **law of excluded middle**, and the schema '$\sim$(p $\cdot \sim$ p)' which expresses the **law of non-contradiction**. Tautologies are said to be **analytically true** statements in that their truth can be determined solely by an analysis of their logical form.

Examples:

p	(p $\vee$ $\sim$ p)
T	T F
F	T T
	(2) (1)

p	$\sim$	(p $\cdot$ $\sim$ p)
T	T	F F
F	T	F T
	(3)	(2) (1)

A **contradiction** is a statement whose schema has only F's under the main operator in its truth table; that is, its logical form makes it impossible for it to be true. Contradictions are said to be **analytically false** statements in that their falsity can be determined solely by an analysis of their logical form. The schema 'p $\cdot \sim$ p' is a contradiction.

A **contingent statement** is one whose schema has both T's and F's under the main operator in its truth table. Contingent statements are neither analytically true nor analytically false; their truth or falsity must be determined by extra-logical means. The schema 'p $\supset \sim$ q' is a contingent statement.

Exercise 3-7

(a) Are propositions with each of the following schemata tautologies contradictions or contingent statements? (b) Construct a truth table to determine your answer in each case.

1. p $\supset$ q
2. p $\supset$ p
3. p $\supset \sim$ p
4. ((p $\supset$ q) $\cdot \sim$ q) $\cdot$ p
5. ((p $\supset$ q) $\cdot \sim$ q) $\vee$ p
6. (p $\vee \sim$ p) $\supset$ (p $\cdot \sim$ p)
7. (p $\vee \sim$ p) $\supset$ (p $\cdot \sim$ q)
8. $\sim$(p $\supset$ q) $\equiv$ ($\sim$ p $\vee$ q)
9. ($\sim$ p $\supset$ q) $\equiv$ (p $\vee$ q)
10. ($\sim$ p $\supset$ q) $\equiv$ ($\sim$ p $\vee$ q)

4.
proposi-
sitional
logic

Truth-Functional Propositions and Arguments

A **truth-functional proposition** is a compound statement which is such that if we know the truth value of each of its component statements and the meanings of the logical operators, the truth or falsity of the compound statement can be determined. Of course, an individual truth-functional proposition is not an argument. An argument, it will be recalled, is a group of statements, one of which is designated the conclusion, which the other statements (the premises) purport to support.

Examples:
All cats are carnivores.
Morris is a cat.
Therefore, Morris is a carnivore.

Either Mary is telling the truth or Joan is telling the truth.
It is not the case that Mary is telling the truth.
Therefore, Joan is telling the truth.

Both examples are valid arguments, but for reasons that will become clear later, the methods of this chapter are not sufficiently powerful to enable us to prove the validity of the first example.

Contradictory Premises and Tautologous Conclusions

Since as logicians we are concerned with the relationships between premises and conclusions, we want to know whether or not a particular deductive argument is valid or invalid. A **valid deductive argument** has previously been defined as one which is such that *if* the premises are true, then the conclusion *must* be true. Given this definition of validity, two consequences result. First, any argument with an inconsistent set of premises is necessarily valid, because it is impossible for all its premises to be true at the same time. Second, any argument whose conclusion is a tautology must be valid, because it is impossible for the conclusion to be false.

Examples:
It is raining and it is not raining. (Contradiction)
Therefore, it is snowing.

It is snowing.
Therefore, either it is raining or it is not raining. (Tautology)

Abbreviating and Schematizing Truth-Functional Arguments

Just as it was possible to abbreviate truth-functional propositions by using propositional constants and symbols for the various logical operators, it is also possible to abbreviate a group of truth-functional statements which comprise an argument. In doing so, we must make certain that we use different propositional constants to represent each different component proposition, and the same propositional constant to represent the same proposition whenever it occurs in the argument.

Example:
If the World Trade Center towers are the world's tallest buildings, then oranges are vegetables.
The World Trade Center towers are the world's tallest buildings.
Therefore, oranges are vegetables.

$$W \supset O$$
$$\underline{W}$$
$$\therefore O$$

Just as it is possible to display the form of a truth-functional compound statement by using propositional variables and the symbols for logical operators, it is also possible to schematize a truth-functional argument. The schema for a last example is shown below.

Example:
$$p \supset q$$
$$\underline{p}$$
$$\therefore q$$

Once an argument schema has been set up, either a simple or a compound proposition may be substituted for the propositional variables in the argument schema. This produces a **substitution instance** or an **interpretation** of the argument schema. However, only *propositions* can be substituted for propositional variables, and the same propositions must be substituted for *every* occurence of any given propositional variable in a particular argument schema. Unlike a propositional schema, an argument schema is valid or invalid. A **valid argument schema** is one for which there is no possible substitution of propositions that would result in an argument with true premises and a false conclusion.

Exercise 4-1
(a) Write an abbreviation for each of the following truth-functional arguments. Be sure to provide a dictionary for each abbreviation, indicating the proposition which each propositional constant represents. (b) Write an argument schema for each argument.

1. Either Fido is in the basement or he is in the backyard.
   Fido is not in the basement.
   Therefore, Fido is in the backyard.
2. Either Fido is in the basement or he is in the backyard.
   Fido is not in the backyard.
   Therefore, Fido is in the basement.

3. If all dogs are carnivores, then Fido is a carnivore.
   All dogs are carnivores.
   Therefore, Fido is a carnivore.

4. If all dogs are carnivores, then Fido is a carnivore.
   Fido is not a carnivore.
   Therefore, it is not the case that all dogs are carnivores.

5. If the law of noncontradiction does not hold, then logical thought is not possible.
   Logical thought is possible.
   Therefore, the law of noncontradiction holds.

6. Either this chair is made of walnut or it is made of mahogany or it is made of teakwood.
   It is not made of walnut.
   Therefore, it is made of mahogany or teakwood.

7. If we are going to the state park for a picnic, then we will take Johnny or Billy along.
   We are going to the state park for a picnic.
   Therefore, we will take Johnny or Billy along.

8. If we are going to the state park for a picnic, then we will take Johnny and Billy along.
   We are going to the state park for a picnic.
   Therefore, we will take Johnny and Billy along.

9. If we are going to the state park for a picnic and we are taking Johnny along along, then we will take Billy along.
   We are going to the state park for a picnic and we are taking Johnny along.
   Therefore, we will take Billy along.

10. If we are going to the state park for a picnic or we are taking Johnny along, then we will take Billy along.
    We are going to the state park for a picnic.
    Therefore, we will take Billy along.

11. If we are going to the state park for a picnic or we are taking Johnny along, then we will take Billy along.
    We are taking Johnny along.
    Therefore, we will take Billy along.

12. If it is raining and the wind blows, then water will get in the tent.
    It is raining.
    The wind is blowing.
    Therefore, water will get in the tent.

13. If it is raining, then if it is getting cold, my car won't start.
    It is raining and it is getting cold.
    Therefore, my car won't start.

14. If snow is falling, then it is getting cold.
    If it is getting cold, then my car won't start.
    Snow is falling.
    Therefore, my car won't start.

15. If the statement under discussion is an equivalence, then it contains an implication.
    Either the statement under discussion is a disjunction or it is an equivalence.
    The statement under discussion is not a disjunction.
    Therefore, the statement under discussion contains an implication.
16. Either the statement under discussion is a disjunction or it is an equivalence.
    If the statement under discussion is an equivalence, then it contains an implication.
    The statement under discussion does not contain an implication.
    Therefore, it is a disjunction.
17. The statement under discussion is either a conjunction or it is a disjunction.
    It is either a conjunction or an implication.
    If it is a disjunction, then it is not an implication.
    Therefore, it is a conjunction.
18. The statement under discussion is either a truth-functional proposition or it is a command.
    If it is a truth-functional proposition, then it is a compound proposition.
    If it is a compound proposition, then it contains a logical operator.
    The statement under discussion does not contain a logical operator.
    Therefore, it is a command.
19. The statement under discussion is either a truth-functional proposition or it is a command.
    If it is a truth-functional proposition, then it is a compound proposition.
    If it is a compound proposition, then it contains a logical operator.
    The statement under discussion is not a command.
    Therefore, it contains a logical operator.
20. If this solution is an acid, then litmus paper placed in it will turn red; and if it is a base, the litmus paper will turn blue.
    The solution is either an acid or a base.
    Therefore, the litmus paper will either turn red or blue.
21. If this solution is an acid, then litmus paper placed in it will turn red; and if it is a base, the litmus paper will turn blue.
    The litmus paper did not turn red and it did not turn blue.
    Therefore, the solution is not an acid and it is not a base.
22. If Herb is a Hoosier, he is from Indiana.
    If Herb is a Buckeye, he is from Ohio.
    If Herb is either from Indiana or Ohio, he is an American.
    Herb is either a Hoosier or a Buckeye.
    Therefore, Herb is an American.
23. If Pete can come tonight, then either Gary or Ralph can come.
    If Gary can come, then Sam can come.
    If Sam can come, then Ted can come.
    If Pete can come, then Ted cannot come.
    Pete can come.
    Therefore, Ralph can come.

24. If either Pete or Gary can come, then either Ralph can't come or Sam can't come.
    If Ralph can't come, then Ted can't come.
    Gary and Ted can come.
    Therefore, Sam can't come.

Testing Validity by Truth Tables

The **truth-table method** for testing the truth-functional validity of arguments requires that we construct a truth table for each premise and the conclusion of an argument schema. If, in this table, there is any row in which there are Ts und under the main operator of each premise and an **F** under the main operator of the conlcusion, then the argument schema is truth-functionally invalid, since this shows that it is possible for an argument with this form to have all true premises and a false conclusion. However, such a schema, in some cases, may be proved valid when tested by the methods of other systems of logic such as the syllogistic and quantificational logic discussed in other chapters.

Examples

p ⊃ q
p
∴ q   Valid.

		(Premise)	(Premise)	(Conclusion)
p	*q*	*p ⊃ q*	*p*	*q*
T	T	T	T	T
F	T	T	F	T
T	F	F	T	F
F	F	T	F	F

p ⊃ q
~p
∴ ~q   Invalid, because the second row has both true premises and a false conclusion.

		(Premise)	(Premise)	(Conclusion)
p	*q*	*p ⊃ q*	*~p*	*~q*
T	T	T	F	F
F	T	T	T	F
T	F	F	F	T
F	F	T	T	T

Exercise 4-2

Test the truth-functional validity of each of the following argument schemata by the truth-table method. (a) Construct a truth-table for each answer. (b) Is it valid or invalid?

1. $\underline{\quad q \quad}$
   $\therefore p \supset (p \cdot q)$

2. $\underline{p \supset q}$
   $\therefore p \supset (p \cdot q)$

3. $\underline{q \supset p}$
   $\therefore p \supset (p \cdot q)$

4. $p \lor q$
   $\underline{\sim p}$
   $\therefore q$

5. $p \lor q$
   $\underline{\quad p \quad}$
   $\therefore \sim q$

6. $p \supset q$
   $\underline{\quad q \quad}$
   $\therefore p$

7. $p \supset q$
   $\underline{\sim p}$
   $\therefore \sim q$

8. $p \supset q$
   $\underline{q \supset r}$
   $\therefore p \supset r$

9. $p \supset q$
   $p \lor r$
   $\underline{\sim r}$
   $\therefore q$

10. $p \supset q$
    $q \supset r$
    $\underline{\sim r}$
    $\therefore \sim p$

11. $p \supset q$
    $p \supset r$
    $\underline{\sim r}$
    $\therefore \sim q$

12. $p \supset q$
    $p \lor r$
    $\underline{\sim p}$
    $\therefore q$

13. $p \supset q$
    $p \lor r$
    $\underline{\sim q}$
    $\therefore r$

14. $p \supset (q \supset r)$
    $\underline{p \supset q}$
    $\therefore r$

15. $p \supset (q \supset r)$
    $\underline{p \supset q}$
    $\therefore q \supset r$

16. $p \supset (q \supset r)$
    $\underline{p \supset q}$
    $\therefore p \supset r$

Testing Validity by the Short Truth-Table Method

Since the full truth-table method becomes cumbersome as the number of propositional variables in an argument schema increases, a short truth-table method may be used in such cases. In using it, we begin by assigning an **F** to the conclusion and then backtrack to see if it is possible to assign truth values to the component statements such that all of the premises can be assigned the truth value **T**. If so, the argument is truth-functionally *invalid*. It is recommended that the short truth-table method be used only to prove invalidity, not the validity, of an argument schema.

Example:
$p \supset q$
$\underline{q \supset r}$
$\therefore q \lor r$

Step One:

			(Premise 1)	(Premise 2)	(Conclusion)
p	q	r	p ⊃ q	q ⊃ r	q ∨ r
	F	F	F	F T F	F F F

Step Two:

			(Premise)	(Premise)	(Conclusion)
p	q	r	p ⊃ q	q ⊃ r	q ∨ r
F	F	F	F T F	F T F	F F F

Exercise 4-3

Using the short truth-table method, prove the invalidity of each of the following argument schemata.

1. p · q
    p ∨ r
    ∴ r

2. p ⊃ q
    p ∨ r
    ∴ q

3. p ⊃ q
    p ∨ r
    ∴ q ⊃ ~ r

4. p ⊃ q
    p ∨ r
    ∴ q ∨ ~ r

5. p ⊃ (q ⊃ r)
    p
    ∴ r

6. p ⊃ q
    q ⊃ r
    ∴ p · r

7. (p ⊃ r) · (s ⊃ t)
    r ∨ t
    ∴ p ∨ s

8. (p ⊃ q) ∨ (q ⊃ r)
    p ∨ q
    ∴ q · r

Truth-Functional Arguments and Corresponding Conditionals

For every argument, it is possible to construct a **corresponding conditional state-ment**; that is, a material implication whose antecedent consists of the conjunc-tion of the premises of the argument and whose consequent is the conclusion of the argument. An argument and its corresponding conditional differ in two respects. First, the argument is composed of several statements, whereas the corresponding conditional is a single compound statement. Second, whereas in the argument the premises are asserted to be true, they are not so asserted in the conditional. If an argument is truth-functionally valid, then its correspond-ing conditional is a tautology, and vice versa.

Example:
p ⊃ q
p
∴ q

The validity of this argument schema has been shown by the truth table on page 4-5. The corresponding conditional of this argument schema is:

$$((p \supset q) \cdot p) \supset q$$

From the truth table below, one can see that this corresponding conditional is a tautology, since there are all T's under the main operator. Hence, the argument schema must be valid, inasmuch as its corresponding conditional is a tautology.

p	q	$((p$	$\supset$	$q)$	$\cdot$	$p)$	$\supset$	q
T	T				T	T		T
F	T				T	F		T
T	F				F	F		T
F	F				T	F		T
					(1)	(2)		(3)

The Propositional Calculus

The method of **deductive proof** supplies an alternative to the truth-table method of proving the validity of argument schemata. A deductive proof system, consisting of a set of rules and procedures which makes it possible to prove the truth-functional validity of a deductive argument schemata in a step-by-step fashion, is called a **propositional calculus**. Most deductive proof systems do not provide a decision precedure, and therefore cannot be used to obtain an unequivocal proof of *in*validity; they can be used only to prove validity. Basically, a deductive proof system uses a small number of rules or axioms which are such that when they are used in conjunction with the premises of a valid argument, it can be shown that if all the premises are true, then the truth of the conclusion logically follows.

A deductive proof system for truth-functional arguments is **deductively complete** if any argument which can be proven to be truth-functionally valid using truth tables can also be proven valid using this system's rules and procedures. The number of rules contained in such a system may vary from as few as three to infinitely many. A system of convenient size and substantial utility can be constructed of about twenty rules, and such a system is used in this book.

Inference Rules

Each of the rules of our deductive proof system is a **rule of inference**; that is, each is a basic argument schema which can be proven valid by the truth-table method, and which can be used in constructing a formal proof for other, more complex arguments. It is considered inappropriate to try to prove the validity of any one of these rules of inference using the other rules.

The first eight rules of inference are given below. (Notice that two of the rules—Disjunctive Syllogism and Simplification—have two variations each.)

Modus Tollens (M.T.)

$p \supset q$

$\sim q$

$\therefore \sim p$

Disjunctive Syllogism (D.Syll.)

$p \lor q$ $p \lor q$

$\sim p$ $\sim q$

$\therefore q$ $\therefore p$

Modus Ponens (M.P.)

$p \supset q$

p

$\therefore q$

Simplification (Simp.)

$p \cdot q$ $p \cdot q$

$\therefore p$ $\therefore q$

Conjunction (Conj.)

p

q

$\therefore p \cdot q$

Hypothetical Syllogism (H.Syll.)

$p \supset q$

$q \supset r$

$\therefore p \supset r$

Constructive Dilemma (Dil.)

$(p \supset q) \cdot (r \supset s)$

$p \lor r$

$\therefore q \lor s$

Addition (Add.)

p

$\therefore p \lor q$

Because these rules are valid *argument* schemata, not propositional schemata, they can be applied only to entire lines of a proof, and not to individual components of such lines.

Constructing a Formal Proof

A **formal proof** is the process whereby the conclusion of an argument can be validly derived, using the rules of the system, from a set of statements, each one of which is either a premise of the original argument or has been validly deduced from the premises and/or other statements which have themselves been validly deduced by means of the rules of the system. Theoretically, an infinite number of correct formal deductive proofs can be constructed for any truth-functionally valid argument. The ability to construct a formal deductive proof for a valid argument is dependent on many subjective factors. Thus, failure to construct a formal deductive proof for a particular argument schema is not sufficient to prove that the schema is truth-functionally invalid.

Let us consider how we may construct a formal proof, using as our example the argument schema below:

$p \lor \sim q$

$r \supset q$

$\sim p$

$\therefore \sim r$

The first thing done is to list the propositional schemata in order of their appearance in the original argument, numbering them consecutively and labeling each as a premise in the column on the right. The last line contains the last premise schema, a slash, the symbol for 'therefore,' and the conclusion; in the right hand column we indicate that both a premise *and* a conclusion appear on this line. This procedure for presenting the premises and conclusion of an argument should always be employed when constructing a formal proof.

Example:

1. $p \vee \sim q$ Premise
2. $r \supset q$ Premise
3. $\sim p /\therefore \sim r$ Premise / Conclusion

We then seek to deduce the conclusion of tne argument schema by means of our rules of inference. We can tackle this problem in a variety of ways. One way is to examine the conclusion of the argument schema—in this instance, '$\sim r$'. We can see that the only place the propositional variable 'r' appears in the premises is on line 2 in the schema '$r \supset q$'. We can derive '$\sim r$' from '$r \supset q$' by means of Modus Tollens, if we could assert '$\sim q$'. The propositional variable '$\sim q$' appears in the first premise—'$p \vee \sim q$'. We could infer '$\sim q$' by means of Disjunctive Syllogism, if we could assert '$\sim p$'. You will notice that '$\sim p$' is the premise expressed on line 3. Therefore, our proof falls into place, as shown below.

Example:

1. $p \vee \sim q$ Premise
2. $r \supset q$ Piemise
3. $\sim p /\therefore \sim r$ Premise / Conclusion
4. $\sim q$ D. Syll.,1,3
5. $\sim r$ M.T.,2,4

Notice that we have numbered each additional line, written out the full schema we have deduced, and indicated at the right both the schemata from which this conclusion was deduced and the abbreviation of the rule by which we justify the deduction. Furthermore, a procedural rule, called the rule of rigor, requires that only one rule be used in each step of a deductive proof, and that the rules be used only in the form in which they are given in the system.

There are several helpful rules of thumb for constructing a formal proof. One which we have already mentioned is that we may sometimes find it helpful to examine the conclusion of a particular argument schema and try to work backward from it to the premises, still using the rules as we have given them. Another rule of thumb is that the Hypothetical Syllogism is helpful in removing middle terms when we have a sequence such as '$p \supset q$' and '$q \supset r$'. Also, Simplification is another inference rule which is helpful as a means of eliminating variables which appear as *conjuncts* in one or more premises of an argument schema, but do not appear at all in the conclusion. If we are faced with a situation in which the conclusion contains a variable which is not present in the premises, the rule of Addition might be helpful, since it permits us to add a variable (or a compound) *only as a disjunct*. While such rules of thumb are helpful for constructing proofs, the most effective way to acquire the skills necessary for constructing proofs is continued practice.

Exercise 4-4

Using the eight rules of inference discussed thus far, construct a proof to demonstrate the validity of each of the following argument schemata.

1. $p \supset (q \cdot r)$
     p
    $\therefore r$

2. $p \supset \sim r$
     $q \supset r$
     p
    $\therefore \sim q$

3. $p \supset \sim r$
     $q \lor r$
     p
    $\therefore q$

4. $(p \cdot q) \supset (r \cdot s)$
     $(r \cdot s) \supset (t \cdot u)$
    $\therefore \overline{(p \cdot q) \supset (t \cdot u)}$

5. $(p \cdot q) \supset (r \cdot s)$
     $(r \cdot s) \supset (t \cdot u)$
     $p \cdot q$
    $\therefore t \cdot u$

6. $(p \cdot q) \supset (r \cdot s)$
     $(r \cdot s) \supset (t \cdot u)$
     $p \cdot q$
    $\therefore u$

7. $p \supset q$
     $q \supset r$
     p
    $\therefore p \cdot r$

8. $p \supset q$
     $q \supset r$
     $\sim r$
    $\therefore \sim r \cdot \sim p$

9. $(p \supset q) \cdot (r \supset s)$
     $(q \supset t) \cdot (s \supset u)$
     $p \lor r$
    $\therefore t \lor u$

10. p
     $p \supset q$
     $(p \cdot q) \supset (r \cdot s)$
    $\therefore r \cdot s$

11. p
     $p \supset q$
     $(p \cdot q) \supset (r \cdot s)$
    $\therefore s$

12. p
     $p \supset q$
     $(p \cdot q) \supset (r \cdot s)$
    $\therefore s \lor t$

13. p
     $(p \lor q) \supset (r \cdot s)$
     $s \supset t$
    $\therefore t$

14. p
     $(p \lor q) \supset (r \cdot s)$
     $s \supset t$
    $\therefore t \lor u$

15. $p \supset q$
     $q \supset r$
     $r \supset s$
     $\sim s$
    $\therefore \sim p$

16. $(p \lor q) \supset (r \lor s)$
     $(r \lor s) \supset (t \lor u)$
     $(t \lor u) \supset (v \lor w)$
     $\sim (v \lor w)$
    $\therefore \sim (p \lor q)$

17. $(p \lor q) \supset (r \supset s)$
     $p \supset r$
     p
    $\therefore s$

18. $\sim (p \cdot q)$
    $(p \cdot q) \vee (r \supset s)$
    $\underline{\sim (p \cdot q) \supset \sim s}$
    $\therefore \sim r$

19. $\sim (p \cdot q)$
    $(p \cdot q) \vee ((r \cdot s) \supset (t \vee u))$
    $\underline{\sim (p \cdot q) \supset \sim (t \vee u)}$
    $\therefore \sim (r \cdot s)$

20. $(p \vee q) \vee (r \vee s)$
    $(r \vee s) \supset t$
    $t \supset p$
    $\underline{\sim p}$
    $\therefore q$

Equivalence Rules

The **rule of replacement** allows us to substitute logically equivalent statements in a deductive proof. It asserts that any propositional schema which is produced by replacing all or part of another schema with a schema which is equivalent to the replaced portion, according to one of the equivalences listed below, is validly derivable from the original schema. A more abstract formulation of the rule of replacement is:

The two following schemata are valid inference forms:

$$\frac{\begin{array}{c} \ldots \Phi \ldots \\ \Phi \equiv \Psi \end{array}}{\ldots \Psi \ldots} \quad \text{or} \quad \frac{\begin{array}{c} \ldots \Psi \ldots \\ \Phi \equiv \Psi \end{array}}{\ldots \Phi \ldots}$$

where $\Phi \equiv \Psi$ is one of the equivalences listed below:

De Morgan's Rules (De M.):	$\sim (p \cdot q) \equiv (\sim p \vee \sim q)$
	$\sim (p \vee q) \equiv (\sim p \cdot \sim q)$
Commutation (Comm.):	$(p \vee q) \equiv (q \vee p)$
	$(p \cdot q) \equiv (q \cdot p)$
Association (Assoc.):	$(p \vee (q \vee r)) \equiv ((p \vee q) \vee r)$
	$(p \cdot (q \cdot r)) \equiv ((p \cdot q) \cdot r)$
Distribution (Dist.):	$(p \cdot (q \vee r)) \equiv ((p \cdot q) \vee (p \cdot r))$
	$(p \vee (q \cdot r)) \equiv ((p \vee q) \cdot (p \vee r))$
Double Negation (D.N.):	$p \equiv \sim \sim p$
Transportation (Trans.):	$(p \supset q) \equiv (\sim q \supset \sim p)$
Material Implication (Impl.)	$(p \supset q) \equiv (\sim p \vee q)$
	$(p \supset q) \equiv \sim (p \cdot \sim q)$
Material Equivalence (Equiv.):	$(p \equiv q) \equiv ((p \supset q) \cdot (q \supset p))$
	$(p \equiv q) \equiv ((p \cdot q) \vee (\sim p \cdot \sim q))$
Exportation (Exp.)	$((p \cdot q) \supset r) \equiv (p \supset (q \supset r))$
Tautology ((Taut.):	$p \equiv (p \vee p)$
	$p \equiv (p \cdot p)$

Unlike the first eight rules of inference, the rules of equivalence included under the rule of replacement can be applied to parts of lines in a proof, as well as to entire lines.

Examples:

1. p	Premise
2. ~q ⊃ ~p / ∴ q	Premise / Conclusion
3. p ⊃ q	Trans., 2
4. q	M.P.,1,3

1. p	Premise
2. q / ∴ p ≡ q	Premise / Conclusion
3. q ∨ ~p	Add.,2
4. ~p ∨ q	Comm.,3
5. p ⊃ q	Impl.,4
6. p ∨ ~q	Add.,1
7. ~q ∨ p	Comm.,6
8. q ⊃ p	Impl.,7
9. (p ⊃ q) · (q ⊃ p)	Conj.,5,8
10. p ≡ q	Equiv.,9

It must be emphasized that there are an infinite number of possible *correct* deductive proofs of any truth-functionally valid argument. The only difference is in terms of factors such as simplicity, which in no way affect the proof of validity *per se*. Thus, the second argument above is also proven valid by the following proof.

Example:

1. p	Premise
2. q / ∴ p ≡ q	Premise / Conclusion
3. p · q	Conj.,1,2
4. (p · q) ∨ (~p · ~q)	Add.,3
5. p ≡ q	Taut.,4

Exercise 4-5
Provide a justification for each line of each proof below.

1.
1. p ⊃ q		Premise
2. ~p ⊃ r / ∴ r ∨ q		Premise / Conclusion
3. ~q ⊃ ~p		_____
4. ~q ⊃ r		_____
5. ~~q ∨ r		_____
6. q ∨ r		_____
7. r ∨ q		_____

2.
1. (p ∨ q) ⊃ r		Premise
2. p / ∴ r		Premise / Conclusion
3. p ∨ q		_____
4. r		_____

3. 1. $p \supset (r \supset q)$ Premise
    2. p Premise
    3. $r / \therefore q$ Premise / Conclusion
    4. $r \supset q$ _____
    5. q _____

4. 1. $p \lor q$ Premise
    2. $\sim q \lor r$ Premise
    3. $\sim p \cdot (r \supset s) / \therefore s$ Premise / Conclusion
    4. $\sim p$ _____
    5. q _____
    6. $\sim \sim q$ _____
    7. r _____
    8. $r \supset s$ _____
    9. s _____

5. 1. $\sim (q \lor \sim p)$ Premise
    2. $(p \cdot \sim q) \supset (p \supset r)$ Premise
    3. $r \supset s / \therefore p \supset s$ Premise / Conclusion
    4. $\sim q \cdot \sim \sim p$ _____
    5. $\sim q \cdot p$ _____
    6. $p \cdot \sim q$ _____
    7. $p \supset r$ _____
    8. $p \supset s$ _____

Exercise 4-6
Identify the error(s) in each of the following proofs.

1. 1. $\sim p$ Premise
    2. $\sim q / \therefore \sim (p \cdot q)$ Premise / Conclusion
    3. $\sim p \cdot \sim q$ Conj.,1,2
    4. $\sim (p \cdot q)$ De M.,3

2. 1. $p \supset (q \supset r)$ Premise
    2. $q / \therefore p \supset r$ Premise / Conclusion
    3. $p \supset r$ M.P.,1,2

3. 1. $((p \lor q) \supset r) \supset \sim (p \lor q)$ Premise
    2. $p / \therefore \sim r$ Premise / Conclusion
    3. $p \lor q$ Add.,2
    4. $\sim \sim (p \lor q)$ D.N.,3
    5. $\sim ((p \lor q) \supset r)$ M.T.,1,4
    6. $(p \lor q) \cdot \sim r$ Impl. and D.N., 6
    7. $\sim r$ Simp.,3

4. 1. p ∨ q   Premise
    2. ~ q ⊃ ~ r   Premise
    3. r / ∴ ~ p   Premise / Conclusion
    4. ~ ~ r   D.N.,3
    5. ~ ~ q   M.T.,2,4
    6. ~ p   D.S.,1,6

5. 1. (p ∨ q) ⊃ (r ∨ s)   Premise
    2. ~ p / ∴ ~ q ∨ (r ∨ s)   Premise / Conclusion
    3. q ⊃ (r ∨ s)   D.S.,1,2
    4. ~ q ∨ (r ∨ s)   Impl.,3

Exercise 4-7
Using the rules of inference discussed thus far, including the ten rules of replacement, construct a proof to demonstrate the validity of each of the following argument schemata.

1.   p ∨ q
     (q ∨ p) ⊃ (r ∨ s)
     (s ∨ r) ⊃ ~ q
     ∴ p

2.   q ⊃ ~ p
     p
     ∴ ~ q

3.   p ∨ (q ∨ r)
     (p ∨ q) ⊃ ~ s
     ~ r
     ∴ ~ s

4.   ~ r · ~ s
     (p ∨ q) ⊃ (r ∨ s)
     ∴ ~ (p ∨ q)

5.   ~ r · ~ s
     (p ∨ q) ⊃ (r ∨ s)
     ∴ ~ p · ~ q

6.   ~ r · ~ s
     (p ∨ q) ⊃ (r ∨ s)
     ∴ ~ q

7.   ~ r · ~ s
     (p ∨ q) ⊃ (r ∨ s)
     ∴ ~ q ∨ t

8.   ~ r · ~ s
     (p ∨ q) ⊃ (r ∨ s)
     ∴ ~ q · ~ r

9.   ~ r ∨ ~ s
     (p · q) ⊃ (r · s)
     ∴ ~ (p · q)

10. ~ r ∨ ~ s
     ~ (r · s) ⊃ (p · q)
     ∴ q ∨ t

11. ~ p ∨ q
     (p ⊃ q) ⊃ (p ⊃ r)
     ∴ p ⊃ r

12. ~ p ∨ q
     (p ⊃ q) ⊃ (p ⊃ r)
     p
     ∴ r

13. ~ p ∨ q
     (p ⊃ q) ⊃ (p ⊃ r)
     p
     ∴ q · r

14. ~ (p · ~ q)
     (p ⊃ q) ⊃ (p ⊃ r)
     ∴ p ⊃ r

15. p · ~ r
     (p ⊃ q) ⊃ (p ⊃ r)
     ∴ p · ~ q

16. p · (q ∨ r)
     ~ (p · r)
     ∴ q

17. $p \cdot (q \lor r)$
     $\sim p$
  ∴ q

18. $(p \cdot q) \supset r$
    $(p \cdot r) \supset q$
    p
  ∴ $r \equiv q$

19. $(p \cdot q) \equiv (r \lor s)$
    r
  ∴ $p \cdot r$

20. $\sim p \lor (q \cdot r)$
    $r \supset p$
  ∴ $p \equiv r$

Conditional Proof

Not every argument which can be proven valid using truth tables can be proven valid using these eighteen rules of inference. The addition of the **rule of Conditional Proof** makes our deductive proof system **deductively complete**; that is, it makes the system such that it is possible to prove the validity of every argument which can be proven valid with truth tables.

The method of Conditional Proof involves assuming an additional premise which is actually the antecedent of a conditional (if . . . then . . .) statement that is necessary in the proof, and then deducing the consequent of the desired statement from the assumption and the original premises. The step ending the Conditional Proof must be a conditional statement, with the assumed premise as its antecedent.

Steps derived from the assumed premise are said to be *within the scope* of the assumption. As soon as the rule of Conditional Proof is asserted, the scope of the assumption is ended, and the assumption is said to be *discharged*. No formula which has been derived within the scope of the assumption (and which is, therefore, possibly dependent on the assumption) may be used outside its scope. This is because Conditional Proof asserts only that *if* the assumption (the antecedent of the conditional) is true, the consequent is also true; it does not assert that the assumption is, in fact, true. Any number of assumptions can be made, providing they are eventually discharged, leaving the conclusion dependent only on the premise(s) of the original argument schema.

Examples:

1. $p \supset q / \therefore p \supset (p \cdot q)$	Premise / Conclusion
2. p	Assumption
3. q	M.P.,1,2
4. $p \cdot q$	Conj.,2,3
5. $p \supset (p \cdot q)$	C.P.,2,4

1. $(p \lor q) \supset (r \cdot s)$	Premise
2. $\sim r / \therefore \sim s \supset \sim q$	Premise / Conclusion
3. q	Assumption
4. $q \lor p$	Add.,3
5. $p \lor q$	Comm.,4
6. $r \cdot s$	M.P.,5,1
7. s	Simp.,6

8. $q \supset s$	C.P.,3-7
9. $\sim s \supset \sim q$	Trans.,8

Exercise 4-8

Prove the validity of each of the following argument schemata using the rules of inference including the Conditional Proof.

1. $\dfrac{q}{\therefore p \supset (p \cdot q)}$

2. $\dfrac{p \supset (q \supset r)}{\therefore (p \cdot q) \supset r}$

3. $\dfrac{\begin{array}{c} p \supset (q \supset r) \\ p \supset q \end{array}}{\therefore p \supset r}$

4. $\dfrac{q \supset r}{\therefore p \supset (q \supset (r \lor s))}$

5. $\dfrac{p \supset r}{\therefore p \supset (q \supset (r \lor s))}$

6. $\dfrac{(p \cdot q) \lor (r \cdot s)}{\therefore \sim p \supset (r \cdot s)}$

7. $\dfrac{p \cdot (q \lor r)}{\therefore \sim q \supset (p \cdot r)}$

8. $\dfrac{\begin{array}{c} r \equiv s \\ p \lor r \end{array}}{\therefore \sim p \supset (r \cdot s)}$

9. $\dfrac{s}{\therefore p \supset (q \supset (r \supset s))}$

10. $\dfrac{r}{\therefore p \supset (p \lor q)}$

Indirect Proof

The **Indirect Proof**, also called the *reductio ad absurdum proof*, is a special case of Conditional Proof. In this, we assert the negation of the conclusion as our assumed premise and then derive a contradiction from it, which then permits us to derive the conclusion of the argument schema.

Example:

1.	$p \supset (q \supset r)$	Premise
2.	$\sim s \supset (p \lor r)$	Premise
3.	$p \supset q / \therefore s \lor r$	Premise / Conclusion
4.	$\sim (s \lor r)$	Assumption
5.	$\sim s \cdot \sim r$	De.M.,4
6.	$\sim s$	Simp.,5
7.	$p \lor r$	M.P.,2,6
8.	$\sim r$	Simp.,5
9.	p	D.S.,7,8
10.	q	M.P.,3,9
11.	$q \supset r$	M.P.,1,9
12.	r	M.P.,10,11
13.	$r \cdot \sim r$	Conj.,8,12
14.	$s \lor r$	I.P.,4-13

The deductive proof system provided in this chapter is deductively complete— that is, any argument which can be proven to be truth-functionally valid by means of truth tables can also be proven valid by means of our nineteen rules of inference (or twenty if the Indirect Proof is considered a separate rule).

However, our deductive system does not provide a mechanical decision procedure, a mechanical procedure that guarantees that in a finite number of steps we will have proven that a given argument is valid or invalid. The system of rules provided cannot be used at all to prove invalidity. Failure to derive the desired conclusion after a specified number of steps could just as well indicate a failure on the part of the individual to find the proper sequence of steps, as it could indicate the invalidity of the argument. Therefore, if after trying for a reasonable length of time to construct a proof, one has not been able to do it, it would be appropriate to test the argument by the short truth-table method, which does enable us to prove invalidity.

Exercise 4-9
Prove the validity of each of the following argument schemata using the method of Indirect Proof.

1. $\sim q \supset (\sim p \cdot r)$
   $\sim r$
   $\therefore q$

2. $p \supset (q \cdot r)$
   $\sim q$
   $\therefore \sim p$

3. $p \lor (q \cdot r)$
   $p \lor t$
   $t \supset \sim (q \cdot r)$
   $\therefore p$

4. $(r \lor q) \supset p$
   $p \supset (s \cdot t)$
   $\sim s \lor \sim t$
   $\therefore \sim (r \lor q)$

5. $\sim p \supset q$
   $\sim (\sim p \cdot q)$
   $\therefore p$

6. $(p \cdot q) \supset r$
   $\sim p \supset r$
   q
   $\therefore r$

7. $p \equiv q$
   $\sim r \lor p$
   $\therefore r \supset q$

8. $p \cdot q$
   $\sim (p \supset q)$
   $\therefore r \supset s$

Exercise 4-10
Prove the validity or invalidity of each of the following argument schemata by any of the methods discussed in this chapter.

1. $p \supset (q \supset r)$
   r
   $\therefore p \supset q$

2. $r \supset s$
   $p \supset q$
   $p \supset s$
   $\therefore q \lor r$

3. $p \supset q$
   $r \lor p$
   $\sim r$
   $\therefore q$

4. $p \lor q$
   $p \supset r$
   $r \supset s$
   $\sim r$
   $\therefore q$

5. $p \lor q$
   $p \lor r$
   $q \supset \sim r$
   $\therefore p$

6. $(p \cdot q) \supset (r \lor s)$
$r \supset p$
$\sim r \lor \sim s$
q
$\therefore p \supset s$

7. $p \supset q$
$r \supset s$
$(q \lor s) \supset t$
$p \lor r$
$\therefore t$

8. $p \supset (q \lor r)$
$q \supset s$
$s \supset t$
$p \supset \sim t$
p
$\therefore r$

9. $p \supset (q \cdot r)$
$\sim s \lor \sim t$
$s \supset (p \lor u)$
$u \supset (r \supset t)$
$\therefore u \lor \sim s$

10. $p \supset q$
$\sim r \supset \sim q$
$\sim s$
$q \supset (\sim r \lor p)$
$s \supset (t \lor u)$
$t \supset (p \lor s)$
$\therefore s \supset (\sim p \supset q)$

5.
quanti-
fica-
tional
logic

Quantificational Logic

Quantificational logic incorporates the symbols, definitions, and deductive rules of the *propositional logic* studied in Chapters 3 and 4, but adds to them. In so doing it becomes a more powerful tool for analyzing statements and arguments.

In propositional logic, statements are the basic unit; and unless a statement is a truth-functional compound, it can be treated only as a whole and symbolized by a propositional constant. The internal structure of statements cannot be symbolized. However, in quantificational logic, the internal structure of statements can be symbolized. The names of individuals, their properties, and their relations to one another can be specified symbolically; in addition, it is possible to give symbolic expression to the terms of quantification—'all,' 'some,' etc.—to which the propositional logic is necessarily blind.

Thus, quantificational logic can deal with those arguments in which the logical relation of one statement to another is dependent on the internal structure of each of the two statements in question.

Example:
All dogs are carnivorous.
Shadow is a dog.
Therefore, Shadow is carnivorous.

This is a valid argument. But in order to prove that it is valid we must be able to symbolize it in such a way that the presence of the common terms in the premises and conclusion is shown. For instance, our symbolization of the argument above must show that 'dog' is contained in both premises and 'carnivorous' and 'shadow' are each contained in a premise and the conclusion. This presence of common terms can be shown if the argument is symbolized using quantificational logic (as will be done later), but not if it is symbolized using propositional logic. Since in propositional logic only statements taken as a whole can be symbolized, the three statements comprising this argument can only be expressed in the following schema:

Example:
p
q
∴r

It is impossible from this symbolizing of the argument to show that it is valid.

The Grammar of Quantification

As was the case in propositional logic, the logical operators '∼', '∨', '·', '⊃', and '≡', are used in quantificational logic to symbolize the logical relations between statements. However, in quantificational logic they can also be used in symbolizing the internal structure of individual statements. In addition, quantificational logic employs the following symbols: the **universal quantifier**, usually '(x)', '(y)', '(z)'; the **existential quantifier**, usually '(∃x)', '(∃y)', '(∃z)'; **individual variables** (usually 'x', 'y', 'z'); **individual constants** ('a' through 't'); and **predicates**, usually abbreviated by the capital letters 'A' through 'Z'.

The basic units of quantificational statements are predicates in association with one or more individual variables or individual constants.

Examples:
Fx or Fxy (variables)
Fa or Gab (constants)
Gxa or Gby (both variables and constants)

We will start with expressions containing only individual constants, for they are easier to discuss. An **individual constant** stands for the name or definite description of some individual thing, person, event, number, etc. A **predicate** is an expression that, joined with one or more individual constants, expresses a complete statement.

Examples:
1. 'Ck' = 'Kathy is playing cards'
   Where 'C' = 'is playing cards'
         'k' = 'Kathy'

2. 'Tbd' = 'Bill is taller than dad'
   Where 'T' = 'is taller than'
         'b' = 'Bill'
         'd' = 'dad

A **monadic** predicate is a predicate which is joined with only one individual variable or one individual constant (e.g., the predicate 'C' in statement 1 above). A monadic predicate, joined with an individual constant, constitutes a **singular statement** (e.g., statement 1 above). A **dyadic** predicate is a predicate which is joined with two individual variables, or two individual constants, or one of each. (The predicate 'T' in example 2 above is dyadic.) A dyadic predicate, along with its two variables or constants, constitutes a **relational** expression; that is, it expresses a relation between the two variables or two constants or between a variable and a constant. A dyadic predicate, when joined with two individual constants, constitutes a **nonquantified relational statement** (e.g., statement 2 above). Predicates joined with three or more individual variables or individual constants or mixtures thereof are called **polyadic** and form complex relational expressions. Polyadic predicates joined only with individual constants form **complex relational statements.**

If a predicate is joined with one or more individual variables (perhaps along with individual constants) the resulting expression is not a statement—that is, it has no truth value—and is called an **open sentence.** (Such expressions are called 'open sentences' because they are not statements but can be converted into statements by systematic substitution of individual constants for their individual variables.)

Examples:
3. 'Cx' = 'x is playing cards'
4. 'Txd' = 'x is taller than dad'

The individual variable 'x' (or 'y' or 'z' in other cases) functions in expressions such as these like the indefinite pronoun 'it.' Since 'x' does not refer to anything in particular, the expressions containing it are neither true or false. Hence any such expression has no truth value, is not a statement, and could not occur as a line in a deductive proof.

Although 'Cx' is not a statement, each of the following expressions is a statement and could occur as a line of a proof:

Examples:
5. 'Ca' = 'Al is playing cards'
6. '(x)Cx' = 'Everything in the universe is playing cards'
7. '(∃x)Cx' = 'At least one thing is playing cards'

Sentence 5 is a singular statement, and it is possible to determine whether it is true or false. In sentence 6, the presence of the universal quantifier '(x)' determines that the 'x' in 'Cx' will mean 'everything in the universe'. In sentence 7, the presence of the existential quantifier '(∃x)' determines that the 'x' in 'Cx' will mean 'at least one thing'. Hence in both cases 'x' has a definable meaning, and thus it is possible to determine whether the sentence is true or false.

Scope, Bound Variables, and Free Variables
Examine the following sentence:

Example:
8. (x)((Fx · Gx) ⊃ Hx)
'F' = 'is a fowl'
'G' = 'is a goose'
'H' = 'honks'

The fact that the whole expression '(Fx · Gx) ⊃ Hx' is contained within the outermost set of parentheses indicates that the whole expression is within the **scope** of the universal quantifier '(x)'. (Parentheses are not needed to indicate scope for noncompound expressions such as '(x)Cx' above.) This means that every 'x' occurring within '(Fx · Gx) ⊃ Hx'—every 'x' within the scope of '(x)'—is to have its meaning specified by '(x)': 'everything in the universe'. Thus, sentence 8 can be read: "For every x in the universe, if x is a fowl and x is a goose, then x honks."

Any individual variable (here any 'x') is said to be **bound** if it lies within the scope of a quantifier of the same letter (here '(x)'). In the case of sentence 8, all three occurrences of 'x' in the sentence—that is, all the occurrences in the expression '(Fx · Gx) ⊃ Hx'—are bound because all are within the scope of the quantifier '(x)'. But this would not be true if sentence 8 were changed in the following manner:

Example:
9. (x) (Fx · Gx) ⊃ Hx

In sentence 9 the whole expression '(Fx · Gx) ⊃ Hx' is not enclosed in parentheses, hence the whole expression is not within the scope of '(x)'. Only that part enclosed in the set of parentheses whose left parenthesis follows immediately after the quantifier—that is, only 'Fx · Gx'—is within the scope of the quantifier. As a result, only the 'x's joined to the predicates 'F' and 'G' are bound. The 'x' joined to the predicate 'H' is not within the scope of the quantifier '(x)' and is thus not bound. Since it is not a bound variable, it is by definition a **free** variable. Since the variable 'x' joined to the predicate 'H' is outside the scope of the quantifier '(x)', it does not have its meaning specified by the quantifier '(x)': it does not mean 'everything in the universe'. As a matter of fact, there is no way of telling what this 'x' means. Only bound variables have definable meanings—meanings determined by the quantifiers within whose scope they fall—free variables do not. Since sentence 9 contains a free variable, with no definable meaning, it has no meaningful English translation.

Universally and Existentially Quantified Statements

When all the variables in a sentence are bound, the sound expresses a statement, a **quantified** or **generalized** statement. No sentence containing a free variable expresses a statement. Only a sentence expressing a statement can occur as a line in a proof.

From this point on in the text of this chapter summary (though not in the exercises) we will assume that all sentences discussed are those which express statements, those which could be used as steps in a proof. We also will assume that we have not symbolized a statement correctly if we have written an expression containing a free variable.

A **generalized** or **quantified statement** is a statement in which the entire expression following the quantifier lies within the scope of that quantifier. A statement is **universally generalized** or **universally quantified** if it begins with a universal quantifier (with no negation sign preceding it), and the entire following expression lies within the scope of this quantifier. A statement is **existentially generalized** or **existentially quantified** if it begins with an existential quantifier (with no negation sign preceding it), and the entire following expression lies within the scope of this quantifier.

Examples:
Universally quantified:
  (x) ((Fx · Gx) ⊃ Hx)
Not universally quantified:
  ~ (x) ((Fx · Gx) ⊃ Hx)
Existentially quantified:
  (∃x) ((Fx · Gx) ⊃ Hx)
Not existentially quantified:
  (∃x) (Fx · Gx) ⊃ Hx
  ~ (∃x) ((Fx · Gx) ⊃ Hx)
A compound of one universally quantified and one existentially quantified statement:
  (x) (Fx · Gx) ⊃ (∃x) Hx

A universally quantified statement is true if and only if every instance of its open sentence is true. For example, '(x)Cx' is true if and only if all possible substitutions for 'x' in 'Cx' result in true statements. If we take the predicate 'C' to mean 'is playing cards', as defined above, then 'Cx' will mean 'x is playing cards' and there are many substitutions for 'x' which yield false statements—for example, 'The pyramid of Cheops is playing cards.' Thus the universally quantified statement '(x)Cx' is not true. The universal quantifier '(x)' refers to everything in the universe, unless the **universe of discourse** it refers to is specifically restricted to all persons, all animals, or the like.

An existentially quantified statement is true if and only if at least one instance of its open sentence is true. For instance, '(∃x) Cx' is true as long as at least one substitution for 'x' in 'Cx' results in a true statement, that is, if at least one person in the universe is playing cards.

The most generally useful form of universally quantified statement is the **universal conditional**, that is, a statement such as '(x) (Sx ⊃ Px)', which approximates in meaning the 'All S are P' statement of traditional logic.

Example:
10. '(x) (Sx ⊃ Px)' = 'For all x, if x is a sequoia, then x is a pine.'
11. 'All S are P' = 'All sequoias are pines.'

The most generally useful form of existentially quantified statement is the **existential conjunction**, that is, a statement such as '(∃x) (Sx · Px)', which approximates in meaning the 'Some S are P' statement of traditional logic.

Examples:
12. '(∃x) (Sx · Px)' = 'There is at least one x such that x is a smoker and x is a person.'
13. 'Some S are P' = 'Some smokers are persons.'

When two different variables are used with dyadic predicates, two quanti-fiers are needed to produce a quantified statement.

Examples:
14. (x) (y) (Dxy ⊃ Cxy)
15. (∃x) (y) (Px · Py) ⊃ Lxy)

The Predicate of Identity
If we wished to symbolize Thomas Hobbes' dictum "Man is a wolf to man," we could, using 'W' = 'is a wolf to', and limiting the universe of discourse to humans, express the dictum as follows:

Example:
16. (x) (y) Wxy

This could be read as 'For any person x and for any person y, x is a wolf to y.' From statement 16, however, would follow this statement:

Example:
17. (x) Wxx

This could be read as: 'For any person x, x is a wolf to x (to himself).' This **reflexive** relation, a relation of any person to himself or herself, was not intended by Hobbes. He did not wish to say that man is a wolf to *himself*, but only to *other* men. So the reflexive relation should be eliminated, if possible. This can be done by using the **predicate of identity**, 'I', where 'Ixy' = 'x is identical with y'.

Example:
18. (x) (y) (~ Ixy ⊃ Wxy)

This can be read as: 'For any person x and for any person y, if x is not identical with y, then x is a wolf to y.' This, finally, is the meaning Hobbes intended.

Exercise 5-1
Open sentences are called *atomic* if, like 'Ax' or 'Fxy', they contain no truth-functional operators. For each of the following, write the open sentences that you would use in a quantificational analysis of the statement. Use letters only for variables; express predicates in words.

1. If a woman is a college graduate, she is not stupid.
   _____

   _____

2. None but players of the first rank entered the tournament.
   _____

   _____

3. All five-legged creatures are hideous.

_____

_____

4. All the cheap goods in the store are either shoddily made or defective.

_____

_____

5. If all centipedes are nonmammals then all mammals are noncentipedes.

_____

_____

6. Every human is either alive or not alive.

_____

_____

7. There are no humans that are not mammals.

_____

_____

8. Emil is in the tournament and there is a player who is in the tournament whom Emil cannot beat.

_____

_____

9. Members of the L family greet everyone they meet, provided that they remember their names.

_____

_____

10. Some actors that are award winners are not Academy Award winners.

_____

_____

Exercise 5-2
For each of the following, indicate your abbreviations for open sentences and singular statements, and express in quantificational symbolism.

1. Susan is always on time for biology class.

_____

_____

2. New movies are not always the best movies.

_____

_____

3. All members of the Dean's List are students with good grades.

_____

_____

4. Most heavy drinkers prefer scotch.

_____

_____

5. No one who is an atheist believes in God.

_____

_____

6. None but players of the first rank entered the tournament.

_____

_____

7. All the cheap goods in the store are either shoddily made or defective.

_____

_____

8. If all centipedes are nonmammals then all mammals are noncentipedes.

_____

_____

9. Emil is in the tournament and there is a player who is in the tournament whom Emil cannot beat.

_____

_____

10. Members of the L family greet everyone they meet, provided that they remember their names.

_____

_____

_____

Exercise 5-3

Give, as closely as possible, colloquial English equivalents for the quantificational statements given below.

1. (x) (Mx ⊃ ~ Fx)
   'Mx' = 'x is male'
   'Fx' = 'x is female'

_____

2. (x) Fx ⊃ (∃x) (Dx)
   'Fx' = 'x is finite'
   'Dx' = 'x is dead'

_____

_____

3. $\sim (x)(Cx \supset Dx)$
   'Cx' = 'x is a canine'
   'Dx' = 'x is a dog'

---

4. $(\exists x)(Cx \cdot Dx)$
   'Cx' = 'x is a canine'
   'Dx' = 'x is a dog'

---

5. $(x)(Fx \lor Ex)$
   'Fx' = 'x is a friend'
   'Ex' = 'x is an enemy'

---

6. $(x)(Ax \supset Ex) \supset (\exists x)(Ax \cdot Fx)$
   'Ax' = 'x applied for the job'
   'Ex' = 'x expected that the job demanded a college education'
   'Fx' = 'x was familiar with the writings of Homer'

---

7. $(x)(y)((Ox \cdot Wyx) \supset Rxy)$
   'Ox' = 'x is a member of the O family'
   'Wyx' = 'y owes x money'
   'Rxy' = 'x remembers the name of y'

---

8. $(x)(y)((\sim Tx \cdot Ty) \supset \sim Bxy)$
   'Tx' = 'x is in the tournament'
   'Bxy' = 'x has beaten y'

---

9. $(x)(Wx \supset (\exists y)(My \cdot \sim Lyx))$
   'My' = 'x is a musician'
   'Wx' = 'y is a musical work'
   'Lyx' = 'y likes x'

---

10. $(x)(y)(((Mx \cdot My) \cdot Kxy)) \supset Lxy)$
    'Mx' = 'M is a member of the orchestra'
    'Kxy' = 'x knows y intimately'
    'Lxy' = 'x likes y'

Rules for Deduction

In propositional logic there are methods for proving the validity and/or invalidity of any argument. Some of these methods are "failproof" except for human or computer error. There are no such systems of proof in quantificational logic. But it has been proved that by adding to the rules of propositional logic certain rules specifically for quantificational deductions, it is possible to derive the conclusion of any valid argument.

The rules to be added are as follows:

1. **Universal Instantiation.** From a universally generalized statement, one may infer a statement from which the initial quantifier has been deleted and the corresponding variables replaced, uniformly, by any constant 'a' through 't'. In annotating such a deduction, write 'U.I.'

   Example:
   1. (x) Fx   Premise
   2. Fa   U.I., 1

2. **Existential Instantiation.** From an existentially generalized statement, one may infer a statement from which the initial quantifier has been deleted and the corresponding variables replaced, uniformly, by any constant 'a' through 't'. In annotating such a deduction, write 'E.I.' *Provided that* the constant selected does not appear in the line instantiated from, or in any earlier line of the deduction.

   Example:
   1. (∃x) Fx   Premise
   2. Fa   E.I., 1

3. **Universal Generalization.** From a statement containing a constant, one may infer a universally generalized statement in which a quantifier new to the statement has been prefixed, and in which the constant is uniformly replaced by the variable of the new quantifier. In annotating such a deduction, write 'U.G.' *Provided that* the statement generalized upon is not a premise; and that the constant replaced does not occur either in a premise from which that statement has been derived or in a statement derived by Existential Instantiation.

   Example:
   1. (x) Fx   Premise
   2. Fa   U.I., 1
   3. Fa ∨ Ga   Add., 2
   4. (x) (Fx ∨ Gx)   U.G., 3

4. **Existential Generalization.** From a statement containing a constant, one may infer an existentially generalized statement in which a quantifier new to the statement has been prefixed, and in which the constant is replaced in one or more occurrences by the variable of the new quantifier. In annotating such a deduction, write 'E.G.'

Example:
1. Fa   Premise
2. (∃x) Fx   E.G., 2

5. **Quantifier Exchange.** From a universally or existentially generalized statement, or from the negation of either, one may infer a statement with opposite quantifier and with opposite sign preceding and following the quantifier. In annotating such a deduction, write 'Q.E.'

Example:
1. (∃x) ~ (Fx ∨ Gx)   Premise
2. ~ (x) (Fx ∨ Gx)   Q.E., 1

Universal Instantiation and Universal Generalization are generally employed jointly, as are Existential Instantiation and Existential Generalization. To deal with a quantificational argument by truth-functional analysis it is necessary to remove quantifiers, and instantiation permits the removal of quantifiers from a generalized statement. Generalization permits their reintroduction after truth-functional analysis is completed.

The restrictions placed on the rule of Universal Generalization make it the most difficult of the five rules to use correctly. The "provided that" clause of this rule should be carefully observed. The restrictions placed on the use of the rule of Existential Instantiation should also be noted.

Exercise 5-4
In each of the cases below, if one follows the pattern of the English sentences, it is natural to symbolize the two members of each pair differently. For example, in No. 1 it is natural to symbolize 'Some apples are rotten' as '(∃x) (Ax · Rx)' and 'Some rotten things are apples' as '(∃x) (Rx · Ax),' in each case abbreviating 'x is an apple' as 'Ax' and 'x is rotten' as 'Rx.' On any correct symbolization of each pair, the resulting quantificational statements will be logically equivalent.

For each pair, (a) symbolize, using the abbreviations indicated above, plus 'Fx' for 'x is a fruit' and 'Px' for 'x is a pear'; and (b) show that the members of each pair are logically equivalent by deducing each from the other.

1. a. Some apples are rotten.
   b. Some rotten things are apples.
2. a. Some apples are not rotten.
   b. Some things that are not rotten are apples.

3. a. All apples are fruits.
   b. No non-fruits are apples.
4. a. All apples are fruits.
   b. All non-fruits are non-apples.
5. a. All apples are fruits.
   b. No apples are non-fruits.
6. a. No apples are pears.
   b. No pears are apples.
7. a. It is not the case that all fruits are apples.
   b. Some fruits are not apples.
8. a. All apples are fruits.
   b. It is not the case that some apples are not fruits.
9. a. No apples are pears.
   b. It is not the case that some apples are pears.
10. a. It is not the case that no fruit are apples.
    b. Some fruit are apples.

Exercise 5-5
For the following arguments, (a) symbolize the premises and conclusion (indicating abbreviations and what they stand for), and (b) deduce the conclusion from the premises.

1. No tomatoes grow on trees, and no squash grow on trees. Since acorns grow on trees, they are neither squash nor tomatoes.
2. Members of the T family speak to everyone whose name they remember; they also gossip about everyone they speak to. Consequently, if any member of the T family remembers anyone's name, they gossip about that person.
3. If someone is injured on the job, every member of group Z is alerted automatically. Felice, who is a member of group Z, has not been alerted. Therefore, no one has been injured on the job.
4. Some three-year-old horses are neither thoroughbreds nor trotters. Only three-year-old thoroughbreds are eligible for the Belmont Stakes. Hence, some three-year-old horses are not eligible for the Belmont Stakes.
5. If the horse that finishes first is disqualified, the second horse is placed first unless it is disqualified also. Since we know that Lazy Bill finished first and was disqualified, and Maizy Dae, who finished second, was not placed first, we can conclude that Maizy Dae was disqualified also.
6. (For the following argument, which is an enthymeme, a 'transitivity premise' must be added—that is, a premise analogous to 'If anything is larger than a second, and the second is larger than the third, then the first is larger than the third.' Supply such a premise.) Ellen runs faster than Harry and Harry runs faster than Joanne. Therefore, Ellen runs faster than Joanne.

7. All human beings are entitled to equal respect. Sally and John are human beings. Sally, therefore, is entitled to as much respect as John.

8. No farmers are executives. Bill is an executive, so he is not a farmer.

9. All beauty contest queens are beautiful and some college graduates are beauty contest queens. Consequently, some college graduates are beautiful.

10. All politicians are liars. Some women are politicians. Thus, it follows that some women are liars.

11. Terriers and poodles are dogs. Cairns are terriers. Therefore, Cairns are dogs.

12. Universities are either financially sound or bankrupt. Universities are not all bankrupt. Thus, it follows that there are financially sound universities.

Exercise 5-6
(a) Symbolize the conclusion of each of the following arguments. (b) Deduce the conclusion from the symbolized premises. In each case, 'Cx' is an abbreviation for 'x is a cow'; 'Hx' is an abbreviation for 'x has horns'; and 'Ux' is an abbreviation for 'x is a unicorn'.

1. Premises: '(x) (Cx ⊃ Hx) ⊃ (∃x) Ux' and '(x) ~ Ux'.
   Conclusion: There are cows that have no horns.

2. Premises: '(∃x) (Cx · Hx)' and '(x) ~ Hx'
   Conclusion: Everything is an unicorn.

3. Premises: '(∃x) (Cx · Hx) ⊃ (x) Ux' and '(∃x) ~ Ux'.
   Conclusion: All cows are hornless.

6. enumerative induction

Inductive versus Deductive Arguments

A **deductive argument** is any argument such that if the premises are true, then the conclusion must also be true. That is, the premises provide absolute support for the conclusion; or, in other words, the conclusion is completely contained in the premises. The addition of one or more premises in no way affects the support which the premises provide for the conclusion. Deductive arguments are valid by virtue of their form. A false premise in a valid deductive argument is not sufficient to prove the conclusion false, and it in no way affects the validity of the argument.

Examples:
All swans are white.
Therefore, swan D is white.

If all carpenters are skilled workers, then Tom is a skilled worker.
All carpenters are skilled workers.
Therefore, Tom is a skilled worker.

An **inductive argument** is an argument that does not satisfy the definition of a deductive argument as given above. Thus, it is any argument such that even if all the premise are true, the conclusion may still be false. That is, the premises provide, at most, only partial support for the conclusion; or, in other words, the conclusion is, at most, only partly contained in the premises. The addition of further premises may change the support provided for the conclusion:

Examples:
Swan A is white.
Swan B is white.
Swan C is white.
Therefore, all swans are white.

All robins are birds and can fly.
All sparrows are birds and can fly.
All eagles are birds and can fly.
All penguins are birds.
Therefore, all penguins can fly.

Enumerative Inductions

An **enumerative induction** is an argument whose premise(s) comprise a listing of cases, concerning either individuals or classes of individuals, to support conclusions about individuals or classes of individuals. On the basis of the different relationships between the premises and the conclusion, it is possible to distinguish between two types of enumerative inductive argument.

An inductive argument which is such that the falsity of one or more premises may lessen the probability of the conclusion, but cannot necessitate the falsity

of the conclusion, is an **induction by analogy**. An analogy is a comparison between two or more things or ideas in which similarities are pointed out.
Analogies are sometimes used to clarify or explain a difficult or unfamiliar
concept. In such cases, an analogical argument generally does not exist.

Examples:
Induction by Analogy:
Tim is a graduate of Harvard Law School and earns a lot of money.
Susan is a graduate of Harvard Law School and earns a lot of money.
Bob is a graduate of Harvard Law School.
Therefore, Bob probably earns a lot of money.

Analogical Explanation:
The repetition of the opening motive of Beethoven's *Fifth Symphony*
throughout the composition may be likened to Paul Klee's painting
Fugue in Red. There is one basic form in both, which is stretched, con-
densed, and colored in a variety of different ways.

An inductive argument with a universal conclusion, in which at least one of
the premises is such that its falsity could necessitate the falsity of the conclusion,
is an **inductive generalization**. An inductive generalization may contain premises
either about individuals or about classes of individuals, but it cannot possibly
have a particular conclusion, regardless of whether the premises are general or
particular.

Examples:
War and Peace is a novel by Tolstoi and is a great book.
Anna Karenina is a novel by Tolstoi and is a great book.
Resurrection is a novel by Tolstoi and is a great book.
Therefore, all novels by Tolstoi are great books.

All elephants are mammals and are warm-blooded.
All giraffes are mammals and are warm-blooded.
All lions are mammals and are warm-blooded.
All humans are mammals and are warm-blooded.
Therefore, all mammals are warm-blooded.

Note that if the first premise in the first example above was false because
Tolstoi did not, in fact, write *War and Peace*, the falsity of the premise would
not imply the falsity of the conclusion. However, if this premise was false
because Tolstoi did write *War and Peace* and it is not a great book, then this
would imply that it is false that *all* novels by Tolstoi are great books. It is this
feature that qualifies the argument as an inductive generalization.

Exercise 6-1
Determine whether each of the following is an induction by analogy or an inductive generalization.

1. All ants are insects and are social animals. All bees are insects and are social animals. All termites are insects and are social animals. Therefore, all insects must be social animals.
2. All ants are insects and are social animals. All bees are insects and are social animals. All termites are insects and are social animals. All flies are insects. So, all flies are social animals.
3. Rudolf Nureyev was trained by Alexander Pushkin and is a great ballet dancer. So were Mikhail Baryshnikov and Valery Panov, and they're great ballet dancers. Therefore, one may infer that all dancers trained by Alexander Pushkin are great ballet dancers.
4. Susan, Veronica, and Caroline are all intelligent women, and each reads *Ms.* magazine. Betty Ann is also an intelligent woman, so she also reads *Ms.* magazine.
5. All past presidents of the United States were men. Therefore, all future presidents probably will be men.
6. *The Mousetrap* and *Murder on the Orient Express* are both by Agatha Christie. Both are also interesting detective stories. *Murder Ahoy* is by Agatha Christie, so it too is probably an interesting detective story.
7. Joe, Frank, Carol, and Mike are all successful business executives and they all read the *Wall Street Journal*. Consequently, one can infer that all successful business executives read the *Wall Street Journal*.
8. John, Peter, Susan, and Frieda are friends of Bob and graduates from Michigan State, so probably all of Bob's friends are Michigan State graduates.
9. American, Eastern, and Braniff all charge the same coach fare for flights from Chicago to New York. Therefore, all airlines that have flights from Chicago to New York charge the same coach fare.
10. Scott Meredith is the literary agent for Norman Mailer, Gore Vidal, and Jacqueline Susann and all their books sell well. Meredith just took on Spiro Agnew as a client. So, Agnew's book will probably sell well.

Inductive and Deductive Strength
The support that the premises provide for the conclusion of an inductive argument can vary from just less than absolute support to no support whatsoever. Inductive arguments can be evaluated only in terms of their relative strengths. The relative strengths of inductive arguments *with the same set of premises* are inversely proportional to the deductive strengths of their conclusions. Of two statements, one is **deductively stronger** than another if and only if the first implies the second and the second does not imply the first. Likewise, of two statements, one is **deductively weaker** than another if and only if the second implies the first and the first does not imply the second. Statements are of

equal deductive strength if they imply each other. In the examples below, the arguments are arranged in order of decreasing inductive strength.

Examples:
All books which Mike has recommended were interesting.
Therefore, some of the books which Mike will recommend will be interesting.

All books which Mike has recommended were interesting.
Therefore, the next book which Mike will recommend will be interesting.

All books which Mike has recommended were interesting.
Therefore, all of the books which Mike will recommend will be interesting.

All books which Mike has recommended were interesting.
Therefore, Mike's recommendation of a book makes a book interesting.

While the arguments above are listed in order of decreasing inductive strengths, the conclusion statements of these arguments are arranged in order of increasing deductive strength.

Exercise 6-2
Place the following arguments in order of decreasing inductive strength.

1. Standard premise for all conclusions that follow:
   Every adult member of the Smith's family is a college graduate.
   Conclusions:
   a. Therefore, Mr. and Mrs. Smith's eight-year-old son and twelve-year old daughter will probably be college graduates.
   b. Therefore, all of Mr. and Mrs. Smith's three children will be college graduates.
   c. Therefore, at least one of Mr. and Mrs. Smith's children probably will be a college graduate.
   d. Therefore, Mr. and Mrs. Smith's eight-year-old son probably will be a college graduate.
   e. Therefore, being a member of the Smith family causes a person to be a college graduate.
2. Standard premise for all conclusions that follow:
   All articles of clothing designed by Pierre Cardin in the past have been expensive.
   Conclusions:
   a. Therefore, being an article of clothing designed by Pierre Cardin causes that article of clothing to be expensive.
   b. Therefore, all articles of clothing designed by Pierre Cardin are expensive.
   c. Therefore, all articles of clothing in Pierre Cardin's new line of evening dresses will be expensive.

   d. Therefore, some articles of clothing in Pierre's Cardin's new lines will be expensive.

   e. Therefore, all articles of clothing in Pierre Cardin's new lines of evening dresses and coats will be expensive.

3. Standard Premise for all conclusions that follow:

     All lions observed to date are carnivorous, warm-blooded mammals.

    Conclusions:

   a. Therefore, all lions are carnivorous, warm-blooded mammals.

   b. Therefore, the very next lion observed will be a carnivorous, warm-blooded mammal.

   c. Therefore, at least one lion that will be observed in the future will be a carnivorous, warm-blooded mammal.

   d. Therefore, being a lion causes an animal to be a carnivorous, warm-blooded mammal.

   e. Therefore, the next six lions observed in the future will be carnivorous, warm-blooded mammals.

4. Standard premise for all conclusions that follow:

     All South American countries have had at least one coup d'état in the past fifty years.

    Conclusions:

   a. Therefore, Chile will have a coup d'état in the next fifty years.

   b. Therefore, every South American country will have a coup d'état in the next fifty years.

   c. Therefore, at least one South American country will have a coup d'état in the next fifty years.

   d. Therefore, being a South American country will cause it to have a coup d'état in the next fifty years.

   e. Therefore, all South American countries have at least one coup d'état every fifty years.

Exercise 6-3
Place each of the arguments in Exercise 6-2 in order of increasing inductive strength.

Exercise 6-4
Place the conclusions of each of the arguments in Exercise 6-2 in order of decreasing deductive strength.

Exercise 6-5
Place the conclusions in each of the arguments in Exercise 6-2 in order of increasing deductive strength.

Criteria for Evaluating Enumerative Inductions
Three factors are important when evaluating the relative strength of enumerative inductions: positive and negative analogy, number of observed cases, and the relevance of the characteristics being compared or contrasted.

The way in which the individuals or classes of individuals cited in an enumerative induction are alike is called **positive analogy**; the way in which they are different is called **negative analogy**. Most interesting enumerative inductions involve premises which describe observed cases about individuals and/or classes of individuals and have conclusions concerned with an unobserved case about an individual and/or a class of individuals.

In general, an enumerative induction becomes weaker as the negative analogy *between observed and unobserved cases* increases, assuming everything else remains the same. In general, the stronger the positive analogy *between observed and unobserved* cases, the stronger the enumerative induction, assuming everything else is unchanged. Increasing the negative analogy *among the observed cases* in an enumerative induction will not usually weaken the argument; in fact, it may strengthen it, since the greater the negative analogy among the observed cases, the greater the number of possible unobserved cases that would have a positive analogy with the observed cases.

In general, as the number of observed cases mentioned in the premises of an enumerative induction increases, the stronger the argument will be. But as the number of observed cases increases, the inductive support given by each *additional* observed case decreases. However, an enumerative induction with only a few observed cases, or even one, is not necessarily a weak argument. Likewise, an enumerative induction with a large number of observed cases is not necessarily a strong argument.

The relevance of the characteristics being compared or contrasted will affect the strength of an enumerative induction. However, the determination of those characteristics which are relevant is not always a simple task, since there is no formal logical procedure which enables us to list all the possible relevant factors. To a considerable extent, determining what is relevant depends on an individual's perception, rather than on some absolute standard.

Exercise 6-6

Read each argument below carefully. Determine whether the addition of the suggested premise(s) weakens or strengthens the argument in terms of positive and negative analogy, relevance, and/or the number of observed cases.

1. All bees are insects and can fly.
   All flies are insects and can fly.
   All wasps are insects and can fly.
   Therefore, probably all insects can fly.
   a. Add the following premise only: All butterflies are insects and can fly.
   b. Add the following premise only: All moths are insects and can fly.
   c. Add the following premise only: All fleas are insects and do not fly.
   d. Add the following premise only: All spiders are insects and do not fly.
   e. Add premises a and b.
   f. Add premises a, b, and c.

2. The Thomases are Irish Catholic and have always voted Democratic.
   The O'Connors are Irish Catholic and have always voted Democratic.
   The Caseys are Irish Catholic and have always voted Democratic.
   The Flynns are Irish Catholic and have always voted Democratic.
   The Kellys are Irish Catholic.
   Therefore, the Kellys probably have always voted Democratic.
   a. Add the following premise only: Mrs. Kelly's brother was the Republican candidate for mayor last year.
   b. Add the following premise only: The Kelly's are registered Democrats.
   c. Add the following premise only: The Kelly's are very active in the Democratic party.
   d. Add the following premise only: The Thomases, O'Connors, Caseys, and Flynns are first-generation immigrants and the Kellys are fifth-generation immigrants.
   e. Add the following premise only: Ninety-five percent of Irish Catholic voters vote Democrat in every election.
   f. Add premises a and d.
   g. Add premises b and e.
   h. Add premises c and d.

3. The Franklins purchased a 1975 Maytag washing machine and have had excellent service.
   The Peppers purchased a 1975 Maytag washing machine and have had excellent service.
   The Goldslags purchased a 1975 Maytag washing machine and have had excellent service.
   The Corleones purchased a 1975 Maytag washing machine. Therefore, the Corleones will probably have excellent service.
   a. Add the following premise only: The Franklins', Peppers', Goldslags', and Corbeils' washing machines hold 24 pound loads, whereas the Corleones' washing machine holds a 16 pound load.
   b. Add the following premise only: The Franklins, Peppers, Goldslags, and Corbeils all use *White*, the soap powder recommended by the Maytag company, whereas the Corleones use *Wash*, the most inexpensive brand of soap powder.
   c. Add the following premise only: The Franklins, Peppers, Goldslags, and Corbeils all use a bleach and fabric softner in addition to soap powder, whereas the Corleones do not.
   d. Add the following premise only: The Petersons purchased a 1975 Maytag washing machine and have had excellent service.
   e. Add the following premise only: All the washing machines were manufactured at the same plant, tested by the same inspector, and purchased from the same store.
   f. Add the following premise only: The Corleones washing machine was a floor model, whereas all the other machines were new, and factory sealed.

    g. Add premises a, c, and d.

    h. Add premises e, and f.

4. John went to Excel high school and won a scholarship to college.

    Mary went to Excel high school and won a schloarship to college.

    Peter went to Excel high school and won a scholarship to college.

    Frances went to Excel High School and won a scholarship to college.

    Susan goes to Excel High School.

    Therefore, Susan probably will win a scholarship to college.

    a. Add the following premise only: John, Mary, Peter, Frances, and Susan each have B+ or better averages.

    b. Add the following premise only: When John, Mary, Peter and Frances graduated from Excel High School, the school had a special program preparing students for scholarship examinations; no such program exists now.

    c. Add the following premise only: John, Mary, Peter, and Frances only won scholarships to the state university; Susan has only applied for a scholarship at Harvard.

    d. Add the following premise only: John, Mary, and Susan took advanced courses in high school, whereas Peter and Frances did not take advanced courses.

    e. Add the following premise only: John, Mary, Peter and Frances scored between 600 and 650 on their college boards, whereas Susan scored between 700 and 750 on her college boards.

    f. Add premises a, d, and e.

    g. Add premises b and c.

Statistical Inductions

There are two types of statistical induction: a statistical induction by analogy and a statistical generalization. A **statistical induction by analogy** is an induction by analogy in which a numerical value appears as the quantifier for the subject term in the premises and/or conclusion. As with inductions by analogy, a statistical induction by analogy is such that the falsity of one or more of its premises cannot guarantee the falsity of its conclusion.

Example:

    Seventy-five percent of last year's graduating students from Excel High School received scholarships to college.

    Therefore, seventy-five percent of this year's graduating students from Excel High School will receive scholarships to college.

A **statistical generalization** is an inductive generalization in which a numerical value appears as the quantifier for the subject term in the premises and/or conclusion. As with inductive generalizations, a statistical generalization is such that it is possible that the falsity of at least one of its premises could necessitate the falsity of its conclusion.

Example:
Ninety percent of the students who graduated from Mouthpiece Law School last year passed the bar examination on the first try.
Ninety percent of the students who graduated from Mouthpiece Law School two years ago passed the bar examination on the first try.
Ninety percent of the students who graduated from Mouthpiece Law School three years ago passed the bar examination on the first try.
Therefore, ninety percent of the students who graduate from Mouthpiece Law School every year pass the bar examination on the first try.

The same criteria which are used to evaluate the relative strengths of enumerative inductions are used to evaluate the relative strengths of statistical inductions. The positive and negative analogies among observed cases and between observed and unobserved cases are important, as are the relevance of the characteristics shared by the observed and unobserved cases, and the number of observed cases cited in the premises.

In statistical inductions, the less precise the conclusion, the stronger the inductive support for it. However, often a middle point must be reached that provides both a sufficiently strong argument and a sufficiently precise conclusion to be useful for the desired purpose.

Exercise 6-7
Place the following arguments in order of decreasing inductive strength.

1. Standard premises for all conclusions that follow:
    Seventy-eight percent of 100 observed students graduating from law school last year passed the bar examination on the first try.
    Seventy-one percent of 100 observed students graduating from law school two years ago passed the bar examination on the first try.
    Seventy-three percent of 100 observed students graduating from law school three years ago passed the bar examination on the first try.
    Sixty-nine percent of 100 observed students graduating from law school four years ago passed the bar examination on the first try.
    Seventy-five percent of 100 observed students graduating from law school five years ago passed the bar examination on the first try.
    Conclusions:
    a. Therefore, at least sixty-nine percent of 100 observed students graduating from law school this year will pass the bar examination on the first try.
    b. Therefore, some of 100 observed students graduating from law school this year will pass the bar examination on the first try.
    c. Therefore, exactly seventy-two percent of 100 observed students graduating from law school this year will pass the bar examination on the first try.

    d. Therefore, between sixty-five and eighty percent of 100 observed students graduating from law school this year will pass the bar examination on the first try.

    e. Therefore, at least seventy-nine percent of 100 observed students graduating from law school this year will pass the bar examination on the first try.

2. Standard premise for all conclusions that follow:

      Ten percent of the 200 books published by our company last year sold 10,000 copies or more.

    Conclusions:

    a. Therefore, exactly ten percent of the books published by all companies last year sold 10,000 copies or more.

    b. Therefore, at least ten of the next 100 books our company publishes this year will sell 10,000 copies or more.

    c. Therefore, some of the next 100 books our company publishes this year will sell 10,000 copies or more.

    d. Therefore, exactly ten of the next 100 books our company publishes this year will sell 10,000 copies or more.

Exercise 6-8

Place the conclusions of each of the arguments in Exercise 6-7 in order of decreasing deductive strength.

Exercise 6-9

Read each argument carefully. Determine whether the addition of the suggested premise(s) weakens or strengthens the argument in terms of positive and negative analogy, relevance, and/or the number of observed cases.

    Seventy-five percent of 500 observed students graduating from law school last year passed the bar examination on the first try.

    Therefore, at least seventy-five percent of all students graduating from law school pass the bar examination on the first try.

    a. Add the following premise only: All of the 500 observed students graduated from the same law school.

    b. Add the following premise only: Of the 500 observed students 100 had straight A averages, 100 had B+ averages, 100 had B averages, 100 had C+ averages, and 100 had C averages.

    c. Add the following premise only: All of the 500 observed students were on their school law review.

    d. Add the following premise only: All of the 500 observed students were males.

2. Forty-one percent of 100 observed families watched *Rhoda* last week.

    Thirty-nine percent of 100 observed families watched *Rhoda* two weeks ago.

    Fifty percent of 100 observed families watched *Rhoda* three weeks ago.

    Forty-six percent of 100 observed families watched *Rhoda* four weeks ago.

Therefore, between thirty-nine and fifty percent of the families to be observed this week will watch *Rhoda*.

a. Of the 100 observed families in each group, all of them had their televisions turned on to *Maude* which precedes *Rhoda* on the same channel.

b. The same 100 families constituted the sample each week, but this week a new 100 families will be sampled.

c. Of the 100 observed families in each group, all of them lived in New York City.

d. Of the 100 observed families in each group, all had watched *The Mary Tyler Moore Show* each week for the past two years.

e. Of the 100 observed families in each group, ten lived in New York, ten lived in Philadelphia, ten lived in Atlanta, ten lived in Miami, ten lived in Chicago, ten lived in St. Louis, ten lived in Memphis, ten lived in Akron, ten lived in New Orleans, and ten lived in San Francisco.

f. A new sample of 100 families was used each week.

The Principle of Induction

It is often asserted that all inductive arguments are grounded in the **principle of induction**, which can be formulated as the assertion that events in the future will resemble events in the past, or that unobserved cases will resemble observed cases—in other words, that similar things behave similarly in similar circumstances. It is sometimes argued that, if this principle is considered to be a suppressed premise, all inductive arguments can be reduced to deductive arguments.

From a practical viewpoint, there are several objections to this reduction. One is in establishing the truth of the principle of induction itself: critics maintain that if we try to do so by the pragmatic argument that it has worked in the past and, therefore, will continue to work in the future, we are justifying induction by an inductive argument, so the proof is circular. A second obstacle lies in the problem of resemblance: do the two cases resemble each other in all relevant ways? One criterion for determining the relevance of a statement is whether its addition to the premises of an argument affects the relative strength of the argument. But this criterion also uses an inductive argument to justify the principle of induction. Finally, even when the principle of induction is added, inductive arguments do not necessarily become deductive, for the addition of more premises can still affect the truth value of the conclusion.

It has been argued that there is no way to justify the principle of induction, just as there is no way to justify an axiom in mathematics. But such arguments are themselves inductive, since they are based on an analogy. They do not prove that the principle of induction *cannot* be justified.

7.
hypo-
thetico-
deduc-
tive
method

The Possible Elimination of Inductions by Analogy

As we have seen in the preceding chapter, by the addition of suitably chosen premises, any inductive argument can be reformulated as a valid deductive argument. However, this does not necessarily improve the quality of the argument, since the premises added are usually weak. Nevertheless, there are several alternative methods of formulating inductive arguments which some logicians have suggested might improve their logical quality or make them simpler to evaluate.

Some logicians have argued that the distinction between inductions by analogy and inductive generalization is unnecessary, and that only deduction and inductive generalization are needed. They reformulate the single-step induction by analogy into a two-step argument, consisting of an inductive generalization followed by a valid deductive argument.

Example:
One-step induction by analogy:
Raven A is black.
Raven B is black.
Raven C is black.
Therefore, Raven D is black.

Two-step argument involving inductive generalization and deduction:
Raven A is black.
Raven B is black.
Raven C is black.
Therefore, all ravens are black.

All ravens are black.
D is a raven.
Therefore, D is black.

Although the two-step method arrives at the same conclusion from the same set of premises as does the single-step method, the two are not equivalent. The one-step method is at least as good as, if not better than, the two-step method, inasmuch as the latter does not recognize differences in the relative inductive strengths of certain arguments. For example, one could deduce in the second step of the example above the conclusion 'At least one raven in addition to A, B, and C is black.' This argument, however, can be no stronger than the induction in the first step to 'All ravens are black.' But as we saw in the last chapter, a given set of premises generally gives stronger support to a conclusion which is deductively weaker than some other conclusion (and 'At least one raven is black' is deductively weaker than 'All ravens are black.')

Exercise 7-1

Reformulate each of the following ordinary-language arguments as (a) a one-step argument—that is, an induction by analogy; and as (b) a two-step argument containing an inductive generalization followed by a valid deductive argument. (c) Indicate in which cases the two arguments are equivalent, and in which cases one is stronger than the other.

1. We will probably have a big snow storm this year, since we had big snow storms last year, two years ago, three years ago, and four years ago.
2. The Smiths, Parkers, Roberts, Mitchells, and Conners all own Fisher receiver-amplifiers and get excellent performance. So, probably the Carters who just bought a Fisher receiver-amplifier will get excellent performance.
3. Chimpanzees A, B, C, D, E, and F each engaged in grooming behavior. Consequently, at least one other chimp will engage in grooming behavior.
4. My grandfather, my father, and my older brother went bald before they were thirty years old, so I probably will, too.
5. *Swan Lake*, composed by Tchaikovsky, is a great ballet score. And *The Nutcracker* also composed by Tchaikovsky, is a great ballet score. *Sleeping Beauty* was composed by Tchaikovsky, so it too must be a great ballet score.
6. The movie I saw on the *Late Show* yesterday was interesting, and the movie I saw on the *Late Show* the night before that was interesting. Therefore, at least one movie I will see on the *Late Show* in the future will be interesting.
7. Regina is an intelligent woman and reads *Ms.* magazine. Barbara and Johanna are intelligent women, and they also read *Ms.* magazine. Elizabeth is intelligent, so probably she reads *Ms.* magazine.
8. Italy, Germany, Spain, and France are European countries and have shown aggressive tendencies. Therefore, at least one other European country will probably show aggressive tendencies.
9. There were interesting people at Joe's last three parties, so undoubtedly there will be interesting people at Joe's party tonight.
10. Juan, Kim, Pete, and Michel all attend Princeton and each had combined college board scores over 1100. Five thousand other students go to Princeton, too; therefore, at least one other student's combined college board scores must be over 1100.

The Hypothetico-Deductive Method

The hypothetico-deductive method differs from the more formal mode of enumerative induction presented in Chapter 6, in that it purports to reflect more accurately the way people do in fact reason. The **hypothetico-deductive method** involves a temporal sequence of three steps.

Step One: Formulating a Generalization The first step of the hypothetico-deductive method involves the formulation of a generalization in the form of a working hypothesis. The generalization 'All ravens are black' is an example of such a working hypothesis. It is important to note that in this context we are not concerned with the mental processes by means of which this generalization was reached; our only concern here is with the justification that can ultimately be provided for the generalization.

Step Two: Deducing Observation Statements   The second step consists of validly deducing observation statements—that is, statements whose truth or falsity can be determined by direct observation—from the generalization. From the generalization 'All ravens are black,' it is possible to deduce a theoretically infinite number of observation statements.

Example:
All ravens are black.
Therefore, the next raven I observe (X_1) will be black.
Therefore, the 15th raven I observe (X_2) will be black.
Therefore, the last raven observed by General Zinger (X_3) was black.
Therefore, the next raven I observe in Kansas (X_4) will be black.

Note that all of the observation statements are about specific individuals. Although other generalizations are also validly deducible from the hypothesis (for example, 'All ravens observed in New Mexico are black'), the hypothetico-deductive method is concerned only with deducing statements about specific individuals, the truth or falsity of which can be determined by direct single observations.

Step Three: Testing Observation Statements   The third step of the hypothetico-deductive method is the testing of the observation statements to determine whether each is in fact true or false, for the falsity of an observation statement logically implies the falsity of the generalization from which it was derived.

The process of deducing and testing observation statements obviously ends when any one of the deduced observation statements is found to be false. If no falsifying instance is found, the process could be continued indefinitely. A basic rule of thumb is that the greater the "logical effort" expended to deduce and test those observation statements which are most likely to be factually false, the greater the probability that, if they prove to be true, the generalization is true as well.

The hypothetico-deductive method is closely related to the method of inductive generalization. Once the generalization has been hypothesized, and the observation statements deduced and confirmed by means of the hypothetico-deductive method, an inductive generalization can be constructed, using the confirmed observation statements as premises and the generalization as conclusion.

Example:
The first raven I observed (X_1) was black.
The 15th raven I observed (X_2) was black.
The last raven observed by General Zinger (X_3) was black.
The raven I observed in Kansas (X_4) was black.
Therefore, all ravens are black.

This formulation of the argument brings out the important fact that the rule of thumb for the hypothetico-deductive method (to make the greatest possible logical effort to falsify the generalization) corresponds to a basic criterion for evaluating inductive generalizations—that the greater the negative analogy among observed cases (premises), the stronger the support they are likely to provide for a related generalization. It is important to note, too, that some logicians view the second and third steps of the hypothetico-deductive method as being directed toward the *verification* of the generalization, whereas others view them as being directed toward the *falsification* of the generalization.

Exercise 7-2
For each of the generalizations given below, indicate which of the observation statements are such that if they are false, the generalization must also be false.

1. All wild chimpanzees use tools, engage in grooming behavior, and live in social groups. (Assume that it is true that A, B, C, D, E, F, G, and H are wild chimps.)
   a. Wild Chimp A engages in grooming behavior.
   b. Wild Chimp B uses twigs to dig out ants from tree bark.
   c. Wild Chimp C uses tools.
   d. Wild Chimps D, E, and F live in the same social group.
   e. Chimp G is wild, since he uses tools, engages in grooming behavior, and lives in a social group.
   f. Wild Chimp H lives in a social group.
2. Every new Volkswagen bug gets at least 20 miles to a gallon of gas during the first six months.
   a. The Finleys' new Volkswagen bug which they got a month ago will get at least 20 miles to a gallon of gas for at least five more months.
   b. Since Bugs Unlimited, which sells only new Volkswagen bugs, opened exactly one month ago and it takes exactly one month to receive the car you order, all of the Volkswagen bugs sold there will get at least 20 miles to a gallon of gas for the next six months.
   c. The Morgansterns' Volkswagen bug which they bought new seven months ago does not get at least 20 miles to a gallon of gas.
   d. The Bonos' five month old Volkswagen bug will get at least 20 miles to a gallon of gas until September 1, since they received it on May 1.
   e. The Benvengas bought a new Volkswagen bug three months ago and it gets 40 miles to a gallon of gas.

3. Whenever the price of a product increases and the supply decreases, fewer persons buy the product.
   a. The price of color televisions increased and the supply decreased six months ago. Fewer people will buy color televisions now than before the price increase and supply decrease.
   b. The price of electric knives has just increased and the supply just decreased. Mr. Smith will not buy an electric knife.
   c. The price of home heating oil has increased and the supply decreased. The people living in Florida are buying less home heating fuel than before the price increased and the supply decreased.
   d. The price of milk has increased in New York City. Fewer people in New York City will buy milk than before the price of milk increased.
   e. The supply of milk has decreased in New York City. Fewer people in New York City are buying milk than before the supply of milk decreased.

Exercise 7-3
Each of the hypotheses given below is followed by five sets of observation statements, all of which are deducible from the hypothesis (sometimes in conjunction with other premises). Assume that all the observation statements have been confirmed. To support each hypothesis, construct five different inductive arguments, using a different set of observation statements for each; then list these arguments in order of decreasing inductive strength.

1. All birds have beaks.
   a.   i. A bluebird observed in Canada had a beak.
       ii. A pigeon observed in New York had a beak.
       iii. A red robin observed in Ireland had a beak.
       iv. A sparrow observed in England had a beak.
       v. A raven observed in Russia had a beak.
   b.   i. An ostrich observed in Kenya had a beak.
       ii. A bluejay observed in France had a beak.
       iii. A nightingale observed in China had a beak.
       iv. A parrot observed in Argentina had a beak.
       v. A penguin observed in Alaska had a beak.
   c.   i. A crow observed in New York had a beak.
       ii. A pigeon observed in New York had a beak.
       iii. A finch observed in New York had a beak.
       iv. A swallow observed in New York had a beak.
       v. An oriole observed in New York had a beak.
   d.   i. A ptarmigan observed in Alaska had a beak.
       ii. A parrot observed in Argentina had a beak.
       iii. A cockatoo observed in Chile had a beak.
       iv. A penguin observed in Canada had a beak.
       v. A seagull observed in Newfoundland had a beak.

e.   i. A robin observed in Spain had a beak.

    ii. A sparrow observed in France had a beak.

    iii. A pigeon observed in Italy had a beak.

    iv. A bluejay observed in Portugal had a beak.

    v. A oriole observed in Switzerland had a beak.

2. All dogs are carnivores.

  a.   i. Frenchie, a miniature poodle, is a carnivore.

     ii. Natasha, a Russian wolfhound, is a carnivore.

     iii. Pierre, a standard poodle, is a carnivore,

     iv. King, a German shepherd, is a carnivore.

     v. Lassie, a collie, is a carnivore.

  b.   i. Peanut, a Yorkshire terrier, is a carnivore.

     ii. Elizabeth, a cairn terrier, is a carnivore.

     iii. Lad, a Scottish terrier, is a carnivore.

     iv. Charles, a West Highland terrier, is a carnivore.

     v. Sidney, an Australian terrier, is a carnivore.

  c.   i. Friskie, an Alaskan husky, is a carnivore.

     ii. Saber, a malamute, is a carnivore.

     iii. Chico, a chihuahua, is a carnivore.

     iv. Sasha, an afghan, is a carnivore.

     v. Heather, a mixed breed, is a carnivore.

  d.   i. Lassie, a collie, is a carnivore.

     ii. Frenchie, a miniature collie, is a carnivore.

     iii. Lassette, a miniature collie, is a carnivore.

     iv. Pierre, a standard poodle, is a carnivore.

     v. BonBon, a toy poodle, is a carnivore.

  e.   i. King, a German shepherd, is a carnivore.

     ii. Duke, a German shepherd, is a carnivore.

     iii. Duchess, a German Shepherd, is a carnivore.

     iv. Princess, a German shepherd, is a carnivore.

     v. Lady, a German shepherd, is a carnivore.

Exercise 7-4

Indicate which of the following statements could be confirmed or falsified by direct observation. For those which cannot be, try to suggest observations which could serve to test them. Compare your answers with those of other members of the class.

1. The last page of *Webster's Seventh New Collegiate Dictionary* is 1223.
2. All of the earth's continents once formed a single land mass.
3. Light travels 186,000 miles per second.
4. Right now I am having the sensation of seeing a solid blue tie.
5. This sculpture is made of an aluminum alloy.
6. Charles I ruled Great Britain from 1625 to 1649.
7. That dog over there is a poodle.

8. Tom laughed a lot last week during the movie *Young Frankenstein.*
9. The capital of Corsica is Ajaccio.
10. Most American families own television sets.
11. 2 + 2 = 4.
12. The lights are on in the Oval Office of the White House right now.
13. The *Mona Lisa* is a beautiful painting.
14. The United States is the largest energy consumer in the world.
15. Susan is an M.D.

Crucial Experiments

A special case of the hypothetico-deductive method, the method of **crucial experiment** is sometimes cited to characterize the procedure for choosing between two "competing" theories or generalizations. Given two logically inconsistent generalizations, it is possible to derive observation statements from them which are such that a single observation will make one false and the other true. Thus, a single observation will force the falsification of at least one of the generalizations, and will usually provide at least some confirmation of the other. The method of crucial experiment is often illustrated by examples from the history of science, such as the heliocentric and geocentric theories.

The method of crucial experiment is not as simple and clear-cut as one might assume. One important objection is the fact that few, if any, observation statements can be deduced directly from a single generalization. Generally, observation statements can be deduced only from a complex conjunction of other generalizations, assumptions, definitions, and observation statements. This being the case, the falsification of one observation statement does not necessarily falsify the original generalization; the fact that the deduced observation statement was false could just as reasonably be attributed to one or more of the other statements. Then too, some statements deducible from a generalization are such that they cannot be "directly" observed. Other conditions that have affected cases of crucial experiments include psychological factors, religious beliefs, aesthetic considerations, and so on.

Scientific Method

Many philosophers and scientists have argued that the hypothetico-deductive method, or some variation of it, is and/or should be *the* scientific method. The argument used to justify the claim that this *should* be so resembles the inductive argument in support of the principle of induction, and is subject to criticisms of circularity. Another difficulty with the argument is that a careful examination of the history of science provides little if any evidence that science has, in fact, developed in this way.

An even more serious problem in trying to characterize the nature of science is the apparent fact that the statements of science cannot be neatly and simply categorized as either theoretical statements (or generalizations) or observation statements. There is even the possibility that individuals from different cultures (or with different theoretical training) actually see different things when exposed to the same stimuli. If this is true to any significant extent, then observations would not necessarily provide a basis for resolving theoretical disputes.

Given that science is, at the least, a body of knowledge contained in a set of statements, logic can be used to identify and evaluate the logical relations among these statements. Many scientific statements belong to one of two basic types: statements about specific observable events, and universal generalizations. Logic can be used to determine whether or not a specific statement is true or false solely by virtue of its logical form. More important, the logician can determine whether one statement is validly deducible from one or more other statements; whether two statements are logically inconsistent; and whether one statement provides any inductive support for another. Perhaps the most significant of these is the determination of inconsistency, since it is generally agreed that inconsistency is undesirable in *any* system. When an inconsistency is found, it must be decided which of the two statements to reject, but this decision goes beyond the scope of logic proper. Although logic alone cannot provide adequate answers to many questions concerning what science is and/or should be, the problems cannot be identified, nor adequate solutions provided, without some use of logic.

Exercise 7-5

For each of the following cases, discuss ways in which (a) the generalized hypothesis could rationally be retained while rejecting the observation statement, and (b) the hypothesis could be rejected while retaining the observation statement. (c) Which strategy seems most reasonable for the given case? Could a crucial experiment be constructed?

1. At one time, it was hoped that a drug known as **L-DOPA** would cure or at least slow the progression of Parkinson's disease. It had been hypothesized that the disease was caused by a deficiency in the brain of dopamine, a transmitter of nerve messages, and that all persons with a sufficient amount of dopamine would, in effect, not have the disease. **L-DOPA** has the effect of correcting the dopamine deficiency. The results of recent tests on 60 patients shows that the drug does reduce many of the symptoms of the disease, but the patients using it apparently do not live any longer than the patients who do not use it. (The scientists concluded that this meant that they should reject their hypothesis and look for a new cause of the disease.)

2. It has been hypothesized that lecithin is a "cholesterol fighter"—that is, lecithin causes the cholesterol level in the blood to decrease. In 1956, a study was conducted in which 15 persons (six other persons were dropped from the study because of allergic reactions) were given six tablespoons of lecithin daily, and the average fall in serum cholesterol was 30 percent. Another study showed that every time an average person eats two eggs (which contain lecithin), the cholesterol level in his or her blood increases.

3. Horoscopes are supposed to be deductions from a complex set of general hypotheses concerning causal relations between the stars, planets, and

individual persons. Look up your horoscope in yesterday's paper. Do your experiences of yesterday confirm or refute the astrological hypothesis?

4. James Burnham, a columnist, in the *National Review* (April 27, 1973) wrote the article below entitled "Everyman His Own Teacher." In it he claims that different people have used their observations of the Vietnam war to confirm a multiplicity of conflicting hypotheses. Evaluate this argument.

We are presently being exhorted by our sages to learn the lessons of Vietnam. "We *must* learn them," they warn us, so that "there will never be another Vietnam," and they generously tick the lessons off for our benefit. Not unexpectedly, each instructor harvests from the Vietnam story the lesson he has sown. To the pacifist, Vietnam has proved that war is wrong; to the isolationists of both the old and the new models, that we should steer clear of entanglements beyond our shores; to the fiery chauvinist, that we should have finished things off in a week with a couple of well-placed H-bombs; to the computer strategists, that we failed to understand that the cold war is over; to the New Left theoreticians, that peace can be won only by the overthrow of imperialism; to the Birchites, that U.S. policy is controlled by 'them'. This Vietnam lesson-drawing proves once more, it would seem, that the only thing we learn from history is that we learn nothing from history.

5. A lie-detector expert has hypothesized that plants react to the thoughts of human beings in their vicinity. He claims that these reactions can be registered on lie-detector type devices attached to the plants. He has conducted many tests which he says confirm the hypothesis. However, when repeating the tests for a well-known plant physiologist, no such responses were observed. The lie-detector expert explained that nothing registered because the plants had "fainted" when they sensed that the plant physiologist in her studies used the procedure of incinerating plants and otherwise harming and destroying them.

6. One hypothesis concerning the social cause of unrest and aggression is known as the "twenty-five-year itch hypothesis." This hypothesis maintains that every twenty-five to thirty years the memories of social unrest, war, or aggression die with the generation that was involved in these activities. The young generation is then willing to defy institutions and engage once again in these activities. Asked his opinion of the hypothesis, Herman Kahn, a social commentator and think-tank administrator, said the following: "It is an attractive theory but I don't think it is accurate. I suspect the analogy is drawn from one single instance—the time that elapsed between 1914 and 1939, and I for one would hesitate to generalize from one observation. If one goes further back in history: in the Napoleonic wars young men in France had been blooded over and over again but were still willing to go to war. They liked war is some real sense. In America, on the other hand, 25 or 30 years after the Civil War there was no sign of any generational unrest, any thirst for a fresh conflict coming to the surface."

8.
mills
method

Kinds of Cause

No generalization which is arrived at solely by means of an enumerative induction is strong enough to support the inference of a causal connection between two or more associated events. That is to say, the fact that Y has always followed X in the past does not prove that X is the *cause* of Y.

When people seek to determine the causes of events, it is generally so that the events may be repeated, prevented, or at least predicted in the future. The word 'cause' may be used in a number of different senses. The **efficient cause** is the preceding event or events which trigger the event in question. For instance, suppose a child throws a rubber ball, which bounces off the floor and then off a wall and then hits her mother on the head. The efficient cause of the mother's being hit on the head would be the force transmitted to the ball from the motion of the child's arm. The **material cause** is the material out of which a thing is made. The material cause of the ball hitting the mother on the head is the fact that it is made of rubber, with certain properties that caused it to bounce when it struck the floor. The **formal cause** is the form of the object involved in the event. The formal cause of the mother being hit on the head is the particular shape of the ball, which caused it to bounce in the direction that it did. The **final** or **purposive cause** is the aim or goal of an action. If the child intended to hit her mother on the head with the ball, this would be the final cause.

As we can see, there are usually many causal factors associated with any given event. When the efficient causes occur in a temporal sequence, with each event producing the next and leading up at last to the event which is to be explained, a **causal chain** can be said to exist. For instance, in our example, the child first had to pick up the ball, then throw it on the floor; then the ball bounced off the floor, then it hit the wall, then it bounced off the wall, and then it hit the mother in the head. The last event in a causal chain (here the ball bouncing off the wall) can reasonably be designated the **proximate cause** – that is, the one closest to the event whose cause is being sought. It is the proximate cause that is assumed to precipitate directly the caused event. The other links in the causal chain are more or less **remote causes**. Thus, the child picking up the ball, throwing it on the floor, and so on, are all remote causes. However, this is not a precise distinction, and some people might argue that the proximate cause was the child's throwing the ball.

Because of the tendency to interpret 'cause' as equivalent to 'proximate efficient cause,' the more neutral term 'condition' is sometimes used by logicians. Two types of condition can be distinguished: necessary and sufficient.

A **necessary condition** is one in the *absence* of which the event *cannot* take place.

Example:
Oxygen is a necessary condition for a match flame.

A **sufficient condition** is one in the *presence* of which the event *is sure to* take place.

Example:
The striking of a dry match against a suitable rough surface in the presence of oxygen is a sufficient condition for a match flame.

In our example above, the sufficient condition is a conjunction — that is, a combination or joining together — of several necessary conditions. There are other cases in which a necessary condition is a disjunction of two or more conditions; that is, the presence of one or another (but not all) of several conditions is necessary to produce the caused event.

Example:
A person goes to the refrigerator and finds that a milk container is empty. There are at least four possibilities, each of which by itself could account for the empty milk container: someone drank the milk, or someone emptied the milk from the container, or the milk evaporated, or the container had a leak in the bottom.

In the example above, the necessary condition is a disjunction of all four possibilities (and of any others that one might think of). Any one of these by itself is a sufficient condition of the milk container being empty.

When an event occurs, it follows by definition that all necessary conditions, and thus at least one sufficient condition, for its occurrence are present. To prevent the occurrence of an event, one would search for and then eliminate the necessary condition(s); to produce an event, one would search for sufficient condition(s), and then take steps to create them.

Exercise 8-1
In each of the following paragraphs, determine the proximate and remote causes of the events specified. (Letters identify sentences.)

1. *Event:* Susan's new record album by the Grand Funk gets scratched.
   (a) Susan had been saving her lunch money all week so that she could buy the new album by Grand Funk. (b) She could barely sit through her Latin class. (c) When the last bell at Old Bridge High School rang, Susan left the building quickly. (d) She saw a school bus go by, and waved to some of her friends on board. (e) She went to the Main Street record store. (f) There she found a pile of the new album in the front of the store. (g) She slipped off the top record and went to the cashier. (h) She remarked that the record was already among the top ten. (i) "Four dollars and eighty-nine cents with tax," the cashier said. (j) Susan gave the cashier five singles and waited for her record and change. (k) She then took a bus home. (l) On the way, she read the record jacket notes and looked at the cover design. (m) The song she liked the best, having heard the album on the radio, was cut four on side two. (n) When her stop came, she jumped out of her seat and made a fast exit. (o) Down the block, she passed Mr. Langston walking his dog, and

greeted him. (p) At home, she rushed into her room. (q) She tossed her coat on the bed. (r) Then she took the record out of its jacket and put on side two. (s) In her rush, she forgot to lift the cueing mechanism. (t) She picked up the playing arm and moved it across to the fourth cut. (u) Then she let it go, and to her horror she saw it drop immediately. (v) It hit the record heavily and then slid across it, making a grinding sound. (w) "Oh, no," she cried. (x) She realized that she had forgotten to raise the cueing mechanism. (y) She did so now and put the arm once again above the fourth cut. (z) She lowered the cueing mechanism and the playing arm descended slowly and gracefully. (a') Then she heard loud clicks as the needle hit the scratches on the record.

2. *Event:* Frank scrapes his leg.

(a) Penelope Triscot and her four-year-old son, Frank, were walking through the park. (b) It was a sunny spring afternoon. (c) The temperature was 63°. (d) Mrs. Triscot noticed a group of other parents sitting on benches near the playground area. (e) She recognized some of them as neighbors. (f) Giving her son a little tug on the arm, Mrs. Triscot walked in the direction of the playground area. (g) One neighbor, John Stevenson, suggested that Frank and his daughter, Miriam, might enjoy the slide. (h) Mrs. Triscot thought it would be good fun. (i) She remembered how much she had enjoyed slides when she was a child. (j) She and Frank and John and Miriam walked to the slide. (k) Three other children were just leaving it. (l) Mr. Stevenson lifted the children to the top of the slide and then released them. (m) The children enjoyed the slide down the metal chute. (n) They shouted and laughed as they went down. (o) At the bottom of the slide, Mrs. Triscot caught the children before they fell off the end. (p) At the end of one trip, Miriam fell down and got a big dirt smudge on the seat of her pants. (q) The parents and children had been playing for about five minutes when suddenly Mrs. Triscot heard a scream somewhere behind her. (r) She turned sharply to see what was wrong. (s) A large German shepherd was sniffing at a little girl, who was screaming with fear. (t) Not recognizing the dog, Mrs. Triscot began running to the little girl. (u) Before she had gone more than a few steps, the little girl's mother had seen the situation and reached her child. (v) Then suddenly Mrs. Triscot heard another, familiar voice crying behind her. (w) She turned around and saw Frank on the ground at the foot of the slide, looking up at her and crying. (x) She hurried toward him, picked him up, and he stopped crying almost immediately. (y) Mrs. Triscot looked for bruises and found a small scratch on Frank's left leg.

Exercise 8-2

The following excerpts are adapted from newspaper reports. Each presents what purports to be a causal chain of events. Try to identify (a) the final event of the causal chain, (b) the proximate cause, and (c) the remote cause(s). Discuss your answers with other members of your class.

1. In 1949, Ivar Hennings, then chairman of the South Bend Bait Company, had a solution to the "threatening" problem of Communism. According to Mr. Hennings, "the furnishing of quality tackle would lead to more fishing, which promotes a clean mind, healthy body, and leaves no time for succumbing to Communistic or Socialist propaganda — simultaneously building for a better America." Lower taxes would also help to solve the problem, he said.

   New York *Times,* May 1, 1974

2. Discontent has been aggravated by a famine that killed tens of thousands of people last year in rural areas of Ethiopia. This was followed by steep rises in fuel prices caused by the world energy crisis, and by other price increases that have severely pressed both the rural and the urban population.

   New York *Times,* February 27, 1974

3. Freon, a nonflammable hydrocarbon containing fluorine and chlorine, is used as a refrigerant and as a propellant in aerosol spray cans. Some scientists maintain that freon may destroy the earth's ozone radiation shield, which filters out the sun's dangerous ultraviolet rays.

   "Freon itself does not harm the ozone layer, but when it reaches the upper levels of the stratosphere the ultraviolet light of the sun triggers the release of chorine from freon. Chlorine in turn breaks down the ozone that serves the earth as a shield from most of the sun's ultraviolet light."

   According to Dr. Donald M. Hunten, chairman of a five-member panel of the National Academy of Sciences, which is studying the problem, "Studies have shown that just about all the freon ever used in aerosol spray cans now resides in the earth's atmosphere. The reason is that freon does not dissolve in water and does not combine with anything to drift harmlessly away. The use of freon has grown at a rate of 15 percent per year over the last five years." Hunten maintains that "about 10 percent of the freon released to the atmosphere has already reached the stratosphere, where most of the atmospheric ozone is."

   Thomas O'Toole, Washington *Post*

4. A panel of scientists appointed by the National Research Council supported the theory that the proposed Supersonic Transport (SST) would dangerously deplete the ozone layer.

   "The panel was created to assess the argument that the introduction of oxides of nitrogen into the stratosphere by exhaust from a fleet of about 500 supersonic transports would initiate a series of ozone-depleting chemical reactions.

   "The nitric oxides, this argument goes, would serve as catalysts. That is, they would participate in the reactions but remain afterward to stimulate further reactions in an open-ended manner. The effect would be to convert ozone, whose molecules are formed of three oxygen atoms, into oxygen gas, which consists of paired oxygen atoms. Ozone, in the region between 10 and 30 miles aloft, strongly absorbs the lethal wavelengths of ultraviolet sunlight. The SSTs would operate in the lower part of this region.

"Last year (1971) Dr. Harold Johnston, a leading authority on atmospheric chemistry at the University of California in Berkeley, contended that within one year the projected SST fleet might halve the amount of ozone in the atmosphere. This, he said, could blind all animals, including human beings, except those remaining indoors or under water."

Walter Sullivan, New York *Times*
November 5, 1972

5. "The immediate cause of Jackie Robinson's death at age 53 was apparently a heart attack. But to many doctors a more fundamental process was involved: diabetes and its complications.

"The former Brooklyn Dodger's heart attack, which came after a decade of failing health, was his third since 1968, two of the Manhattan specialists who cared for him said in interviews. These two previous heart attacks had left him with a need for cardiology care to treat his congestive heart failure.

"The Dodger second baseman had also conculted several other kinds of specialists in the 20 years he knew he had diabetes because during this interval Mr. Robinson had developed most of the conditions that can complicate the endocrine disease. The first black major leaguer lost the sight of one eye and was becoming progressively blind in the other, despite treatments with a laser beam. A week ago today [October 22, 1972], he suddenly lost even more sight from a hemorrhage in his 'good' eye.

"In 1961, his knee, already damaged by arthritis caused by the trauma of sliding around the bases on the playing field, was further injured by a serious infection. The staphylococcal bacteria that caused the knee infection also poisoned his blood system with a near fatal case of septicemia and temporarily threw his diabetes out of control until antibiotics and more insulin helped him recover.

"Mr. Robinson also suffered from burning sensations and other pains in his legs that had resulted from a combination of diabetic damage to the nerves and arteries in his legs. So discomforting were these symptoms, his doctor said, that Mr. Robinson had to give up golf.

"Also, his blood pressure was abnormally high for many years. Though hypertension can be another complication of diabetes, Mr. Robinson's physicians said they considered it an unassociated problem in his case. Cardiologists have reported that hypertension is found with unusually high frequency among blacks."

Lawrence K. Altman, New York *Times*
October 29, 1972.
Reprinted by permission.

Exercise 8-3

1. Assuming ordinary circumstances:
    a. Is being 18 years of age or older a necessary condition for being eligible to vote in a national election? a sufficient condition?

b. Is being a male a sufficient condition for being elected president of the United States? a necessary condition?

c. Is being a dog a sufficient condition for being a canine? a necessary condition?

d. Is the disjunction of being a man, or a woman, or a boy, or a girl a sufficient condition for being human? a necessary condition?

e. Is the presence of clouds a necessary condition for a snowfall? a sufficient condition?

f. Is being shot with a gun a necessary condition for death? a sufficient condition?

g. Is the conjunction of an ounce of vodka, 6 ounces of orange juice, ice cubes, and a glass a sufficient condition for the creation of a screwdriver? a necessary condition?

2. Smart University offered five scholarships to seniors majoring in biology. Ten candidates applied. Their qualifications are shown in the chart below.

Student	Overall B Average	A Average in Biology	Family Income Under $5000	Recommendations by Two Professors	Brothers or Sisters at the School	Intention to Teach
1	X	X	X	X		X
2	X	X	X	X	X	X
3	X	X				X
4	X		X	X		X
5	X	X	X	X	X	
6	X	X		X	X	
7	X		X	X		X
8	X				X	
9	X	X		X	X	X
10	X		X	X		X

Students 1, 2, 4, 5, and 7 received the scholarships. What can you identify as probably necessary and/or sufficient conditions of receiving the scholarship?

Mill's Methods

Mill's methods are a set of inductive methods frequently used to determine the necessary and/or sufficient conditions of an event. The methods were named after John Stuart Mill, a nineteenth-century British philosopher who did much to popularize them. Whereas Mill's own formulations of the methods used the notion of cause, we will discuss them in terms of the more precise concepts of necessary and sufficient condition. Each of Mill's methods uses a variation of the process of **eliminative induction**; that is, it considers a number of possibilities, and then eliminates most of them in order to arrive at necessary and/or sufficient condition(s). None of Mill's methods establishes the truth of any causal proposition absolutely; they merely purport to establish them to a reasonable degree of probability.

The Method of Agreement

The **method of agreement** states that if, in every case in which an event occurs, a particular condition is present, and no other factor is common to all occurrences, then that condition is probably a necessary condition of the event.

Example:
During the past eighteen months, three different departments of a large retail store — toys, radios, and housewares — have each suffered unexplainable inventory losses. The management of the store begins an investigation. They first secure a list of all employees who have worked in each of these departments during the eighteen-month period. Only one person, Mark Hustler, worked in each department at the time of the thefts. Furthermore, the inventory losses in each department started about two weeks after Mark joined the department's staff. The management concludes that Mark's presence is probably a necessary condition for the inventory losses. They decide to watch him carefully to see if they might catch him in the act.

The absence of a factor may be a necessary condition for an event. For instance, the lack of calciferol is a necessary condition for rickets, a bone disease.

The Method of Difference

The **method of difference** states that if the conditions in two cases *appear* to be essentially the same, but the caused event or phenomenon occurs in only one of them, then we should search for some other difference. The condition which exists in the case containing the caused phenomenon, but not in the other, is probably the sufficient condition of the phenomenon.

Example:
Students A, B, C, D, and E all ate breakfast in the school cafeteria. Students A, B, and C had oatmeal, scrambled eggs, bacon, and coffee. Students D and E had scrambled eggs, bacon, and coffee. Students A, B, and C later that day each had a severe case of diarrhea; students D and E suffered no such effects. Using Mill's method of difference, we may conclude that probably the oatmeal was a sufficient condition of the diarrhea.

The Joint Method of Agreement and Difference

In the **joint method of agreement and difference**, we first use the method of agreement to find a probable necessary condition. Then a number of cases in which the phenomenon under study does *not* occur are examined. Without worrying about whether this second group of cases resembles the first group in all other respects (as is necessary when using the method of difference), these cases are examined to see if the suspected causal factor is missing. If it is missing from all of them, not only will our belief that this factor is indeed a necessary condition of the phenomenon be further justified, but we will have reason to believe that it may be a sufficient condition as well.

Example:

In a particular elementary school, there were four sixth-grade classes. Each class was taught by a different teacher, and each was heterogeneously grouped; that is, students varied considerably in ability and achievement within each class. The whole sixth grade was given a standardized spelling test. Twenty students of the 100 who took the test scored 90% or better. There were about five high scorers in each class. Surprised that 20 percent of the students had done so well, the principal of the school decided to see if there was anything in the background of these students that would have caused their high scores. Examining their records, he found that they had IQs varying between 90 and 135. Their grades offered no clues, since in the past some had done well in language arts and others had done poorly. The one thing all students had in common was the same fifth-grade teacher, Miss Geng, whom the principal knew to be an excellent teacher and very strong on spelling skills. He investigated further and found that none of the students who had scored below 90 percent had ever had Miss Geng. He concluded that Miss Geng was probably a necessary, and perhaps a sufficient, condition for the students achieving 90 percent or better on the spelling test.

The Method of Concomitant Variation

The **method of concomitant variation** is useful when one seeks the cause of changes which occur along a continuum. It states that if a change in one phenomenon is found to occur every time a certain change in another phenomenon occurs, and if the degree of change in one phenomenon varies consistently with the degree of change in the other, then either (1) the change in the first phenomenon is the cause of the change in the second; (2) the change in the second phenomenon is the cause of the change in the first; or (3) a third factor is the cause of the change in both. **Positive concomitant variation** occurs when both factors vary in the same direction. **Inverse concomitant variation** occurs when the factors vary in opposite directions.

Examples:
Positive concomitant variation:
A sociologist conducted a survey to determine if there was any relationship between the amount of education and the voting behavior of citizens in national and local elections. She surveyed 1,800 citizens; the sample was representative of the overall population in terms of geographic region, age, sex, marital status, and income. She discovered that as the amount of education increased, the likelihood that the citizen voted in the national and local elections increased proportionately. She concluded that education was the cause, or part of the cause, of the increased voting behavior. (She noted also the possibility that the increase in education and the increase in voting were both caused by some third, unidentified factor.)

Inverse concomitant variation:
As the amount of resistance to an electric current in a light bulb increases, the brightness of the light decreases; as the amount of resistance decreases, the brightness of the light increases.

Exercise 8-4
Each of the following accounts involves the use of one of Mill's methods. For each, tell (1) which method was used; (2) whether the causal condition discovered was necessary, sufficient, or both.

1. The Visor Television Company shipped 1,000 portable television sets to a large department store chain. During the next three months, 115 of the sets were returned. In each case, the picture reception was good, but there was no sound. Examining the first group of ten returned sets, a plant inspection supervisor noticed that, in every set, a certain wire to the speaker was improperly soldered. She also noticed that the same person—Bill Evans, a fairly new employee—had done the soldering. The supervisor inspected the next group of returned sets and found the same improperly soldered wire in each. She concluded that Bill Evans' faulty soldering was the cause of the problem. She returned the sets to Bill with the necessary instructions; later, as other sets with the same defect were returned, she sent these to him as well.

2. It is now generally accepted that the addition of fluorine to drinking water helps to prevent or reduce tooth decay. One of the experiments by which this fact was established was conducted in two communities on the Hudson River. In each community a group of about 1,000 children was chosen; the children were selected so that each of the two groups had about the same number of cavities. Then, for ten years, a small amount of sodium fluoride was added to the water supply of one community; none was added to that of the other. At the end of the ten-year period, the two study groups were checked again, and the group which had received fluoridated water was found to have significantly fewer cavities than the other group. The fluorine was considered the cause of the difference.

3. A sociologist conducted a survey of ten families to determine the relationship, if any, between a family's total income and its expenditures on recreation and entertainment. A summary of the findings appears in the following table:

Family income	Approximate total recreation and entertainment expenditure	
	In dollars	As a percentage of total income
5,000	500	10.0
7,500	650	8.7
12,500	1,100	8.8
17,500	1,450	8.3
22,500	1,600	7.1
27,500	2,000	7.3
32,500	2,300	7.1
42,500	2,800	6.6
75,000	3,600	4.8
100,000	5,500	5.5

4. Professor Stein frowned as he studied the seven Philosophy 104 examination papers spread out on his desk. All seven contained a major error in the third essay question; and all the errors were essentially the same, even to the wording. He examined the papers again. There was a suspicious similarity in some of the correct answers as well. Clearly there had been cheating, either during the examination or before. He looked up his records of the seven students. Two were sophomores, the rest juniors. Furthermore, they were in two different sections of the course, which meant, according to the standard practice at High Rise University, that they had taken the exam in two different rooms. This seemed to rule out collusion during the time of the exam. Someone must have gotten hold of the questions beforehand, and either studied them with the others, or prepared a crib sheet which the rest had used. Professor Stein called the office of the Dean of Students and asked to know the residences of the students involved. He found that all seven were members of the very exclusive X Fraternity, and lived in its residence. None of the other students in either section of the course were members of X Fraternity, and there was no indication in the papers that any others had participated in this particular piece of cheating. The professor still had no idea how the questions had been obtained, but he concluded that they had been, quite deliberately, circulated only within X Fraternity.

5. Researchers at the state agricultural laboratories were seeking a means of immunizing poultry against a new virus disease, and had developed several varieties of a vaccine which looked hopeful. In order to test them, they

isolated 500 newly hatched chicks for six days, one day longer than the usual incubation period of the disease. Since none of the chicks became ill, it was clear that they had not contracted the virus, either since hatching or while still in the egg. The chicks were then separated into five groups of 100 each, and each of the first four groups was innoculated with a different one of the four vaccines being tested. The fifth group was given no innoculation. All groups were given the same diet and living conditions. A week later, all 500 chicks were deliberately exposed to the virus. Within ten days, 90 of the chicks in group 5 were dead; 48 of those in group 4; 6 of those in group 3; 59 of those in group 2; and 62 of those in group 1. The researchers concluded that the vaccine given to group 3 furnished a high degree of protection against the virus.

6. Phil and Doris McCabe had never had any particular trouble with their telephone, until one fall it went dead three times in two weeks. On each occasion, it came back on by itself in a couple of days. The phone company repairman could find nothing wrong with the instrument or the interior connection, and no one else on the block was having comparable difficulties. The McCabes did not know what to think. Then, a week later, Doris was in the middle of a business call when the phone went dead again. She glared at the receiver, muttered something unladylike, and hung up. Going to the window, she stared out in disgust at the driving November rain. Suddenly she recalled that on each previous occasion when the phone had gone dead, there had also been heavy, driving rain. "I wonder . . . ," she said aloud, and made a point of noting that the rain was slanting in from the east, on a fairly strong wind. That night she told Phil her idea. The next day, Saturday, Phil got out the ladder and checked the east wall of the house. Sure enough, high up under the eaves, where the telephone wires from outside were led into the wall, a small patch of insulation on the wires was worn thin and cracked, and the area was still damp from yesterday's rain. A call to the local newspaper office on Monday—by then the phone had turned itself on again—confirmed that on the three earlier occasions the rain had also been driving from the east. Apparently, given the location of the damaged part of the wire, only such a rain could reach the worn spot and penetrate it, thus temporarily short-circuiting the wires.

7. Ed Kolchak, building manager of the new Parkview Apartments, put down the phone and wearily made a note on his desk pad. Then he buzzed the maintenance man on the intercom. "Tim, go up to 16J and check the thermostat. They're having trouble too."

"Another one!" Tim's voice sounded unbelieving. "Mr. Kolchak, this is crazy! How many's that make—nine, no, ten people telling us their heat don't come on right, just since we started up the furnace three days ago. You reckon mebbe somebody dropped a shoe down the duct or something, when they was building this place?"

"Lord only knows. Go on up and see what you can do, anyhow."

"Okay, Mr. Kolchak. But I sure would like to know—" Tim's voice trailed off as he hung up. Ed grinned wryly at the "shoe" hypothesis. There were always bugs in a new building; with luck they'd clear up before really cold weather set in. If not, there would be a lot more complaining tenants.

The next morning, Tim was waiting at the office when Ed came in at 8:30. "Hey, Mr. Kolchak, you know that thermostat business; I got an idea, only I need your okay to check it out."

"What's that?"

"Well, I remembered last night, all of a sudden, that my brother knows a guy that worked on this place when they was building it, so I got his number and called him up, and asked did he know anything funny about the heating system. He says no and wants to know why, so I told him the trouble we was having, and then he says, 'Hey, you know, maybe there is something.' He says, 'Seems to me I remember some guy telling me the contractor had shortchanged them on thermostats, and they was having to go out and buy some somewhere else to get the job done on time. The guy was real sore about it. Maybe it's those odd-lot thermostats that ain't working right.' You reckon we ought to check it, Mr. Kolchak?"

Ed was impressed. "Sure, go ahead. Maybe you're onto something. You have a list of the apartments involved?—Wait a second." His phone was ringing. He picked it up. "Kolchak here—yes—all right, Mr. Lomaki, we'll look into it. Thanks for letting me know. I'll send someone up right away." He hung up. "Add 16M to that list, Tim."

By the end of the day it seemed that Tim's hunch had been right. All of the malfunctioning thermostats had been manufactured by one company. Tim also checked about twenty apartments where no trouble had been reported, and found that only one of their thermostats was of this brand. Clearly, there was a strong probability that a fault in this particular brand of thermostat was the cause of the heating problem, and Ed Kolchak began making arrangements to have the thermostats replaced.

Exercise 8-5

Many real-life situations are of such a degree of complexity that Mill's methods can be applied to them only in modified form. The following cases are drawn from newspapers, magazines, and other everyday sources. On the basis of the evidence presented and the conclusions derived: (1) determine which, if any, of Mill's methods was used in that case; (2) indicate what additional evidence, if any, would have (a) strengthened the support for the conclusion, (b) weakened the support for the conclusion, (c) falsified the conclusion; (3) where the term 'cause' is used in the statement of the conclusion, specify whether a necessary or a sufficient condition is more probably meant.

1. Dr. Arthur Klatsky conducted a study in which 197 male cardiac patients, each of whom died within 24 hours after a heart attack, were compared with a similar group of cardiac patients who did not die of sudden attacks. There turned out to be significantly more current cigarette smokers in the

sudden-death group than in the other. No significant difference was found in regard to coffee drinking, heavy aspirin use, or alcohol. The researchers concluded that current cigarette smokers were at substantially greater risk than nonsmokers of sudden death from heart attacks. This would seem to substantiate the contention that cigarette smoking is a cause of sudden cardiac death.

2. It has recently been argued that the cause of crime is not poverty but wealth. Jonathan Quick, in an article in the February, 1974, *Freedom News*, points out that, whereas poverty has not greatly increased in recent years, both crime and the number of very rich people have increased dramatically. He explains this combination of events by suggesting that crime is especially profitable for the rich, who are often in a position to exercise considerable influence over decisions of business and government agencies, and who are seldom punished severely even if they are convicted of crimes. Ambitious members of lower classes, seeing that crime pays for the rich, are led to imitate them insofar as they can, thus further increasing the amount of crime. Therefore, concludes Quick, an effective way to reduce crime is to reduce the number of wealthy people.

3. Among British and American troops in North Africa during World War II, the incidence of paralytic poliomyelitis was much higher for officers than for men in the lower ranks. Since none of the obvious hypotheses seemed to explain this discrepancy, some rather wild ones were proposed. One of these took note of the fact that most of the officers drank whiskey, whereas most of the other men drank beer, and suggested that this difference was the the cause of the different rates of polio.

4. It is now known that persons who are exposed in infancy to the polio-carrying virus are likely to develop a natural resistance to it, and escape paralysis. Such exposure is more likely in unhygienic surroundings. Since more enlisted men than officers, in the North African group, came from lower-class social backgrounds and were thus likely to have been exposed to such conditions as children, they were less vulnerable to infection in adult life. A similar hypothesis has been proposed to explain the geo-graphical distribution of another disease, multiple sclerosis. MS, as the disease is often known, is more common in the economically advanced parts of the world—particularly northern Europe and the northern parts of the United States—than in many less advanced regions, including southern Europe, the southern United States, and South America. It is extremely rare in Japan. In South Africa it is relatively rare among native-born whites and those who immigrated to the country at an early age, but more common among those who immigrated after the age of fifteen. In Australia, another country with a high immigration rate, there is no signifi-cant difference between immigrant and native-born whites, but there is a higher MS rate in the temperate south than in the more tropical north.

    Early exposure to infection appears to be a probable condition in all the low-MS regions—usually, but not always, because of either the poor hygiene associated with economic backwardness, or the presence of a tropical climate favorable to the spread of infection. Japan and white South Africa are, of course, neither tropical nor economically backward; but in Japan human excrement was until recently a common fertilizer, and in South Africa the majority of white children are cared for by black servants whose own living conditions are poor and primitive. Since Australian whites, as a whole, lack similar close contact with the native population, the immigrant-native difference found in South Africa is not duplicated here. It is therefore hypothesized that MS is a normal virus infection of childhood, and that those who are infected at this time usually develop a natural resistance which protects them from the later effects of the disease.

5. Some medical researchers have recently found evidence of a possible correlation between beer drinking and certain types of cancer. Drs. James E. Enstrom and Norman E. Breslow compared the 1960 per capita consumption of beer in 41 states with the mortality rates in those states for 20 types of cancer. They found statistical correlations with at least 7 types, of which the strongest was with cancer of the large intestine and rectum. They emphasized, however, that the presence of a correlation does not, by itself, prove that beer causes cancer.

6. Doctors have long been puzzled by the occurrence of sudden fatal heart attacks in persons who were, until the attack, in apparently good health. Recent studies by Dr. William A. Greene revealed that, in one group of 26 employees of a single company who died of such sudden heart attacks, nearly all had been suffering a period of depression for some time. This depression was then interrupted by some sudden event, usually unpleasant, which made them anxious or angry, or otherwise upset their emotional and physical reactions. Usually the heart attacks and death followed shortly thereafter. Greene concluded that the combination of depression and sudden arousal probably contributed importantly to the deaths.

7. One of the more common signs of heart trouble is the painful condition known as angina pectoris. This is caused by a shortage of oxygenated blood supply to the heart muscle, and can be a forerunner of a damaging or fatal heart attack. The usual treatment for it today is coronary bypass surgery, in which the circulation is shunted around the obstruction in the coronary artery that is directly causing the trouble. Cardiologist Dr. Henry Russek has questioned the value of this, believing that surgery itself entails considerable risk and that effective, less dangerous treatment with drugs is possible. He treated one group of 102 severe angina patients for six years with a combination of several drugs, and found that their death rate during this period was about the same as that for the general population in the same age range. In contrast, in a talk reported in the March 4, 1974 *Time* magazine, he cited statistics which appeared to show that those who receive coronary bypass surgery have a higher death rate than the general

population, as well as a high incidence of major nonfatal postoperative complications. He concluded that drug treatment is safer than surgery, and at least as effective.

8. A study of regular marijuana smokers by Columbia University researchers indicates that marijuana use may cause a depression of the body's immune system, rendering the user more susceptible to disease. The pertinent evidence was summarized in the March 4, 1974 issue of *Time* magazine as follows:

   Taking T-lymphocytes, or immunologically active white blood cells, from the pot smokers and from healthy, nonsmoking volunteers, the doctors mixed the cells in test tubes with substances known to elicit immune responses. Cells from both groups responded to the foreign substances by multiplying, but those taken from the marijuana users reproduced 40% less than those from controls, a result suggesting that regular marijuana users may be more susceptible to disease.

9. Between 1968 and the end of 1972, there were 147 attempts to hijack United States aircraft, and 91 of these were successful. Thirty-one attempts were made in 1972 alone. In 1973 there was only one hijacking— of an Air Force helicopter—and the hijacker was arrested two days later. What caused this abrupt drop? Did potential hijackers suddenly lose interest? Did some secret organization of hijackers send out the word to "lie low"? Was public outrage a factor?

   Early in 1973, President Nixon ordered establishment of the screening procedures now standard at commercial airports, whereby passengers and all their carry-on luggage and other material pass through special X-ray units before boarding their planes. Some people have objected to this procedure on the grounds that it violates their constitutional right to privacy and constitutes an "unwarranted search and seizure." Proponents of the procedure argue that it is the cause of the virtual elimination of hijackings, and that if it were to be discontinued, hijackings would again occur (as they do in Europe and the Middle East) and people would be more seriously inconvenienced or even killed.

10. Recessions cause an increase in deaths from heart disease, kidney failure, and stroke, claims Dr. Harvey Brenner of Johns Hopkins University. Statistics over the past 68 years, he says, show that periods of economic downturn are consistently followed by waves of deaths from all these causes, as well as a rise in infant mortality, and that suicides, murders, and traffic deaths increase during a recession. So do the numbers of patients admitted to mental hospitals. Brenner attributes all these phenomena to the increased stress suffered by individuals at these times, whether from unemployment, from fear of unemployment, or from the struggle to secure basic necessities. He notes that the use of alcohol and tobacco increases during a recession, and holds that these two factors, plus others such as a rise in blood pressure and cholesterol level, are sufficient to cause

many of the heart-attack, stroke, and kidney-failure deaths, as well as to increase the number of mothers who give birth to infants unable to survive.

11. In Canada, as in the United States, there has been a trend away from capital punishment, even for convicted murderers. Law-enforcement officials and some others have been worried by this, believing that execution of some criminals would deter others from committing similar crimes. Among the statistics cited to support this view are the following: in 1963, the first year in which no one was hanged, there were 217 murders in Canada. In 1971, after eight years without a single hanging, there were 426. This data is regarded by many as evidence that abandonment of capital punishment has caused an increase in the murder rate. Therefore, it is claimed, a return to capital punishment would cause a reduction in the number of murders.

12. Mothers in the United States long ago abandoned breast-feeding of their babies in favor of bottle-feeding. Today, many of them are coming back to the breast. But now mothers in underdeveloped countries have begun to adopt bottle-feeding, and nutritional experts are concerned about the possible effects on infants' health. In these countries, cow's milk is often expensive, and packaged formulas are even more so, so a mother may dilute the milk—perhaps with impure water—before giving it to her baby. Or she may prepare a formula wrong, because she does not understand the directions on the package. Furthermore, cow's milk does not contain, as human milk does, precisely the right blend of ingredients for the needs of human babies. Thus a baby may need more cow's milk than human milk to achieve equally good nutrition.

In fact, doctors have noted that, as bottle-feeding has increasingly replaced breast-feeding in many of the underdeveloped countries, babies have begun showing signs of severe malnutrition at earlier and earlier ages. This appears to support the contention that in poor countries bottle-feeding causes an increased level of infant malnutrition.

13. In a study of the effects of LSD on memory, subjects were given doses containing either no LSD, 50 micrograms, or 100 micrograms of the drug. Of four memory skills tested after administration of the dose, scores on three were somewhat lower for the 50-microgram subjects than for the no-LSD group, and still lower for those subjects who had received 100 micrograms. The researchers concluded that the use of LSD caused the memory loss.

14. Researchers studying the effects of various types of fat in the diet concluded that margarine may cause more hardening of the arteries than various cholesterol-containing substances such as beef fat, butterfat, and powdered eggs. Although margarine is made with vegetable oils which are originally low in saturated fats, part of the oil is converted in the manufacturing process to saturated forms, called "trans" fats. In a controlled study, swine were fed for eight months on diets containing either

"trans" fats or one of the cholesterol-containing substances mentioned above. They were then slaughtered, and the condition of their arteries studied. Those fed with "traps" fats were the ones which showed the highest degree of arterial damage.

9. probability

Two General Principles

An adequate theory of probability must satisfy at least two requirements. First, a statement which is absolutely true has a probability of 1, whereas a statement which is absolutely false has a probability of 0, and any statement which is neither absolutely true nor absolutely false has a probability between 0 and 1.

Examples:
Every person born will eventually die. (*Probability of 1*)
Every person born will never die. (*Probability of 0*)
A male born and living in the United States will live until he is 68
    years of age. (*Probability between 0 and 1*)

A second requirement is that the sum of the probabilities of any logically inconsistent statements (that is, statements not more than one of which can be true at any given time) must be no greater than 1. Not more than one of the following statements can be true at any given time, although they all could be false.

Examples:
The next throw of this die will show a two.
The next throw of this die will show a three.
The next throw of this die will show a four.

Consequently, the sum of the probability that the first is true, the probability that the second is true, and the probability that the third is true cannot be more than 1.

Exercise 9-1

Would the probability of each of the following events be 1, 0, or a fraction in between? If in between would it be about .5, nearer to 1, or nearer to 0?

	1	0	Nearer to .5	Nearer to 1	Nearer to 0
1. A two-year-old child will die within the next six months.	☐	☐	☐	☐	☐
2. A mugging will be committed in New York City next week.	☐	☐	☐	☐	☐
3. The Arctic ice cap will completely melt in the next year.	☐	☐	☐	☐	☐
4. From this complete deck of ordinary playing cards, the next card I draw will be black.	☐	☐	☐	☐	☐
5. The moon is made of green cheese.	☐	☐	☐	☐	☐

	1	0	Nearer to .5	Nearer to 1	Nearer to 0
6. From this container that contains only white balls, the next ball I draw will be white.	☐	☐	☐	☐	☐
7. This green oak leaf has engaged in photosynthesis.	☐	☐	☐	☐	☐
8. From this complete deck of ordinary playing cards, the next card I draw will not be black.	☐	☐	☐	☐	☐
9. It will rain somewhere in the next month.	☐	☐	☐	☐	☐
10. Man is capable of landing on the moon.	☐	☐	☐	☐	☐

Exercise 9-2
Can the sum of the probabilities for any of the following pairs of statements be more than 1? Why, or why not?

	No	Yes
1. It will snow next week; it will not snow next week.	☐	☐
2. John will pass biology; John will fail biology.	☐	☐
3. Susan will pass logic this semester; Susan will not pass logic this semester.	☐	☐
4. The child which Mrs. Smith gave birth to yesterday was a boy; the child which Mrs. Smith gave birth to yesterday was a girl.	☐	☐
5. A Republican will lose the presidential election in 1980; a Democrat will lose the presidential election in 1980.	☐	☐

Three Theories of Probability
All logicians agree with the two general restrictions discussed above. However, when one tries to specify the probability of any statement to any degree of precision beyond that imposed by these generally accepted restrictions, the differences among competing theories of probability become very apparent. The three theories of probability that we will consider differ primarily in terms of the assumptions that must underlie the judgment establishing the probability of any statement. The theories are known as the classical (or *a priori*) theory, the relative frequency theory, and the subjectivist (or personalistic) theory.

The **classical theory**, or *a priori* theory, is based on two assumptions. The first is that all possible events are known. The second, called the **principle of indifference**, is that the probability of the occurrence of each event is equal to that of the others, unless there is good reason to believe otherwise. The probability that the favorable event will occur is determined by dividing the number of possible favorable events by the total number of equally possible events. This idea can be expressed by the following formula, in which A stands for the favorable event, P(A) stands for the probability of this event, m stands for the number of possible favorable events, and n stands for the number of all possible events:

$$P(A) = \frac{m}{n}$$

Thus, according to the classical theory, the probability that, upon throwing a standard die, the number four will show would be calculated as follows:

Example:
$$P(\text{Throwing a four}) = \frac{1}{6}$$

Critics have challenged the basic assumption of the classical theory that for any given situation, all possible events are being considered. They argue that there are almost always some possible events which we do not take into consideration when computing probabilities—for instance, the die may land on its edge. Furthermore, this theory cannot be used when statistical or other evidence indicates that not all possible events are equally probable.

All of the several versions of the **relative frequency theory** are based on the direct observation of concrete cases. This theory stipulates that the probability of an event is determined by dividing the number of observed favorable events by the total number of observed events.

This idea can be expressed by the following formula, in which P(A) is the probability of the favorable event A, m is the number of observed favorable events, and n is the total number of observed events.

$$P(A) = \frac{m}{n}$$

Thus, according to the relative frequency theory, the probability that a plane would crash would be calculated by observing a sample of randomly selected planes and counting the number of these planes that crashed. Assuming that 1000 planes were observed and two crashed, the probability would be calculated as shown below.

Example:
$$P(\text{Plane will crash}) = \frac{2}{1000} = .002$$

One difficulty faced by most version of the relative frequency theory stems from the assertion that probabilities based on observations of past cases are applicable to future cases only in the long run. That is, it is improper, or sometimes even meaningless, to assign a probability value to a single event.

The **subjective theory** defines probabilities as being grounded in the beliefs of individual persons. Thus, a variety of different probabilities can be assigned to the same particular event. For example, Jimmy the Greek may give 6 to 1 odds that the Yankees will defeat the Mets, whereas Tony the Bookie may give 3 to 1 odds in favor of the Yankees on the same game. Their probabilities for the same event would be different, as shown below.

Examples:
Jimmy the Greek:
$$P(\text{Yankees will beat Mets}) = \frac{6}{6+1} = \frac{6}{7}$$

Tony the Bookie:
$$P(\text{Yankees will beat Mets}) = \frac{3}{3+1} = \frac{3}{4}$$

There are several restrictions which significantly limit the assignment of probabilities according to the subjectivist theory. First, the two general rules mentioned earlier apply, for the person making the assignment of probability. Second, the rules of the probability calculus, discussed later, must also be observed. A significant feature of the subjectivist theory is that it requires that, insofar as possible, all of an individual's beliefs be considered in establishing his probability for a particular event, and the rules of the probability calculus provide a means of doing this. Many critics feel that the mere fact that different probabilities can be assigned to the same event by different persons (or by the same person at different times) is sufficient for rejecting the theory.

Exercise 9-3
Calculate the probability of each of the following, in terms of the theory specified.

1. (Classical theory) The state you are living in holds a weekly lottery. If 525,000 tickets have been sold, what is the probability you will win
   (a) if you hold two tickets, or (b) if you hold ten tickets?
2. (Relative frequency) If the number of plane crashes among domestic airlines in the United States is 156 out of a total of 342,576 domestic flights, what is the probability that the next domestic flight you take will crash?
3. (Subjectivist theory) A politician believes that the odds are 5 to 1 that he will win a particular election. (a) What is his probability for the event?
   (b) What is his probability that he will lose the election?
4. (Classical theory) A person is asked to pick a card from a well-shuffled deck of ordinary playing cards without a joker. What is the probability that the

person will (a) draw an eight, (b) draw a numbered card (ace, two ... ten), (c) draw a black picture card (king, queen, or jack), (d) draw a red numbered card, (e) draw the two of diamonds.

5. (Subjectivist theory) A month before the big football game, Benny the Bookie gives odds of 5 to 4 that Team A will defeat Team B. Two weeks before the game, Benny learns that Team B's superstar quarterback has been seriously injured and will play no other games this season. Benny quickly changes his odds, giving new odds of 3 to 1 that Team A will defeat Team B. What was Benny the Bookie's (a) old probability, and (b) new probability that team A will win?

6. (Relative frequency theory) According to actuarial statistics, out of 100,000 newborn females, 800 do not survive to their third birthday. (a) What is the probability that a newborn female will survive to her third birthday? (b) What is the probability that a newborn female will not survive to her third birthday?

7. A man is in a Las Vegas gambling casino, observing a particular roulette wheel. In the past 50 turns of the wheel, the ball has landed on a black number 35 times, and on a red number 15 times. (Roulette wheels have an equal number of red and black squares.) What is the probability that on the next turn the ball will land on a red square? (a) Assume the relative frequency theory, and (b) assume the classical theory.

8. (Relative frequency theory) Siamese cats are born either with a bend in the tip of their tails or with crossed eyes, but not both. Of 75 randomly observed Siamese cats, 45 had bends in the tip of their tails and 30 had crossed eyes. What is the probability that the next Siamese cat you observe (a) will have a bend in the tip of its tail, (b) will have crossed eyes?

9. (Classical theory) A bag contains 50 jellybeans: 20 licorice, 15 cinammon, and 15 papaya. What is the probability that a blindfolded child who selected one jellybean from the bag will select a licorice one?

The Probability Calculus

The procedure for determining the probabilities of compound events has been codified in a formal axiom system known as the **probability calculus.** Given the probability of the occurrence of each of several simple events, the probability calculus enables us to calculate the probability of their occurring in various combinations.

The probability calculus presupposes that there is some independent procedure for establishing the probabilities of individual events before attempting to calculate the probability of any combination of these events. The probability of a simple event's occurring by itself is called the **initial probability**, and it may be calculated by any of the three theories discussed above. For the sake of simplicity, we will use the classical method for determining initial probabilities.

In the probability calculus, a **complex event** is viewed as a whole composed of a number of simple events. For instance, the probability of being dealt a royal flush in hearts consists of the component events of being dealt the ace of hearts, the king of hearts, the queen of hearts, the jack of hearts, and the ten of hearts. The process of calculating the probability of the whole from the probabilities of the parts depends, as we shall see, on understanding the way in which the various parts are related.

The Restricted Conjunction Rule

Independent events are events such that the occurrence of one has no effect on the occurrence of the other(s); that is, if one event occurs, the probability of the occurrence of the other event(s) is not changed. For example, suppose Jane and Jack are each holding a penny. They both toss their respective pennies in the air. What is the probability that both will turn up heads? These are independent events, since the probability of the occurrence of one in no way affects the probability of the occurrence of the other. The probability of both pennies turning up heads can be determined by using the restricted conjunction rule.

The **restricted conjunction rule** states that if x and y are independent events, then the probability of both x and y occurring is equal to the probability of x occurring multiplied by the probability of y occurring. The restricted conjunction rule may be formulated as follows:

If x and y are independent events, then
$$P(x \text{ and } y) = P(x) \times P(y)$$

Using our example of Jane and Jack each tossing a penny, the probability that both coins will turn up heads may be calculated using the restricted conjunction rule.

Example:
P(Jane's penny coming up heads and Jack's penny coming up heads) =
$$\frac{1}{2} \times \frac{1}{2} = \frac{1}{4} = .25$$

The General Conjunction Rule

Dependent events are events in which the occurrence of one of the events affects the circumstances of the other(s) in such a way that the probability of the other(s) occurring is no longer what it would have been if the first event had not occurred. For example, suppose there are ten balls in an urn, five of which are white and five of which are black. What is the probability that a blindfolded man will select three black balls on three successive tries? These are dependent events, since each selection of a ball changes the composition of the balls in the urn and, therefore, the probability of selecting a black ball. The probability of picking three black balls in three successive tries can be determined by using the general conjunction rule.

The **general conjunction rule** is used to calculate probability values of the joint occurrence of a number of simple events (whether dependent or independent). The rule states that if x and y are any two events whatever, then the probability of their joint occurrence is equal to the probability of **x** occurring multiplied by the probability of **y** occurring given that **x** has already occurred. The general conjunction rule may be formulated as follows:

If **x** and **y** are any events whatever (either dependent or independent) then
P(**x** and **y**) = P(**x**) × P(**y** given **x**)

Using our example of the man selecting balls from an urn, the probability that he will select three black balls on three successive tries may be calculated using the general conjunction rule.

Example:
$$P(\textbf{x} \text{ and } \textbf{y} \text{ and } \textbf{z}) = \frac{1}{2} \times \frac{4}{9} \times \frac{3}{8} = \frac{12}{144} = \frac{1}{12} = .083$$

The restricted conjunction rule can be derived from the general conjunction rule, since if **x** and **y** are independent events, then the probability of **y** given that **x** has already occurred is the same as the probability of **y** itself.

Exercise 9-4
Calculate the probabilities of the following conjunct events. Provide the following information for each: (a) whether the simple events are dependent or independent; (b) the rule to be applied; (c) the initial probabilities computed using the classical theory; (d) the probability of the conjunct event; (e) the equation used to derive the answer.

1. If two normal dice are thrown simultaneously, what is the probability they will both turn up with a 1 on their faces?
2. From a well-shuffled ordinary deck of playing cards (without a joker), a person turns over five cards. What is the probability that the cards will be the ace, king, queen, jack, and ten of spades in that order?
3. Assuming that it is equally probable that a person will be born on any particular date and ignoring the complications of a leap year, what is the probability that two randomly selected people were born on October 20th?
4. There are three urns, each of which contains thirty balls. Urn 1 contains ten white, ten black, and ten red balls. Urn 2 contains fifteen white, five black, and ten red balls. Urn 3 contains twenty white, five black, and five red balls. If a person selects one ball from Urn 1, one from Urn 2, and one from Urn 3 in that order, what is the probability that he will select three black balls?
5. Assuming the same circumstances as in question 4, what is the probability that the person will select a red, white, and black ball in that order?
6. Assuming the same circumstances as in question 4, if a person selected three balls just from Urn 1, what is the probability he would select a red, white, and black ball in that order?

7. The Friendly Ripoff Corporation has five employees, and offices on the tenth floor of an office building. There are four elevators in the building that are all equally accessible. What is the probability that the five employees of the Friendly Ripoff Corporation took elevator number 1 to the offices on a particular morning?

8. A roulette wheel contains an equal number of black and red numbers. What is the probability that on four successive random spins of the wheel, a black number will turn up each time?

9. There are two well-shuffled decks of playing cards with no jokers. If Person A draws a card from one deck, and Person B draws a card from the other deck, what is the probability that both cards will be spades?

10. There is one well-shuffled deck of playing cards with no jokers. If Person A draws a card from the deck, and Person B draws a second card from the same deck, what is the probability that both cards will be aces?

The Restricted Disjunction Rule

All the situations discussed so far have involved **conjunctions** of simple events—complex events whose component events have occurred jointly; that is, the complex event was said not to occur unless a combination of two or more particular component events occurred in a specific sequence. There are other complex events which are **disjunctions**—that is, which may be said to occur when *one or more* of several alternative events occur. There are some events which are such that only one can occur; such events are said to be **mutually exclusive events**. For example, upon throwing a normal die, what is the probability that an even number will turn up? These are mutually exclusive events since on a given toss of the die 1 or 2 or 3 or 4 or 5 or 6 can come up, but only one number can come up on any one throw.

The **restricted disjunction rule** is used to calculate the probability of the occurrence of one or another of two or more mutually exclusive events. This rule states that if x and y are mutually exclusive events, then the probability that either will occur is equal to the probability of x plus the probability of y. The restricted disjunction rule may be formulated as follows:

If x and y are mutually exclusive events, then
$P(x \text{ or } y) = P(x) + P(y)$

We may use the restricted disjunction rule to calculate the probability of throwing an even number on one toss of a normal die. There are six possible events, each of which is equally possible, so the initial probability for any one of them is 1/6. However, there are three favorable events (throwing a 2 or a 4 or a 6). We shall call these three favorable events x, y and z.

Example:
$P(x \text{ or } y \text{ or } z) = P(x) + P(y) + P(z) = \frac{1}{6} + \frac{1}{6} + \frac{1}{6} = \frac{3}{6} = \frac{1}{2}$

The General Disjunction Rule

The components of a disjunction need not be mutually exclusive; that is, it is possible for many events to occur together. For instance, returning to our example of Jane and Jack each tossing a penny in the air, what is the probability that at least one of the two will get heads? The probability of getting heads from one coin is .5 and the probability of getting heads from the other is also .5. Nevertheless, the probability of Jane's getting heads or Jack's getting heads cannot be .5 + .5, since this would equal 1 or certainty. The restricted disjunction rule does not work because these two events are not mutually exclusive.

The **general disjunction rule** enables us to calculate the probability of the disjunction of any two or more events whatever; that is, it is not restricted to disjunctions of mutually exclusive events. This rule states that, for any two events x and y, the probability that at least one will occur is equal to the sum of the initial probabilities of x and y minus the probability that both x and y will occur, where the probability that both will occur is calculated by the general conjunction rule. The general disjunction rule may be formulated as follows:

For any events x and y, then
$$P(x \text{ or } y) = P(x) + P(y) - P(x \text{ and } y)$$

Using our example above, we can calculate the probability that either Jane's penny will come up heads or that Jack's penny will come up heads or that both will come up heads. (Note that 'or' in the general disjunction rule, and in our example, is to be interpreted in the inclusive sense—that is, as either x or y or both). Using the classical theory to establish the initial probabilities, we find that the probability of Jane's penny coming up heads is 1/2 and the probability of Jack's penny coming up heads is 1/2. Since they are independent events, the probability of them both occurring—that is, $P(x \text{ and } y)$—equals $1/2 \times 1/2$ which equals 1/4, as calculated by the general conjunction rule. Substituting this value in our general disjunction rule, we can now determine the probability of either Jane's penny coming up heads or Jack's penny coming up heads.

Example:
P(Jane's penny coming up heads or Jack's penny coming up heads) =
$$\frac{1}{2} + \frac{1}{2} - \frac{1}{4} = \frac{3}{4}$$

It should be noted that the restricted disjunction rule can be immediately derived from the general disjunction rule, since for mutually exclusive events the probability that both will occur is 0.

Exercise 9-5
Calculate the probabilities for the following disjunct events. Provide the following information for each: (a) whether or not these are mutually exclusive; (b) the rule to be applied; (c) the initial probability of each favorable event

(use the classical theory, when needed, to determine it); (d) where relevant, the value of P(x and y); (f) the probability of the disjunct event; (e) the equation used to derive the answer.

1. An urn contains ten black balls, five white balls, six blue balls, five red balls, and four yellow balls. What is the probability that a person will select either a white ball or a blue ball?

2. Two coins are flipped simultaneously. What is the probability that both will come up heads or both will come up tails?

3. If the probability that a ten-year old boy will survive to his twentieth birthday is .90, and the probability that his five-year old sister will survive to her twentieth birthday is .80, what is the probability that either will survive until his or her twentieth birthday?

4. From a standard deck of playing cards without a joker, what is the probability of selecting an ace, or a king, or a queen, or a jack on a single draw?

5. Assuming the same circumstances as in question 4, what is the probability of selecting either the ace of hearts, or the king of hearts, or the queen of hearts, or the jack of hearts on a single draw?

6. Suppose that there are two urns. Urn 1 contains thirty balls, ten of which are black, ten are white, and ten are red. Urn 2 contains thirty balls, five of which are black, fifteen are white, and ten are red. Suppose that Person A selects one ball from Urn 1, and Person B selects one ball from Urn 2. What is the probability that at least one of them will select a black ball?

7. Assuming the same circumstances as in question 6, what is the probability that either person A or Person B will select a red ball?

8. An urn contains fifty balls, fifteen of which are black, five are white, twenty are red, and ten are yellow. If one ball is selected at random, what is the probability that (a) it will be either white or black, (b) it will be either red or yellow, (c) it will be either black or yellow?

9. A young man has just moved into his own apartment. He is faced with ten sealed cartons, all of the same size and color, and all unlabeled. Three cartons contain books; two contain clothing; two contain dishes, pots, and other kitchen equipment; one contains bedding; and two contain canned and boxed foods. He decides to start by unpacking the kitchen supplies, that is, the dishes, pots, food, etc. What is the probability that the first box he opens will contain either dishes, pots, and other kitchen equipment, or canned and boxed foods?

10. In a group of 1,000 families receiving welfare, 50% of them have only one adult member, and 60% of them have three school-aged children; 35% have both only one adult member and three school-aged children. What is the probability that a randomly selected family will have either only one adult member or three school-aged children (or both one adult and three school-aged children)?

Combining the Rules

There are some complex events for which both conjunction and disjunction rules must be used. For example, suppose there is an urn which contains thirty balls, ten of which are white, ten are black, and ten are red. What is the probability that a man will draw five balls of any one color on his first five tries? There are three mutually exclusive favorable alternatives: getting five white balls, or five black balls, or five red balls. The initial probability of the choice of a white ball, on the classical theory, is 10/30, since there are ten white balls among the total of thirty. Assuming that the first ball chosen is white, the man now has twenty-nine balls from which to choose, only nine of which represent favorable outcomes. So the probability of getting a white ball on the second try, after having gotten a white one on the first try, is 9/29. Using the same methods, we can calculate the probability of getting five balls of one color in the following way:

$$P(\text{Five balls of one color}) = \frac{10}{30} \times \frac{9}{29} \times \frac{8}{28} \times \frac{7}{27} \times \frac{6}{26} =$$

$$\frac{30,240}{17,100,720} = \frac{2}{1131}$$

Since the other two favorable alternatives are mutually exclusive (and are being assumed to be all equally probable), the restricted disjunction rule can be used to calculate the probability of getting five balls of any one color.

$$P(\text{Five white balls or five black balls or five red balls}) =$$

$$\frac{2}{1131} + \frac{2}{1131} + \frac{2}{1131} = \frac{6}{1131} = \frac{2}{377}$$

10.
ardi-
nary
lan-
guage

Uses of Language

Everyday discourse is frequently imprecise and difficult to analyze from a logical viewpoint. Some of the problems of ordinary language are inherent in the language itself. Although language has many uses, the logician is concerned only with sentences that are being used to express propositions which appear in arguments. To determine what, in ordinary language, is within the domain of the logician, systems for classifying ordinary language uses have been developed. One such system of classification is to categorize the uses of ordinary language as cognitive or noncognitive.

A sentence is being used cognitively when it is being used to express a proposition, that is, something of which is proper to say that it is true or false. **Cognitive** uses of language in everyday contexts include explaining, classifying, asserting, and so on. Statements of personal beliefs, attitudes, and feelings may also involve cognitive uses of language. Assuming ordinary context, each of the following sentences is probably being used cognitively.

Examples:
Roses are red, yellow, pink, or white.
Compared with other foreign cars, the Volkswagen is very expensive.
My favorite dessert is chocolate pudding.
I believe that the moon is made of green cheese.

Each of the sentences above in most ordinary contexts would be used to express a proposition; thus, each would qualify as cognitive. Notice that the proposition being expressed by a sentence need not be a true proposition.

A sentence is said to be used noncognitively when it is used to do something other than express a statement or proposition. **Noncognitive** uses of language involve such acts as issuing commands or giving orders, making requests, asking questions, expressing feelings, and arousing emotions. (Note that there is a difference between describing one's feelings, which is a cognitive use of language, and expressing one's feelings, which is a noncognitive use of language.) Assuming ordinary context, the sentences below probably are being used noncognitively.

Examples:
Open the window.
Did you pass your test?
Holy mackerel!

The context in which a sentence is being used is the most important guide for determining whether or not it is being used to express a statement or proposition and is, therefore, logically analyzable. However, it is possible for a sentence to have more than one use within a particular context. For example, in ordinary contexts, the sentence 'The building is falling down!' is being used cognitively; that is, it expresses a proposition which is either true or false. However, the sentence ordinarily is also used to express the emotions of the speaker and to arouse emotions in the hearers. Then too, the sentence also may be used at the same time to express a command, 'Get out of the building fast.'

Exercise 10-1

Assuming ordinary context where not otherwise specified, indicate whether each of the following sentences most likely exemplifies cognitive, noncognitive, or mixed uses of language. Be prepared to explain your answers.

	Cognitive	Noncognitive	Mixed
1. I believe that history will show that Richard Nixon was one of the United States' greatest presidents.	☐	☐	☐
2. Sit down over there, please.	☐	☐	☐
3. There's an earthquake!	☐	☐	☐
4. I can't stand your behavior.	☐	☐	☐
5. Elephants are not mammals.	☐	☐	☐
6. How much did that shirt cost?	☐	☐	☐
7. Well, John is your friend, isn't he?	☐	☐	☐
8. I don't like blondes.	☐	☐	☐
9. Ugh!	☐	☐	☐
10. Don't tell me you don't know Mary—I saw you with her last night!	☐	☐	☐

Neutral versus Emotive Language

It is incorrect to say that any word, phrase, or sentence is, in and of itself, positive, negative, or neutral with regard to the emotive force it carries. It is best to regard the notion of neutral and emotive language as a continuum on which we have, at one extreme, very positive emotive language, and, at the other extreme, very negative emotive language, with neutral language between the two extremes. The same word, phrase, or sentence may appear anywhere on the continuum, depending on the context in which it is used, the intended purpose of the speaker, and the situations and attitudes of the receivers. For example, consider the statement 'Euthansia is the taking of the life of an individual who is hopelessly sick or injured for reasons of mercy and with that individual's consent.' Such a statement uttered by a speaker who favors euthansia probably is intended to carry positive emotive force. To someone in the audience who is strongly opposed to euthansia, such a statement may carry strong negative emotive force, since he or she may perceive the statement to be a gross attempt soft peddle a form of murder or suicide. To another audience member who is neutral about the issue, the statement itself may seem neutral.

Exercise 10-2

Each of the following sentences contains an italicized word or phrase. Rate the probable emotive force of this word or phrase (for the speaker) on a continuum ranging from strongly, moderately, or slightly positive, through relatively neutral, to slightly, moderately, or strongly negative. Take into consideration the sentence in which the word or phrase is used and also the stipulated context.

1. (A friend who has just come aboard another friend's yatch) This is *some boat* you have!
2. (A friend who is on another friend's rowboat, and has just noticed a second leak) This is *some boat* you have!
3. (A friend describing her trip to a New England seacoast town) We saw *some boats*.
4. (A teacher to a six-year-old who has just told about a trip he took with his parents during the summer) That's a *good story*, John. Would you care to tell another one?
5. (A wife to her husband who has just arrived home from work at a 11 P.M. and a little drunk; the husband has just told the wife that he had to work late at the office and the phone lines were out so he couldn't call) That's a *good story*, John. Would you care to tell another one?
6. (A college student to another student) Joan is such a *pig*; she borrowed my book and spilled coffee all over it.
7. (A mother to her toddler who has just smeared chocolate pudding all over his face and tee shirt) You're my favorite little *pig* in the whole world!
8. (A farmer to another farmer) You call those scrawny creatures '*pigs*'?
9. (A demonstrator being carried away by the police) Help, the *pigs* have captured me!
10. (A woman to another woman) John and I have worked very hard at our *marriage*, and I think the results show.
11. (A committed bachelor to a friend who is about to be married) Man, *marriage* is the end of the line; you're about to give up all your freedom, money, and fun.
12. (A lecturer in a college sociology class) The tradition of monogomous *marriage* is not confined to western societies.

Exercise 10-3

Compare your answers to the problems in Exercise 10-3 with those of other members of your class. Discuss the reasons for any differences in rating; do they lie in the sentence itself, in the stipulated context, or in the personal experience and beliefs of the students doing the rating.

Kinds of Disagreement

A **real disagreement** is one in which the statements of the disputants' positions are logically inconsistent—that is, one in which it is logically impossible for both to be true at the same time.

Example:
Person A: John is 5'11' tall.
Person B: John is 6'1" tall.

An **apparent disagreement** or **pseudo-disagreement** is one in which the statements of the disputants' positions are not logically inconsistent—that is, one in which it is logically possible for both to be true at the same time.

Example:
Person A: I believe John is 5'11" tall.
Person B: I believe John is 6'1" tall.

A **merely verbal disagreement** is a type of pseudo-disagreement in which a key word or phrase is being used with different meanings.

Example:
Person A: John is tall.
Person B: John is not tall.

If Person A considers anyone who is over 5'10" to be tall and Person B considers anyone who is over 6'6" to be tall, then this is a merely verbal disagreement.

Exercise 10-4
Indicate whether each of the following pairs of sentences exemplifies a real or apparent disagreement, and if apparent, whether the disagreement is merely verbal. If you regard a disagreement as apparent rather than real, be prepared to explain why.

	Real	Apparent	Apparent/ Verbal
1. *Mike:* I have strong opinions about politics.	☐	☐	☐
Pete: I am not very interested in politics.	☐	☐	☐
2. *Person A:* I think *Rhoda* is a boring show.	☐	☐	☐
Person B: I think *Rhoda* is a very entertaining show.	☐	☐	☐
3. *Person A:* The Smiths are a poor family.	☐	☐	☐
Person B: The Smiths are not a poor family. (Persons A and B agree that the total income of the Smith family is $4800 per year.)			

	Real	Apparent	Apparent/ Verbal
	☐	☐	☐

4. *Person A:* President Nixon was impeached, since charges were brought against him by the House Judiciary Committee.
   Person B: President Nixon was not impeached, since he was not tried in the Senate and found guilty of the charges made against him.

5. *Pete:* When I see Bob, I'm going to punch him in the nose for what he told Susan about me.   ☐ ☐ ☐
   Mike: You don't really mean that; you're just upset right now; you'll get over it.

6. *Father:* Listen, son, would you shut off that blasting radio. I can't think with all that noise.   ☐ ☐ ☐
   Son: That's not noise, dad. That's the Rolling Stones' new hit.

7. *Person A:* A straw looks bent when it is placed in a glass of water.   ☐ ☐ ☐
   Person B: No, the straw isn't bent. It's just as straight as it was before.

8. *Person A:* President Ford is a conservative; he opposes school busing.   ☐ ☐ ☐
   Person B: President Ford is not a conservative; he favored a tax rebate.

9. *Person A:* Cairn terriers are the smallest dogs.   ☐ ☐ ☐
   Person B: Scotties are the smallest dogs.

10. *Person A:* I saw a strange object in the sky; I think it was a flying saucer.   ☐ ☐ ☐
    Person B: I think what you saw was a space satellite.

11. *Person A:* There was a flying saucer in the sky five minutes ago; I saw it with my own eyes.   ☐ ☐ ☐
    Person B: You're out of your mind; there are no such things as flying saucers.

	Real	Apparent	Apparent/ Verbal
12. *Person A:* Federico Fellini's first film was *Juliet of the Spirits.* *Person B:* Federico Fellini's first film was *Amarcord.*	☐	☐	☐
13. *Person A:* Duchamp's painting *Nude Descending the Staircase* is a masterpiece.	☐	☐	☐
Person B: It's not a masterpiece; it's not even a hundred years old.	☐	☐	☐
14. *Person A:* Dr. Jekyll and Mr. Hyde were really the same person; the physical appearance of the body is all that changed. *Person B:* No, Dr. Jekyll and Mr. Hyde were two different persons; they both lived in the same body and the body changed appearance when one person was dominant.	☐	☐	☐
15. *Person A:* The sun looks like it revolves around the earth. *Person B:* No, the earth revolves around the sun.	☐	☐	☐
16. *Person A:* Mercury is smaller than Venus in circumference. *Person B:* Mercury is larger than Venus in circumference.	☐	☐	☐
17. *Person A:* John is an excellent student; he got an A in English last semester. *Person B:* John is a terrible student; he got a D in Biology last semester.	☐	☐	☐
18. *Person A:* Robert is a very well-educated person. *Person B:* Robert is not a very well-educated person. (Persons A and B agree that Robert has a high school diploma.)	☐	☐	☐
19. *Person A:* I think *The Tempest* is a great play. *Person B:* I think *The Tempest* is a terrible play.	☐	☐	☐
20. *Person A:* I saw Fred with Marsha last night. *Person B:* I think you saw Bob, Fred's identical twin, with Marsha last night.	☐	☐	☐

Ethical Sentences
The following examples are typical ethical sentences.

Examples:
You should not smoke pot.
C.I.A. spying on Americans in wrong.
You ought to obey all laws.

If ethical sentences express propositions, then they can be subjected to logical analysis, and it is possible for real disagreements to arise over them. Philosophers hold a number of views on whether or not ethical sentences express propositions; seven such views are presented below.

View One: Ethical sentences are a cognitive use of language; therefore, they are logically analyzable.

View Two: Ethical sentences are ordinarily used to express an emotional reaction by the speaker and, therefore, do not express propositions.

View Three: Ethical sentences describe attitudes held by the speaker and, therefore, express either true or false propositions about the attitudes of an individual rather than about actions.

View Four: Ethical sentences are used in most contexts only as commands or directives and, therefore, are nonpropositional. (A contrary view maintains that even though they may express a command or admonition they express propositions as well.)

View Five: Ethical sentences are used to evoke positive or negative attitudes in the hearer, and do not express propositions.

View Six: Still another view asserts that since such terms as 'right,' 'wrong,' 'ought,' and 'ought not' are used in nonethical sentences that express propositions, they are similarly employed in ethical sentences. Opponents of this view maintain that the use of ethical terms in describing nonethical things or events is an ambiguous use of language, and that the terms have different meanings in ethical and in nonethical contexts.

View Seven: Ethical sentences such as 'Murder is wrong' really attribute specific meaning to the word 'wrong,' such as 'productive of human unhappiness,' or 'illegal.' And whether murder does produce human unhappiness or actually is illegal are matters that can be determined to be true or false. Therefore, on this view, an ethical sentence is normally used to express a proposition.

Real disagreements concerning ethical sentences can occur only when both disputants are using these sentences to express the same sorts of proposition. Consider the following example:

Example:
Person A: Killing is always wrong.
Person B: Killing is not always wrong.

If both disputants hold view one, then their disagreement is real. If Person A holds view one and Person B holds view two, then their disagreement is an apparent verbal disagreement.

Exercise 10-5
In the following pairs of sentences, the view of ethical sentences held by each speaker is shown by the number in parentheses following each sentence. Indicate whether each pair of sentences represent a real or an apparent disagreement.

		Real	Apparent
1.	Abortion is always wrong. (4) Abortion is not always wrong. (1)	☐	☐
2.	A child should always obey his parents. (1) A child should not always obey his parents. (1)	☐	☐
3.	Homosexuality is good. (2) Homosexuality is bad. (2)	☐	☐
4.	It's good to have premarital sex. (2) It's bad to have premarital sex. (4)	☐	☐
5.	Abortion is always wrong. (7) Abortion is not always wrong. (5)	☐	☐
6.	A child always should obey his parents. (3) A child should not always obey his parents. (6)	☐	☐
7.	Homosexuality is good. (5) Homosexuality is bad. (1)	☐	☐
8.	It's good to have premarital sex. (4) It's bad to have premarital sex. (4)	☐	☐
9.	Abortion is always wrong. (5) Abortion is not always wrong. (5)	☐	☐
10.	A child always should obey his parents. (7) A child should not always obey his parents. (1)	☐	☐
11.	Homosexuality is good. (3) Homosexuality is bad. (1)	☐	☐
12.	It's good to have premarital sex. (3) It's bad to have premarital sex. (5)	☐	☐
13.	Abortion is always wrong. (1) Abortion is not always wrong. (2)	☐	☐
14.	A child should always obey his parents. (3) A child should not always obey his parents. (3)	☐	☐
15.	Homosexuality is good. (6) Homosexuality is bad. (6)	☐	☐
16.	It's good to have premarital sex. (3) It's bad to have premarital sex. (2)	☐	☐
17.	Abortion is always wrong. (3) Abortion is not always wrong. (4)	☐	☐

	Real	Apparent
18. A child should always obey his parents. (7)	☐	☐
A child should not always obey his parents. (7)		
19. Abortion is always wrong. (1)	☐	☐
Abortion is not always wrong. (6)		
20. It's good to have premarital sex. (2)	☐	☐
It's bad to have premarital sex. (5)		

11.
de·
fini·
tions

The Importance of Definitions

Although the concept of definition is not of great importance to abstract logic, it is of importance in analyzing and evaluating arguments in everyday contexts. For instance, it is necessary to know the meanings of words in a sentence to determine whether or not they express a proposition, and are, thus, logically analyzable. Although logicians generally are not concerned with the truth or falsity of a particular statement, there are some statements that are true or false by definition. Since it is crucial in any non-trivial valid argument that one or more of the components of the conclusion must be identical in meaning with one or more of the components of the premises, definitions are needed to determine if two or more expressions have the same meaning. Though the vagueness of everyday language often is an asset in everyday contexts, it can create problems in disciplines such as logic which demand accuracy of thought and expression. Then too, meaning and definition also may have a powerful impact on people's lives.

Use-Mention Distinction

It is important to distinguish when a word is being used and when it is being mentioned. This **use-mention distinction** can be best illustrated by examples such as those which follow. In each example, the italicized word is being *used* in the first sentence and *mentioned* in the second.

Examples:
Use: *War* is always tragic.
Mention: The word *war* is of Anglo-Saxon origin.

Use: The lilacs *are* green.
Mention: *Are* is a present tense form of the verb to be.

Use: This is something which I will not put up *with*!
Mention: *With* should never end a sentence.

In ordinary language sources, words or groups of words that are mentioned are usually either set off in double quotation marks or italicized.

Examples:
"Anopheles" means "harmful" in Greek.
Literary characters are the source of many words, including *quixotic* and *faustian*.

In this book, when a word or group of words is being mentioned, rather than used, it is set off in single rather than double quotation marks.

Examples:
The word 'mizzle' is not used very frequently.
The sentence 'All men are mortal' expresses a proposition in most ordinary
   contexts.

If a word or group of words is being mentioned within a sentence already
set off in single quotes, these words are placed in double quotes.

Example:
The sentence 'The word "mizzle" is not used very frequently' expresses a
   true proposition.

It is possible to avoid the use of combined single and double quotes by
setting the sentence being mentioned in a separate line, For example, if we say
that

   'Mob' means 'a large disorderly crowd'

expresses a proposition, we need only place the words 'mob' and 'a large disorderly crowd' in single quotes, since by setting the sentence on a separate line,
we are indicating the whole sentence is being mentioned.
   Sentences used to express definitions are often abbreviated as shown below:

Example:
'Mob' = df. 'a large disorderly crowd'

As in ordinary language sources, we will follow the convention of using
double quotes to indicate direct speech or to indicate that the word enclosed
has a special or atypical meaning within a particular context (called 'scare
quotes').

Examples:
Direct Discourse:
The teacher looked at John and said firmly, "Keep your eyes on your own
   test paper or you will be reported to the Dean."

Scare Quotes:
I have no desire to live in a country which is the "winner" of a nuclear war.

Exercise 11-1
Each of the following passages is from an ordinary language source. Some of the
words in each passage are placed in single and/or double quotes. Read each
passage carefully. Does the use of quotes indicate that the word(s): (a) are
being mentioned; (b) are being used in a special or atypical sense; or (c) are
part of direct dialogue or are being quoted directly from another source?

1. For almost half a century, physicists have struggled to understand the four basic sources that exist in nature and to find a single "unified field theory" that would explain them all.
   (*Newsweek*, Dec. 2, 1974)
2. Senator Walter Mondale once confided to a friend that he was not sure he could be elected President because "I don't think there's enough show biz in me."
   (N.Y. *Times*, Nov. 24, 1974)
3. "Proved reserves" [of petroleum] can mean anything from a mere round multiple of last year's production to a careful estimate of reservoirs mapped by test wells.
   (*Scientific American*, Sept., 1974)
4. In physics 'force' means 'the product of mass times acceleration.'
5. 'Tulip tree' =df. '*Liriodenclron tulipifera*'.
6. Direct [wage and price] controls may check "leapfrogging" by unions as they strive to catch up with past inflation and maintain their members' wages relative to those of other workers.
   (N.Y. *Times*, Dec. 8, 1974)
7. Discussions of the term 'intuition' give rise to a great deal of disagreement.
8. ' "Sense" has a wide variety of meanings in English' was the statement Professor Wright made in class.
9. AT&T will accommodate a customer [who wishes to install non-Western Electric equipment and connect it to the Bell System] only if he agrees to buy a Western Electric-made protective device to "couple" [it] with the Bell equipment.
   (*Newsweek*, Dec. 2, 1974)
10. Now that the U.N. General Assembly has overwhelmingly endorsed the P.L.O. [Palestine Liberation Organization] and the Palestinian people's "right to national independence and sovereignty," several Israeli commentators are conceding that Israel has lost its diplomatic struggle with the P.L.O.
    (N.Y. *Times*, Dec. 8, 1974)

Exercise 11-2
Using the rules for single and double quotes to be followed in this text, correctly punctuate the following passages.

1. The definition Man is a rational animal was originally formulated by the Greeks.
2. The definition Expire means die is a synonymous definition.
3. The so-called domino theory was used by the administrations of several American presidents in the 1950's and 1960's to justify American involvement in Vietnam.
4. Law school, says Millard Rund, executive director of the Association of American Law Schools, is a place where society's generalists are educated.
   (*Newsweek*, Dec. 9, 1974)

5. Quasar = df. any of various very distant celestial objects that resemble stars but emit unusually bright blue and ultraviolet light and radio waves.

(Webster's New Collegiate Dictionary)

6. Then Attorney General Elliot Richardson resigned from the Nixon Administration during the Saturday night massacre rather than fire former Special Watergate Prosecutor Archibald Cox when President Nixon ordered him to do so.

(Adapted from N.Y. *Times*, Dec. 15, 1974)

7. All of Descartes' philosophical system follows from the initial argument I think, therefore I am.

8. [Henry Ford II] suggested a 10-cent-per-gallon tax on gasoline to finance aid to the people most seriously hurt by the recession. I realize it may have a short-term adverse impact on auto sales, said Ford, but we will never get a full-fledged recovery in the auto industry if we don't give the nation some elbow room to fight its way out of the recession.

(*Newsweek*, Dec. 2, 1974)

Kinds of Definition

In logic, definitions are used primarily to define words, not concepts or ideas. The term that is to be defined is called the **definiendum**. The word or words used to define it are called the **definiens**. In the following example, 'pongid' is the definiendum and 'anthropod ape' is the definiens.

Example:
'Pongid' = df. 'anthropod ape'

When formulating a definition, it is important to specify the context in which the definiendum is being used. Depending on the type of definiens provided, a definition may be classified as one of several kind: synonymous, enumerative, connotative, and operational.

A **synonymous definition** is one in which the definiens consists of only one word which, in appropriate contexts, can be used interchangeably with the definiendum.

Examples:
'rob' = df. 'steal'
'cop' = df. 'policeman'
'tepid' = df. 'lukewarm'

In an **enumerative definition**, the definiens lists words referring to or presents actual examples of things, properties, relations, concepts, and so on, to which the definiens can be appropriately applied. Enumerative definitions are divided into two categories—ostensive and denotative—depending on the nature of the definiens.

Ostensive definitions provide concrete examples of things to which the definiendum can be applied. For example, a person might provide an ostensive definition of the word 'automobile' by pointing to a Rolls-Royce, a Volkswagen, and a Cadillac, or any other type of car that might be present.

Example:
'the modern Roman alphabet' = df. 'a, b, c, d, e, f, g, h, i, j, k, l, m, n, o, p, q, r, s, t, u, v, w, x, y, z'

Denotative definitions do not require the physical presence of the definiens; rather they list examples of things, or types or classes of things, to which the definiendum applies. The list comprising the definiens specifies what is called the '**denotation**' or '**extension**' of the definiendum.

Example:
'criminal' = df. 'robber, thief, felon, pickpocket, forger, perjurer, briber, murderer, confidence man, and so on.'

Ostensive definitions have advantages: they often are easy to formulate; they can teach concepts that were previously unknown; and they do not depend on preexisting language. But, ostensive definitions also have disadvantages: they depend on the physical presence of the definiens, and they often are more easily subject to misinterpretation than other types of definition.

Denotative definitions usually are easy to formulate, and are sometimes easily understood, especially when the listing in the definiens is complete. On the other hand, the listing of examples in the definiens of a denotative definition often is incomplete, causing the person to misinterpret the meaning of the word. With some words (for example, 'unicorn'), it is impossible to provide examples for a denotative definition.

The definiens in a **connotative definition** pinpoints the meaning of the definiendum by listing a set of properties common to all the things to which the definiendum can be correctly applied, and common only to those things. The sum total of a definiendum's essential properties is variously called the '**intention**' or the '**connotation**' of the definiendum.

Example:
'radio' = df. 'an electronic device that receives transmitted signals of sounds and converts them into auditory sensations and has no capability for the reception of signals that produce visual effects.'

An increase in the intention of a term (the adding of properties) will either diminish the denotation (extension) or leave it unchanged. A decrease in the intension of a definition (the elimination of some of the properties named by the definiens) will either increase the denotation or leave it unchanged.

A definition by genus and difference is a type of connotative definition which consists of specifying the general class of things to which the definiendum belongs, and then further specifying the properties by which the definiendum can be distinguished from other things belonging to the same general class. The general class is called the *genus*, and the distinguishing properties are called either the *differential* or the *difference*. In the example below, the genus is 'an order of mammal' and the difference is 'females have an abdominal pouch for carrying their young.'

Example:
'marsupials' = df. 'an order of mammal in which the females have an abdominal pouch for carrying their young.'

Connotative definitions must list the **essential attributes** of a definiendum. An attribute is considered essential by virtue of being essential to the definition of the word rather than of any physical entity. 'Essential attributes' may be defined as 'those attributes which, when included in the definiens, are most informative, most characteristic of the definiendum, and least open to misinterpretation.'

An **operational definition** is one whose definiens provides a test or a formal procedure which is to be followed in order to determine whether or not the definiendum applies to a certain thing.

Example:
A liquid is 'alkaline' if after immersing a piece of litmus paper in the liquid, the litmus paper turns blue.

Exercise 11-3
Tell whether each of the following definitions is synonymous, enumerative (ostensive or denotative), connotative (possibly by genus and difference), or operational.

1. "Herbivorous' means 'feeding on plants.'
    _____

2. A copy is a reproduction.
    _____

3. Prime numbers: 1, 2, 3, 5, 7, 11, 13, 17, 19, 23, etc.
    _____

4. The piece of music we are listening to now is an example of a string quartet.
    _____

5. An icosahedron is a polyhedron having twenty faces.
    _____

6. Alcoholic beverage: If, as a person drinks more and more of a beverage, the person becomes more and more drunk, the beverage is an alcoholic beverage.

7. Free trade: As applied to international trade, the absence of export and import duties and of regulations which are clearly designed to reduce or prevent such trade. (Sloan and Zurcher, *Dictionary of Economics*)

8. Aleph is the first letter of the Hebrew alphabet.

9. '*Quercus alba*' is the scientific name for the American white oak.

10. A prevaricator is a liar.

11. The face cards in a deck of playing cards are all the Jacks, Queens, and Kings.

12. Allergy: If a substance is placed on a person's skin and the person develops a rash, then that person has an allergy to that substance.

13. Stamina is the same thing as endurance.

14. An iguana is a large herbivorous tropical American lizard.

15. Noon (local time) is that time of day at which the sun is equidistant between the eastern and western horizons.

16. 'Wireless' means 'radio'.

17. Right triangle: Given any triangle, construct a circle around the triangle, using the longest side of the triangle as the diameter of the circle. If all three vertices of the triangle lie on the circle, the triangle is a right triangle.

18. The principal parts of a Latin verb: amo, amare, amavi, amatus.

19. The principal parts of a Latin verb are the first person singular present indicative active, the present infinitive active, the first person singular perfect active, and the perfect passive participle.

20. The principal parts of a Latin verb are those verb forms from which all other possible verb forms can be derived.

Exercise 11-4

Write (a) a synonymous definition, (b) an enumerative (ostensive or denotive) definition, and (c) a connotative definition (perhaps by genus and difference) for each of the following words.

1. Metropolis
2. Movie
3. Shooting star
4. Fabric
5. *Homo sapiens*
6. Loquacious
7. Windpipe
8. Spine
9. Gem
10. Rich

Exercise 11-5

Write an operational definition for each of the following words.

1. Buoyant
2. Transparent
3. Contagious
4. Poison (noun)
5. Even number

Uses of Definitions

In addition to distinguishing some of the different methods by which a word can be defined, it is also important to be aware of the reasons why people formulate definitions, and of the uses to which definitions can be put. Among the most common uses of definitions are to report meaning, to remove ambiguity or vagueness, to introduce a new meaning, to persuade, and any combination of these various uses.

A **reportive** or **lexical** definition is used to report the meaning of a term as it is used and understood by a specific group of people. It can be enumerative, connotative, synonymous, or operational. A lexical or reportive definition is propositional; it express a statement which is either true or false, depending on whether or not it accurately reports the way the word is actually used by members of the group in question.

Examples:

'Typewriter' may be defined as 'a mechanical device operated either manually or electrically, that enables a person to write with type that resembles printer's type on a page by means of a moveable, inked ribbon'

'Typewriter' means 'that thing which our secretary Mary is using at her desk right now'

Not all lexical or reportive definitions report the way an entire language group uses a word; some are limited to reporting the way in which a term is used in a technical or otherwise limited context. Two common types of limited reportive definitions are the theoretical definition and the legal definition. A **theoretical definition** defines a word in terms of the meaning which it carries in a particular scientific theory. Some words have both ordinary and theoretical lexical definitions; others only have theoretical definitions.

Example:
In the psychology of C. G. Jung, the word 'mask' means 'the outer or social aspects of personality.'

A **legal definition** is one that is specified in laws as formulated by a legislative, judicial, or executive body. It serves a limited reportive function when it is used in reference to a definition which is generally accepted within an existing legal system.

Example:
'Blindness' is defined for purpose of receiving benefits under the state welfare laws as 'having less than one tenth of normal vision in the more efficient eye after all refractive corrections have been made by a lens.'

Ambiguity is said to exist when a word or phrase having two or more distinct meanings is used in such a way that it is not obvious from the context which meaning is intended. For example, the sentence 'He gave her a ring' may refer to a man giving a woman a piece of jewelry, or calling her on the telephone. Without knowledge of the context, the word 'ring' is ambiguous.

Vagueness exists when a term is such that it is impossible to tell whether or not it applies to certain borderline cases. For example, the term 'overweight' in ordinary language is vague, since it is impossible to pinpoint exactly when someone fits this category.

Precising definitions are used to eliminate ambiguity or vagueness. Any of the kinds of definition mentioned in the previous section (synonymous, enumerative, etc.) can be used as a precising definition.

Examples:
'Rich means 'having a million dollars in readily liquidable assets.'
For our purposes, the word 'educated' refers only to those persons who have graduated from a four-year high school.

Precising definitions are not evaluated strictly in terms of their truth or falsity. They are judged by whether or not they adequately eliminate ambiguity or vagueness, and whether they do so without distorting the generally accepted meaning of the word.

A **stipulative definition** introduces new meaning. It may define either a newly coined word or a word which has a generally accepted meaning, but which is now being used in a new sense.

Examples:
The word 'delitrious' means 'both tastes delicious and is nutritious'.
In my lectures, the term 'major world powers' should be understood to include 'any country which is a major exporter of oil.'

Since there is no precedent for the newly stipulated use of a word, a stipulative definition cannot be true or false. It can be judged good if it achieves the specific purpose for which it was introduced and bad if it does not. If a new word, or a new meaning for an old word, becomes absorbed into general usage or into the standard vocabulary of a particular discipline, then its definition is no longer stipulative, but rather reportive.

Each of the different kinds of definition can be used persuasively. **Persuasive definitions** usually reflect the beliefs or persuasive intent of the speaker; they are usually intended to influence someone else's evaluation of the definiendum and/or to affect other people's behavior in some significant way.

Examples:
'Pot smokers' may be defined as 'dropouts, malcontents, emotionally insecure persons, and the dregs of society.'
'Pot smokers' may be defined as 'enlightened experimenters, victims of a puritanical and hypocritical society, who have challenged age-old patterns of behavior.'

A definition may have mixed uses, and it is not always clear how a definition is being used in a particular situation. Definitional controversies are apt to arise whenever complex issues and changing ideas are under debate, especially in the courts, where judicial interpretation of existing law may actually broaden or narrow the meaning and applicability of the law. In such cases, there is no fixed usage of definitions.

Exercise 11-6
Each passage below is concerned with the definition of a word, and in some cases a particular context has been supplied. Read each passage carefully and then determine the use to which the definition has been put. Is it (a) reportive or lexical; (b) limited lexical (perhaps theoretical or legal); (c) precising; (d) stipulative; and/or (e) persuasive.

1. A physics teacher defining 'gravity,' stating Newton's law of universal gravitation: Every body of matter in the universe attracts every other body with a force directly proportional to the product of their masses and inversely proportional to the square of the distance between them.

2. A professor to her graduate philosophy seminar: In order to eliminate confusion in this discussion, I propose that we define 'intuition' as 'unmediated knowledge' and find other words to express the other meanings that some of those involved in the discussion are attaching to the word 'intuition'.

3. A statement by Mr. Irving S. Shapiro, chairman of E. I. duPont de Nemours & Co., describing effective training programs for persons who will be working for industrial companies: Nearly 80 per cent of the people who will be of working age in the year 2000 are already on the job or are now in school. These people are the direct bridge to the 21st century. They're what we might call our "people connection" with the future.

(N.Y. *Times*, Dec. 15, 1974)

4. Walter Lippmann, on the duty of public officials: Those in high places are more than the administrators of government bureaus. They are more than the writers of laws. They are the custodians of a nation's ideals, of the beliefs it cherishes, of its permanent hopes, of the faith which makes a nation out of a mere aggregation of individuals.

5. A music teacher to the class: Quality is one of the attributes of a note. By their quality, notes of the same pitch and volume may be distinguished. Quality depends on the extent to which overtones are present with the fundamental.

(Robert Illing, *A Dictionary of Music*)

6. 'Nail' means: 1. A piece of horn-like material growing out of and covering the ends of the fingers and toes of man and most primates; 2. A slender piece of metal, often with a flat head, designed to be hammered into pieces of wood or other materials to hold them together; 3. A British unit of length equal to one sixteenth yard.

7. In addition, the newly discovered subatomic particle may be the first to possess a combination of mathematical properties rather unscientifically known as "charm" (a term first coined by Harvard physicist Sheldon Glashow and Stanford's James Bjorken, that involves such basic characteristics as the way in which the particle is produced and the means by which it breaks up into other particles).

(*Newsweek*, Dec. 2, 1974)

8. Last week famous South African heart surgeon Dr. Christian Barnard performed the first "twin heart" operation, implanting a second heart into a terminally ill cardiac patient to act as a backup for his own diseased heart.

(*Newsweek*, Dec. 9, 1974)

9. A law school professor to his class: Escrow is defined as property placed by one person in the hands of a second person, usually a trust company, for the delivery to a third person upon the fulfillment by the latter of certain specific obligations.

(Sloan and Zurcher, *Dictionary of Economics*)

10. A lobbyist who is against repealing marijuana laws: Marijuana is the devil's weed; it weakens the mind of the user and destroys the fabric of American society.

Exercise 11-7
Next to each word listed below is given a use to which a definition for that word might be put. Write a definition for each word which functions according to the use indicated. Provide a context for each definition where necessary.

1. Forecast (reportive)
2. Closed shop (limited reportive-legal)
3. Politician (persuasive)
4. Pornographic (precising)
5. Z-ray (stipulative)
6. Acceleration (limited reportive-theoretical)
7. Recent (precising)
8. Coup d'etat (reportive)
9. Socialism (persuasive)
10. Bail (limited reportive-legal)

Criteria for Good Definitions
There are some general criteria for good definitions which can be applied to any definiens. These include noncircularity, affirmativeness, accuracy, and clarity.

A **circular definition** is one in which the definiens contains the word that is to be defined, or contains a grammatical variation of this same word. All good definitions should be noncircular.

Example:
'Vagueness' is 'the quality or state of being vague.'

An **affirmative** definiens (one which states those attributes applicable to the word being defined) is generally more efficient at pinpointing a definiendum than a **negative** definiens (one which states what is inapplicable to the word being defined). However, sometimes a negative definition can be good, and sometimes it is the best or only possible definition.

Examples:
An 'optimist' is 'a person who is not a pessimist.' (Negative definiens)
An 'optimist' is 'a person who habitually perceives or expects the best to happen.' (Positive definiens)

A definition should be **accurate**; that is, neither too broad nor too narrow. If it is too broad, it applies not only to the things referred to by the definiendum, but to other things also. If it is too narrow, some concepts or things normally referred to by the definiendum will not be referred to by the definiens.

(Negative definitions are very often too broad.) Unless the definition being offered is a persuasive one, the definiens should convey or describe any positive or negative overtones carried by the definiendum if the criterion of accuracy is to be satisfactorily met.

Examples:
A 'dog' is 'a four-legged carnivore of the canine family.' (Too broad)
A 'building' is 'a man-made dwelling constructed of brick and mortar, or wood.' (Too narrow)

A definition should also possess **clarity**; that is, it should be free from any vagueness or ambiguities which can reasonably be removed. Also, it is important when framing a definition to gauge the knowledge and the vocabulary of the intended audience. The definiens should be more easily understood (that is, contain more familiar terms) than the definiendum. What is a good definition of 'light' to a group of physicists would, in all probability, be incomprehensible to a group of elementary school students.

Exercise 11-8
For each of the following definitions: (a) Indicate which criterion or criteria (noncircularity, affirmativeness, accuracy, clarity or neutrality) is violated.
(b) Considering the context provided, write a good definition of the word to be defined.

1. An art teacher to the class: "A potter's wheel is a wheel used by a potter."
2. An American to a German tourist: "Bread is the staff of life."
3. A lawyer to his client: "Perjury is lying."
4. One electrical engineer to another: "An antenna is a metallic wire or rod."
5. In an art class: "A fresco is not a mosaic."
6. A college student to her little sister: "Saccharin is a white crystalline solid, used as an artificial sweetener, whose formua is $C_7H_5O_3NS$."
7. A college student studying with a fellow student from chemistry class: "Saccharin is a white powder that tastes sweet like sugar."
8. A piano tuner to his son: "A tuning fork is a fork used for tuning instruments."
9. An English teacher to the class: "A novel is a work of fiction."
10. A biology teacher to the class: "An invertebrate is any animal that is not a vertebrate."

Analytic versus Synthetic Statements
There are two types of analytic statement. Those statements that are true or false by virtue of their logical form are called '**syntactically analytic**' propositions. Those which are true or false by definition (that is, by virtue of the meanings of the words in the statements) are called '**semantically analytic**' propositions. A statement which is neither syntactically nor sematically analytic is called a

'synthetic' or 'contingent' proposition. Such statements are used as statements about the world, and their truth or falsity is usually ascertained through empirical observation.

Examples:
It is snowing or it is not snowing. (Syntactically analytic; true)
It is false that if some dogs are carnivores, then some carnivores are dogs.
   (Syntactically analytic; false)
All widows are women. (Semantically analytic; true)
All widows are men. (Semantically analytic; false)
Mount Rushmore is 49,587 feet tall. (Synthetic; false)
Hank Aaron holds baseball's home run record. (Synthetic; true)

Exercise 11-9
Examine each of the following sentences and determine whether the statement expressed is (a) syntactically analytic, (b) semantically analytic, or (c) synthetic or contingent and whether or not they are true or false. Assume the ordinary meaning for all words.

	Syn. Analytic	Sem. Analytic	Syn-thetic	True	False
1. No circles are squares.	☐	☐	☐	☐	☐
2. Either that gem is a diamond or it is not a diamond.	☐	☐	☐	☐	☐
3. My pet dog is a collie.	☐	☐	☐	☐	☐
4. If no circles are squares, then no squares are circles.	☐	☐	☐	☐	☐
5. George Washington was the first President of the United States.	☐	☐	☐	☐	☐
6. If all men are mortal, then some men are mortal.	☐	☐	☐	☐	☐
7. All blind persons are humans.	☐	☐	☐	☐	☐
8. Some humans are blind persons.	☐	☐	☐	☐	☐
9. If all coral snakes discovered to date are poisonous, then all coral snakes are poisonous.	☐	☐	☐	☐	☐
10. Some liars always tell the truth.	☐	☐	☐	☐	☐

	Syn. Analytic	Sem. Analytic	Syn-thetic	True	False
11. The moon revolves around the earth.	☐	☐	☐	☐	☐
12. Either John is alive or he is not alive.	☐	☐	☐	☐	☐
13. All actresses are women.	☐	☐	☐	☐	☐
14. If some businessmen are poets, then some poets are businessmen.	☐	☐	☐	☐	☐
15. It is snowing or it is raining.	☐	☐	☐	☐	☐

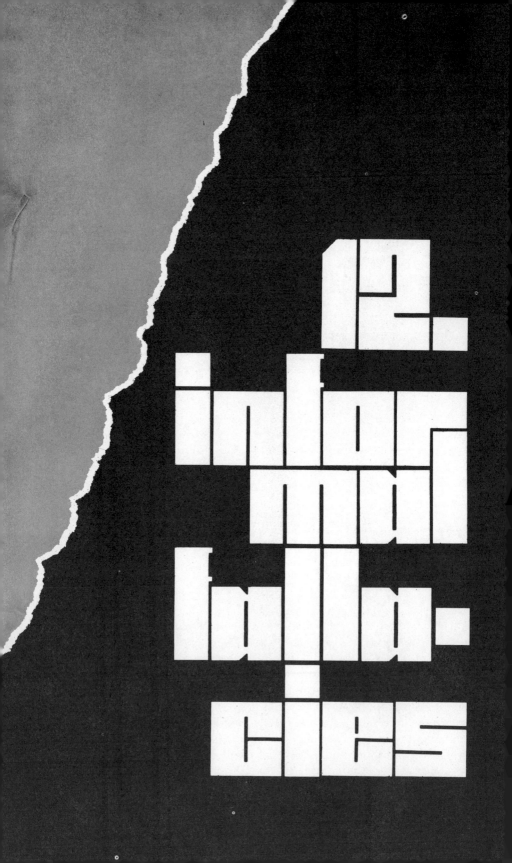

12.
informal fallacies

Defining Informal Fallacies
The term 'fallacy' has been traditionally used by logicians as a synonym for 'bad reasoning.' Commonly used everyday arguments in which there *appears* to be a logical relationship between the conclusion and true premises sometimes prove to be bad arguments. Since they can be recognized with little or no reliance on the methods of formal logic, they are known as **informal fallacies**. A bad argument in everyday discourse may actually involve one or more informal fallacies. Most fallacious arguments can be formulated as either inductive or deductive arguments. However, it is usually necessary to add at least one obviously false or highly questionable premise to an argument which involves an informal fallacy to make it deductively valid. There are literally hundreds of different informal fallacies, and several systems of classification have been devised by logicians. However, we shall only present a listing representative of the most frequently encountered informal fallacies.

Begging the Question
Any argument which is bad because it is circular—that is, because for its intended audience, the conclusion is merely a restatement of something explicitly stated in the premises—is said to commit the fallacy of **begging the question** (also known as *petitio principii*).

> *Example:*
> All people who like the novels of Emily Bronte are persons with excellent literary taste, since persons with excellent literary taste are persons who like Emily Bronte's novels.

The Straw Person Fallacy
When we interpret an individual's statements on a given matter in such a way as to make them most vulnerable to attack and criticism, we are violating the principle of charity and commiting the **straw person fallacy**. This fallacy often involves reducing a relatively complex argument to an overly simple form, thereby leaving out some of its key elements.

> *Example:*
> A college debate team member arguing against ligislation of marijuana: The only possible justification its proponents can give for legalizing marijuana is that marijuana laws cannot be absolutely enforced. Obviously this is a very weak argument, since no one claims that *any* law can be absolutely enforced.

Argument from Ignorance
The fact that a proposition has not been conclusively proven to be true or false—especially when little or no real attempt has been made to verify it—often establishes nothing but one's inability to prove or disprove it. To treat this inability as establishing the truth or falsity of the proposition is to use a fallacious type of argument known as the **argument from ignorance** (sometimes called the

argumentum ad ignorantiam). The basic form of this fallacy is: 'There is no evidence or proof that it is the case that X; therefore, it *is not* the case that X.' When confronted with an argument which appears to have this form, we should make sure that it cannot be reasonably interpreted as a good inductive argument before labeling it as fallacious.

Example:
Cancer is not caused by a virus, since no conclusive evidence of the existence of such a virus has been provided.

Fallacy of False Cause

The notion which underlies the fallacy of **false cause** is that the conjunction in space and time of two events or states of affairs is sufficient to establish the existence of a causal relation between them. A special type of false cause fallacy, the *post hoc ergo propter hoc*, argues that because one event occurs after another another, the earlier was the cause of the later.

Examples:
Seven months after Governor Broderick was elected, the state had a budget deficit, the first in twenty years. Obviously, Governor Broderick is responsible.

Tom was seen in the vicinity of the broken window at about the time that it was broken, so he must have done it.

Argument Against the Person

The fallacy of the **argument against the person** (also called *argumentum ad hominem*) consists of attacking a person's beliefs or assertions by attacking the person himself in one way or another. This fallacy usually appears in one of three forms: the abusive, the circumstantial, and the *tu quoque* or "you, too" form.

The abusive argument against the person uses epithets, or factual but irrelevant data against one's opponent in the hopes of discrediting any statements he may make.

Example:
Although Mr. Wilkins, the defendant's chief witness, claims that he did not see the defendant selling heroin to Mr. Rodgers, there is no reason to accept Mr. Wilkins' statement. After all, we know that Mr. Wilkins is a pot-smoking communist-mongering hippie.

The **circumstantial argument** against the person cites the opponent's personal circumstances as sufficient reason for dismissing a statement he has made; or it may point out a contrast between the opponent's lifestyle and his expressed opinions, thereby suggesting that the opponent's conclusions can be dismissed merely because the opponent is himself hypocritical.

Examples:
Of course, the workers at the factory favor unionization: they're the ones
who will get a pay increase without having to pay for it.
Mr. Smith, how can you favor gun legislation when you own a pistol?

In the *tu quoque* argument against the person, a person attempts to escape
criticism of his position by attacking the position of his opponent, rather than
by directly answering the charges against him.

Example:
Reporter: The CIA under your direction engaged in illegal domestic sur-
veillance, a clearcut violation of the CIA's charter.
CIA official: The CIA under the past three administrations has been required
to pursue such action. To believe that such activity is not necessary and
has not taken place before is naive. It is people like you who would like to
see our country infiltrated with foreign spies.

Appeal to the People
In the **appeal to the people** (also called *argumentum ad populum*) a person
attempts to manipulate the passions, prejudices, and identity of specific audi-
ences. Although such arguments often bypass reasoning altogether, they can
be highly persuasive. However, when sound arguments and pertinent evidence
are made available to an audience, the persuasive power of an appeal to the
people may be weakened.

Examples:
We can't permit him to be arrested because he is one of us. When they arrest
him they arrest each of us in a little way. Fight for your rights! This
police state action should be opposed in your own name.
You should wear 'Brand X' shirts; they're for the discriminating man who is
concerned with quality not price.

Appeal to Pity
In an **appeal to pity** (or *argumentum ad misericordiam*), a person introduces
irrelevant considerations that will arouse sympathy and detract attention from
pertinent evidence. In some cases, however, an appeal to pity may not be completely fallacious. For example, the judge who gave a suspended sentence to
an unemployed man who had stolen a three dollar toy for his child's only
Christmas present may have been correct that pity was sufficient justification
for waiving the prescribed penalty of imprisonment.

Example:
I ask the court to set free this man accused of murdering a policeman. If he
is sent to jail, his poor children will have to grow up without a father, and

will suffer from the taunts of their schoolmates that their father is a convicted felon. Who could do this to such innocent helpless children?

Appeal to Authority

In the **appeal to authority** (also known as the *argumentum ad verecundiam*), a person cites the opinion of a person who has no special expertise on a subject as reinforcement for one's own opinion. Identifying an appeal to authority may be difficult for several reasons: there may be disagreement over who is a genuine authority in the field at a given time, and authorities in the same field often subscribe to conflicting theories and opinions.

Example:
Of course, this is a solid, well-managed insurance company. Three famous football players have endorsed it in TV commercials.

Appeal to Force

The **appeal to force** (or *argumentum ad baculum*) constitutes one of the most effective informal fallacies, since it seeks to obtain the listener's agreement by arousing his fears and intimidating him into agreement. The appeal to force may involve threats of immediate physical violence or threats against a person's status and general well-being.

Examples:
You really should sign this confession now. Otherwise, you will be tried and eventually found guilty. Then there will be no chance of leniency; you'll be given the maximum sentence of life in prison.
If you want to avoid the embarrassment of perspiration-stained clothing, you should use "Dry," the new anti-perspirant deodorant.

Fallacy of Accident

In the fallacy of **accident**, a person applies a general rule to a particular case to which the rule was not intended to apply. This type of fallacy can be attributed either to a poorly formulated generalization or to a careless or intentionally mistaken interpretation of a reasonably well-formulated generalization.

Example:
Money is the root of all evil. Therefore, you should not give a reward to the person who returns your lost wallet.

Fallacy of Hasty Generalization

In the fallacy of **hasty generalization**, a person forms a generalization on the basis of observations of a sample that is unrepresentative or too small. Reasoning of this type is fallacious, since the generalization is based on exceptional, or specially selected, rather than typical, or randomly selected cases.

Example:
Since Babe Ruth, Mickey Mantle, Lou Gehrig and Joe DiMaggio were all great baseball players and members of the Yankees, it follows that all Yankees are great ballplayers and also that all great baseball players are Yankees.

Fallacy of Equivocation
The fallacy of **equivocation** involves the use of a word or phrase that can be interpreted in two or more different ways in the given context. The equivocal element may be used in one sense in the premise(s) and in another in the conclusion; or it may be used in different senses in different premises; or it may be used in such a way that it is impossible to determine the sense in which it is being used.

Example:
Man is a social animal, and no woman is a man. Therefore, no woman is a social animal.

Fallacy of Amphiboly
The fallacy of **amphiboly** occurs when a grammatically ambiguous statement causes a person to interpret the argument as being valid when, in fact, it is not. Amphiboly is not a matter of erroneous reasoning, so much as of erroneous interpretation.

Example:
Four out of five dentists recommend Sugarfree gum so it is obviously good for you. (Amphibolous if a person infers that 'four out of five dentists' means 'four out of *every* five.')

Fallacy of the False Dilemma
The fallacy of the **false dilemma** consists of presenting an argument as if there were fewer possible solutions of the problem than is actually the case. Usually two alternatives are offered in an either–or fashion; but unless both are reasonably correct and one directly contradicts the other, there are generally other available alternatives.

Example:
With the crime rate increasing at the rate way it is, you must either carry a gun with you or live in fear.

Fallacy of the Complex Question
The fallacy of the **complex question** involves asking a question which in reality is a composite of several questions; demanding a single answer; and then applying that answer to both the explicit question and the unasked questions contained within it.

Example:
Questioner: Do you still cheat on your income tax?
Answerer: No.
Questioner: Aha, therefore in the past you have cheated on your income
   tax.

The component questions within a complex question demand independent consideration; therefore, in asking a complex question, one obscures the real issues
involved, and in demanding a single answer, one implies a spurious simplicity.

Fallacy of Accent
The fallacy of **accent** arises when improper stress is placed on some portion of a
premise or conclusion, and, as a result, the meaning of the argument is distorted.
This form of ambiguity is usually intentional, and often arises when a statement
is taken out of context or when a speaker gives it an inflection which conveys
the wrong meaning.

Examples:
Book reviewer: I can't say Mr. Snodgrass's first novel is very promising.
Newspaper advertisement for the same book: ". . . Mr. Snodgrass's first
   novel is very promising," says Mr. Book Reviewer.
Movie critic's comment: "Mr. Gomer Goes to Philadelphia" is a triumph of
   bad direction and bad acting.
Newspaper advertisement for the same movie: Mr. Critic says "Mr. Gomer
   Goes to Philadelphia is a triumph . . . ," so he obviously thinks it's a great
   movie.

Fallacy of Composition
The fallacy of composition involves two forms of erroneous reasoning. The first
occurs when a person erroneously argues that a whole which is a single entity has
a certain characteristic because each of its component parts has that characteristic. The second form occurs when a person invalidly concludes that a collection of elements has a certain characteristic because each element in the collection has this characteristic.

Examples:
Each brick in that building was rectangular in shape, so the building must be
   rectangular in shape.
If you drop a feather from a ten story building, it will float to earth very
   slowly. Therefore, if you drop that pillow from a ten story building, it too
   will float to earth slowly.

Fallacy of Division
The fallacy of **division** is the reverse of the fallacy of composition and, like it,
occurs in two forms. The first form occurs when it is invalidly argued that each

part in a whole has a particular attribute because the whole itself has that attribute. The second form occurs when it is erroneously argued that what is true of a collection of items must also be true of each component item. When the attribute being considered is a distributive attribute—that is, when it refers to properties possessed by the individual members of a collection—the inference will be valid. However, when it is a collective attribute—that is, when it refers to a property possessed only by the totality of members of a collection—the inference will be invalid.

Examples:
The American judicial system is a fair system. Therefore, defendant X got a fair trial.
In the latest poll, 60% of the American people favored the President's handling of the economy. Therefore, of the ten Democrats on the Senate Finance Committee, exactly six favor the President's handling of the economy.

Fallacy of the Irrevelant Conclusion
The fallacy of the **irrelevant conclusion** (also called *ignoratio elenchi*) is committed when a person attempts to disprove a conclusion by presenting information that merely establishes another conclusion rather than refuting the one under criticism. Fallacious arguments of this sort are often used because they are more persuasive and compelling than those which present pertinent information or evidence. In essence, the two parties in such a debate are arguing past one another.

Example:
Person A: All persons who kill a police officer should die!
Person B: Murder, especially the murder of a police officer, is an awful crime, but the death penalty is "cruel and unusual punishment" and, therefore, forbidden by the Constitution.
Person A: My brother was a police officer who was killed during a bank holdup!

Exercise 11-1
Identify the informal fallacy or fallacies committed in each of the following arguments.

1. A mother's protection of her young offspring does not primarily result from any reasoning process on her part, nor from behavior patterns she acquired by learning or imitation. It is primarily the manifestation of her maternal instinct, as one can see, for instance, by observing the instinctive way a cat will protect her kittens from danger.
2. There is no reason to enact new inheritance laws. The advocates of new inheritance laws believe that without laws to prevent children from

inheriting their parents' money and property, we will, in a few generations, have a society in which people no longer work, based on the assumption that it is economic pressure which motivates people to work, and there is no economic pressure on a person who has inherited more money than he or she will ever need. And clearly this assumption is false.

3. President Kennedy died in office because, in this century, every man who was elected to the presidency in a year with a number which ended in zero has died while he was in office.

4. Mr. Ball's argument is exactly what one can expect from a racist like him!

5. As TV watching has increased over the last ten years, so has the crime rate. The more TV people watched, the more crimes they committed. So TV watching causes crime.

6. No one can prove that drivers who were drunk when they had accidents would not have the same accidents had they been sober. It is therefore unwarranted to claim that a driver's state of intoxication increases his likelihood of having an accident.

7. After murdering our lay-down Three No Trump contract in the last rubber, my bridge partner has no reason to criticise me because I went down in a partscore I could have made.

8. Take out a subscription to the *Investigator*, the nation's leading newsweekly, and be as well informed as your neighbors!

9. Insurance salesmen never tell you about the ways their company has to get out of paying insurance claims. You find out about those when you actually file a claim. So who can blame people for padding their claims the next time they have an accident or a burglary?

10. The verdict you give cannot help the victim of this assault; but it can save the defendant from the degradation and despair of prison life and allow him to take care of his wife, who is expecting her third baby.

11. None of my grandchildren play a musical instrument; it must be that young people today don't care about music anymore.

12. Doctors who favor the extermination of rats and mosquitoes do so in violation of their Hippocratic oath, which binds them to do all they can to preserve life and nothing to destroy it.

13. If by the end of class you are still convinced that I have not treated you fairly, you'll stay here in the classroom while the other students go out to the playground.

14. There will be a meteoric rise in food prices by the end of the year. I know this through a man who is a well known meteorologist.

15. Since the age of a person corresponds to the number of birthdays he has had, a son can be older than his own father, provided the father was born on the twenty-ninth of February.

16. The other executives find it helpful to do a few hours' work in the office on Saturday mornings. The young man who was your predecessor never did; that's the reason we replaced him. We hope you won't find that your family can't spare you on weekends.

17. In 1972, Richard Nixon had the choice of fighting the Democrats by devious and sometimes unethical means, or handing the Presidency over to George McGovern, whose foreign and domestic policies would, in Nixon's opinion, have spelled disaster for the country.

18. The guidebook must be mistaken. It says, "the shortest route to the other side of the hill is by the road that circles the base of the hill." There is a path on the map that runs in a straight line from here to the top of the hill and down the other side which must be the shorter route, because a straight line is the shortest distance between two points.

19. If he sent money to Biafra and to Bangladesh because the people there were starving, perhaps he'll send us money, too; because we are always starving by the time dinner is finally on the table.

20. You should begin a meal with a nourishing first course, such as soup. With tomato soup, which contains one part of vegetable solids, fat, flour, and spices for every three parts of water, three-quarters of the nourishment will actually be derived from its water content.

21. When Councilman Rogers was asked whether he had any evidence of police brutality in the community, he replied, truthfully, "There isn't any I have seen." He had, however, received several verbal accounts of police brutality from his constituents.

22. If students who are studying in other countries suffer from homesickness more than students who attend school in the U.S., we may conclude that American students are more mature than foreign students.

23. My twenty-year-old son wants a car of his own; but I wouldn't buy one for him. Why should I? When I was his age, I was lucky if I could borrow my father's car on a Saturday night. And my father, when he was twenty, could not even borrow his father's car, because my grandfather never owned one.

24. John says that he loves me and he must be telling the truth, because a person who says that he loves someone would never lie to the person he loves.

25. Nothing has ever been discovered that travels faster than the speed of light; therefore, it is impossible to travel faster than the speed of light.

26. *Two children playing monopoly:*
    Child A: I will throw the dice first.
    Child B: No, I'll throw first.
    Child A: No, it's only fair that I go first, because it's my game and I'll take it home if I can't go first.

27. The 6th commandment says 'Thou shalt not kill.' Yet you, Reverend Smith, claim that the United States was correct to send fighting men to Vietnam. Surely, you do not mean to contradict God's commandment!

28. There must be something to astrology. For the last week, every single prediction about my sign has come true. For example, on Monday it said that there would be difficulties with a loved one, and that evening my husband and I had a terrible argument. On Tuesday, it said I would hear

from someone unexpected, and a friend from college who I haven't heard from for two years called. It's been that way all week.

29. The world of science contains numerous examples of great men and women who believed in a god, so a god must exist.

30. Of course, you realize that if you fail to vote against the gun control bill, our organization will not support your next reelection drive with a donation as it has done in the past.

31. As sure as I am talking to you, Bob Davis is guilty of embezzlement. You know he has a criminal record; he was convicted of income tax evasion and stock fraud five years ago.

32. *A student to a professor:* If I don't pass your course, I won't graduate on time. I have a good job lined up for July and my fiancé and I are going to be married the day after graduation. I know I've failed all the exams, but I really have tried to understand the material. If I don't pass my whole life will be messed up. Thus, I really do deserve a passing grade.

33. You should not listen to his arguments against legislation prohibiting the sale of cigarettes. He owns stock in two cigarette companies.

34. You shouldn't accept Mr. Jefferson's argument that high school English teachers should have fewer students in their classes since they have to grade so many compositions. After all, Mr. Jefferson is a high school English teacher; he stands to benefit.

35. According to the latest figures from the Controller's office, the city's revenues have fallen off considerably. I suggest that the City Council immediately approve a twenty-five percent across-the-board budget cut for all departments. The people of the city will just have to learn to live with three-fifths of the services they have had up to this time.

36. With a *laissez faire* policy, each member of society acts in a way that will best advance his or her own economic interest. Consequently, all individuals and ultimately society as a whole achieves the maximum economic advantages.

37. The only way to manage a company effectively is to instill fear in your workers. Either you treat employees kindly and they take advantage of you and goof off, or you are tough on them and they'll work hard for you.

38. Our cat died at the animal hospital, then on 65th Street in Manhattan. So, our cat died twice.

39. Things that are difficult to find cost a lot, and secret hiding places are difficult to find, so secret hiding places cost a lot.

40. Me, I'm dead set against a national welfare plan. Why, when I drove through the so-called "poor" part of town the other day, I saw a bunch of guys standing on the corner drinking beer. Man, I'd love for someone to pay me to stay at home and spend the afternoon on the street corner drinking beer and shootin' the breeze.

41. Well Mr. Mayor, it's perfectly fine for you to say that the quality of education in our neighborhood schools is superior. But how do you explain the fact that you send your daughter to a private school?

42. During every recession we had a Republican in office, so the Republicans obviously do not know how to manage the nation's economic affairs.

43. *Father:* Have you finally been paying attention to your teacher lately?
    Son: Yes.
    Father: Go to your room.
    Son: Why?
    Father: For not listening to your teacher in the past.

44. *A statement made by Richard M. Nixon in 1973:* "Mr. Sparkman and Mr. Stevenson should come before the American people, as I have, and make a complete financial statement as to their financial history, and if they don't it will be an admission that they have something to hide."

45. Either Frank is poor or he is rich, and by looking at the car he drives, you can see that he is rich.

46. Great works of art are rare, so Joyce's *Ulysses* is rare.

47. Good roast beef is rare these days, so you shouldn't order yours well done.

48. Since this committee began investigating abuses in nursing home care of the elderly, it has received ten thousand letters from old people in homes, complaining of poor conditions. Quite obviously, every nursing home is filled with abuses.

49. The United States should not give aid to lesser developed countries. We gave aid to India and they developed an atomic bomb. We gave aid to South South Vietnam and the war there has continued. We gave aid to Turkey and they invaded Cyprus.

50. *Book reviewer:* The author provides an incomplete and grossly distorted account of the actual events which took place. The real truth seems to have escaped him completely. The high quality journalism to which the public has a right is completely lacking.
    Publisher's advertisement: The author provides an . . . account of the actual events which took place. The real truth . . . . High quality journalism . . . .

ANSWER KEY

Answers to Introduction

Exercise 1
1. Command. 2. Question. 3. Statement. 4. Command. 5. Exclamation. 6. Command. 7. Question. 8. Exclamation. 9. Statement ('I am a good poker player'); perhaps also a question. 10. Statement ('I don't understand it'). 11. Statement. 12. Command. 13. Question. 14. Command. 15. Statement.

Exercise 2
1. (a) Yes. (b) There is Professor Brown. 2. No. 3. (a) Yes. (b) No penalty would be too great for a man who would dare to betray his native land to its avowed enemies. 4. No. 5. (a) Yes. (b) John and Joan make a nice couple.

Exercise 3
1. (a) He (the defendant) is not guilty. (b) The defendant is insane. 2. (a) Some mammals can fly. (b) Bats can fly. 3. (a) That is not a good French dictionary. (b) It (that French dictionary) does not show how each word should be pronounced. 4. (a) It (the flu) can't be cured with antibiotics. (b) The flu is caused by a virus. 5. (a) The sum of its (this figure's) interior angles is 540°. (b) This figure is a pentagon. 6. (a) It will take two seconds for that rock to fall. (b) It (that rock) is going to fall a distance of sixty-four feet. 7. (a) It (coffee) must contain a stimulant. (b) Coffee keeps people awake. 8. (a) He (Mr. Scott) is a lawyer. (b) Mr. Scott is a judge. 9. (a) The housing bill will never come to a vote on the floor of Congress. (b) The opposition has enough votes to kill it (the housing bill) in committee. 10. (a) This solution is an acid. (b) It (this solution) turns litmus paper red. 11. (a) Tom will not be able to go to the New Year's Eve party at the club. (b) He (Tom) is not a member. 12. (a) Composers do not have to be able to hear music in order to write it. (b) Beethoven was deaf. 13. (a) Starvation will inevitably occur somewhere in the world. (b) The expanding world population will eventually increase beyond the capacity of the total world agricultural resources to feed it. 14. (a) Plastics are becoming more expensive. (b) Oil is becoming more expensive. Plastics are made from oil. 15. (a) It (a body) cannot travel faster than the speed of light. (b) As a body approaches the speed of light, its mass becomes infinite. An infinite source (of energy) would be needed to accelerate it.

Exercise 4
1. (a) No. (b) It is a conditional. 2. (a) No. (b) It is a conditional; also 'Give Joan a call' expresses a command. 3. (a) Yes. (b) *Conclusion:* Logic is distinct from psychology. *Premise:* Logic deals with prescriptive laws whereas psychology deals with descriptive laws. 4. (a) Yes. (b) *Conclusion:* You are an idealist. *Premise:* All Sagittarians are idealists. 5. (a) Yes. (b) *Conclusion:* French is called a romance language. *Premise:* It (French) is derived from Latin. 6. (a) No. (b) 'Don't use that book when you write your paper' is a command. 7. (a) Yes. (b) *Conclusion:* President Nixon was impeachable. *Premise:* He (President Nixon) was involved in obstruction of justice. 8. (a) No. (b) 'Because' is used in a causal sense. 9. (a) Yes. (b) *Conclusion* (unstated): That dime is made of silver. *Premises:* 'That dime is undated' *and* 'All dimes dated 1964 or earlier are made of silver.' 10. (a) No. (b) 'Since' is used in a temporal sense. 11. (a) Yes. (b) *Conclusion:* The United States has always been governed by a president, congress and Supreme Court. *Premise:* That is the form of government specified in the Constitution. 12. (a) Yes. (b) *Conclusion:* That could not have been Helen you met last night. *Premise:* Helen has short brown hair. 13. (a) No. (b) It is a conditional. 14. (a) Yes. (b) *Conclusion:* It (this rock) will scratch glass. *Premises:* 'If a rock is quartz, it will scratch glass' *and* 'This rock is made of quartz.' 15. (a) Yes.

(b) *Conclusion:* It (this rock) is not quartz. *Premises:* 'If a rock is quartz, it will scratch glass' *and* 'This rock will not scratch glass.' 16. (a) No. (b) The passage is exposition.

Exercise 5

1. No dogs are fish.
   No collies are fish.
   Therefore, no collies are dogs.
2. All violets are plants
   All tree are plants.
   Therefore, all violets are trees.
3. If it is raining, then it is cloudy.
   It is cloudy.
   Therefore, it is raining.
4. If it is raining, then it is cloudy.
   It is not raining.
   Therefore, it is not cloudy.
5. Some Englishmen are dentists.
   Winston Churchill was an Englishman.
   Therefore, Winston Churchill was a dentist.
6. All governors are politically powerful.
   Lyndon B. Johnson was politically powerful.
   Therefore, Lyndon B. Johnson was a governor.
7. Some foods are liquids.
   Some nuts are foods.
   Therefore, some nuts are liquids.
8. Some animals are not cats.
   Therefore, some cats are not animals.
9. Water extinguishes fires.
   Water is made of hydrogen and oxygen.
   Therefore, hydrogen extinguishes fires and oxygen extinguishes fires.
10. Tomato juice is a delicious drink.
    Coffee is a delicious drink.
    Therefore, tomato juice-coffee is a delicious drink.

Exercise 6

Note that for part (b) of the answers in this exercise: Where the argument is deductive, it is so in all cases because the premise(s) provide(s) absolute support for the conclusion. Where the argument is inductive, it is so because the premise(s) do(es) not provide absolute support for the conclusion. For inductive arguments the answers given in (b) explain why the support is not absolute in each case.

1. (a) Deductive. 2. (a) Deductive. 3. (a) Inductive. (b) The argument is

weakened if it is true that Bob's parents both have brown eyes. 4. (a) Inductive. (b) The argument is weakened if it is pointed out that John just ate ten pizzas, fifteen pickles, and seven rhubarb pies. 5. (a) Inductive. (b) The argument is weakened if the electric company's estimates of power needs in the past have all been very inaccurate. Also, if the conclusion is interpreted as a command, then this collection of sentences does not express an argument. 6. (a) Deductive. 7. (a) Inductive. (b) The argument is weakened if it is true that many Democrats register as Republicans because there is usually no contest in the Democratic primaries. 8. (a) Deductive. 9. (a) Inductive. (b) The argument is weakened when it is added that a Sagittarian is one born between November 23 and December 21. 10. (a) Inductive. (b) The argument is weakened if there is little or no evidence that there is a relationship between one's birth date and personality characteristics. 11. (a) Inductive. (b) The argument is weakened if it is true that Helen works as a waitress in a truck stop restaurant. 12. (a) Inductive. (b) The argument would be weakened if one considers tool-using or problem-solving behavior of other animals as indications of rational thought.

Exercise 7

Note that there may be other possibilities for (c) in each answer.
1. (a) That is not a rose bush. (b) It doesn't have thorns. (c) All rose bushes have thorns. 2. (a) It (*Rhoda*) is childish. (b) *Rhoda* is a television series. (c) All television series are childish. 3. (a) That is a conifer. (b) It is a pine tree. (c) All pine trees are conifers. 4. (a) Karl is eccentric. (b) All metaphysicians are eccentric. (c) Karl is a metaphysician. 5. (a) He (Gregory) is a Greek Cypriot. (b) Gregory is not a Turkish Cypriot. (c) All Cypriots are either Turkish or Greek. 6. (a) The price of sugar has gone up. (b) If the demand for sugar exceeds the supply, the price of sugar will go up. (c) The demand for sugar exceeds the supply. 7. He (Senator Brandt) is a Democrat. (b) Senator Brandt is a major party candidate. (c) He (Senator Brandt) is not a

Republican. (c) Major party candidates are either Republicans or Democrats. 8. (a) All oaks are living things. (b) All trees are plants' *and* 'All oaks are trees.' (c) All plants are living things.

Exercise 8

Note that there are many other possible answers for (c) and (d) of each answer. 1. (a) I will like the 1972 Beaujolais wine that I am going to drink. (b) 'I liked the 1969 Beaujolais wine that I drank' *and* 'I liked the 1970 Beaujolais wine that I drank' *and* 'I liked the 1971 Beaujolais wine that I drank.' (c) I liked the 1967 Beaujolais wine that I drank. (d) I did not like the 1968 Beaujolais wine that I drank. 2. (a) 'He (Sluggo Jones) is likely to hit a home run today. (b) Sluggo Jones has hit more home runs this season than any other player on the team. (c) Sluggo Jones has already hit four home runs this season off the opposing team's starting pitcher. (d) Sluggo Jones has a sprained wrist. 3. (a) You are more likely to catch the flu than I am. (b) 'There has been an outbreak of the Asian flu in the U.S. this month' *and* 'I have had a flu vaccination' *and* 'You have not had a flu vaccination.' (c) Your father and your sister already have the flu. (d) Studies have shown that the flu vaccination is not very effective in preventing a person from catching the flu. 4. (a) The Karlans will like her pot roast. (b) 'The guests our family has to dinner always like my mother's pot roasts' *and* 'The Karlans are coming to dinner' *and* 'My mother is serving pot roast.' (c) My mother says she has purchased an especially good cut of meat this time. (d) The Karlans are vegetarians. 5. (a) Mr. Harrison is probably a liberal. (b) 'Most east coast newspaper editors are liberals' *and* 'Mr. Harrison is an east coast newspaper editor.' (c) Mr. Harrison is a Democrat. (d) Mr. Harrison has lived all his life in a small conservative New Englahd town and is editor of the town's only newspaper. 6. (a) The automobile as we know it will eventually have to be replaced with other means of transportation by the year 2020. (b) At the present rate of consumption, the known world petroleum reserves will be exhausted by 2005. (c) The rate of consumption will not level off and remain static, but will continue to increase at its present rate so that the known reserves will be exhausted by 1990. (d) It is very probable that a way will be found to produce gasoline and motor oil from other materials and also that new oil reserves will be discovered.

Answers to Chapter 1

Exercise 1-1
1. A 2. O 3. E 4. I 5. A 6. O
7. A 8. E 9. I 10. E

Exercise 1-2
1. (a) All Frenchmen are Europeans.
(b) A (c) All F are E. (d) All S̲ are P̲.
2. (a) No ponderosas are shrubs. (b) E
(c) No P̄ are S. (d) No S̲ are P̲.
3. (a) Some sailors are swarthy persons.
(b) I (c) Some Sa are Sw. (d) Some S̲
are P̲. 4. (a) Some hives are not things
having bees. (b) O (c) Some H are not B.
(d) Some S̲ are not P̲. or (a) Some hives
are things that don't have bees. (b) I̅
(c) Some H are B. (d) S̅ome S̲ are P̲.
5. (a) All kraters are Greek vases. (b̄) A
(c) All K ar̄e G. (d) A̅ll S̲ are P̲.
6, (a) Some Panama hats are things made
in Equador. (b̄) I (c) Some P are E.
(d̄) Some S̲ are P̲. 7. (a) Some fans are
not machines. (b) O (c) Some F are not
M. (d̄) Some S̲ are not P̲. 8. (a) 'Some
paperbacks are in̄expensiv̄e things' *and*
'̄Some paperbacks are not inexpensive
things:̄ (b) I, O (c) 'Some P are I' *and*
'Some P are not I̲' (d) 'Some S̲ are P̲'
and 'Some S̲ are not P̲'. 9. (a) All
invited persons are members of the club.
(̄b) A (c) All I are M̄. (d) All P̲ are S̲.
10. (a) 'All nonautomotive unions are
unions which have settled their strikes *are*
'No automotive unions are unions which
have settled their strikes.' (b) A, E
(c) 'All non A are S' *and* 'No A are S'.
(d) 'All non S̲ are P̲' and 'No S̲ are P̲',

Exercise 1-3
1. (a) Some dogs are pets. (b) Some D
are P. (c) Some S̲ are P̲.

(d)

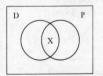

2. (a) All oaks are hardwoods. (b) All O
are H. (c) A̅ll S̲ are P̲.

(d)

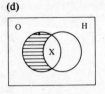

3. (a) No termites are ants. (b) No T are
A. (c) No S̲ are P̲.

(d)

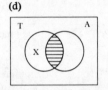

4. (a) Some nebulae are not galaxies.
(b) Some N ar̄e not G. (c) Some S̲ are not
P̲.

(d)

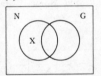

5. (a) All harpies are mythological creatures. (b) A̅ll H are M̄. (c) All S̲ are P̲.

(d)

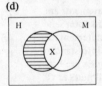

6. (a) Some dancers are persons who can
charleston. (b) Some D are C. (c) Some
S̲ are P̲.

(d)

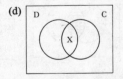

7. (a) No behaviorists are persons who tolerate idle speculation. (b) No B are T. (c) No S̲ are P̲.

(d)

8. (a) All persons who can vote are citizens. (b) All V are C. (c) All P̲ are S̲.

(d)

9. (a) 'Some art collectors are rich persons' *and* 'Some art collectors are not rich persons'. (b) 'Some A are R' *and* 'Some A are not R.' (c) 'Some S̲ are P̲ *and* 'Some S̲ are not P̲'.

(d)

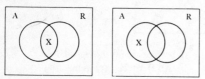

10. (a) All nonexceptive statements are easy to translate into standard form sentences' *and* 'No exceptive statements are easy statements to translate into standard form sentences.' (b) 'All nonEx are Ea' *and* 'No Ex are Ea'. (c) 'All nonS̲ are P̲' *and* 'No S̲ are P̲'.

(d)

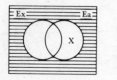

Exercise 1-4
1. (a) Contrariety. (b) False. (c) Undetermined. 2. (a) Subcontrariety. (b) Undetermined. (c) True. 3. (a) Subimplica-

tion. (b) True. (c) Undetermined. 4. (a) Superimplication. (b) Undetermined. (c) False. 5. (a) Contradiction. (b) False. (c) True. 6. (a) Contradiction. (b) False. (c) True. 7. (a) Contrariety. (b) False. (c) Undetermined. 8. (a) Superimplication. (b) Undetermined. (c) False. 9. (a) Subcontraries. (b) Undetermined. (c) True. 10. (a) Contradiction. (b) False. (c) True.

Exercise 1-5
1. Consistent; Dependent. 2. Consistent; Independent. 3. Consistent; Independent. 4. Inconsistent; Dependent. 5. Inconsistent; Dependent. 6. Consistent; Dependent. 7. Consistent; Independent. 8. Consistent; Independent.

Exercise 1-6
1. All dogs are four-legged creatures. (a) All D̲ are F̲. (b) All S̲ are P̲.

(c)   (d)

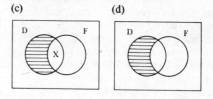

2. No dilemmas are unsolvable problems. (a) No D̲ are U. (b) No S̲ are P̲.

(c)   (d)

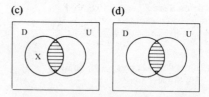

3. Some planets are things which have moons. (a) Some P are M. (b) Some S̲ are P̲.

(c)   (d)

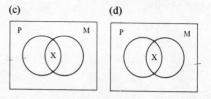

4. Some cats are not animals that can jump well. (a) Some C are not J. (b) Some S are not P.

(c)   (d)

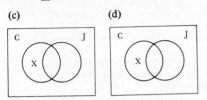

Exercise 1-7

1. (a) None. (b) Undetermined. (c) Undetermined. 2. (a) None. (b) Undetermined. (c) Undetermined. 3. (a) None. (b) Undetermined. (c) Undetermined. 4. (a) None. (b) Undetermined. (c) Undetermined. 5. (a) Contradiction. (b) False. (c) True. 6. (a) Contradiction. (b) False. (c) True. 7. (a) None. (b) Undetermined. (c) Undetermined. 9. (a) None. (b) Undetermined. (c) Undetermined. 10. (a) Contradiction. (b) False. (c) True.

Exercise 1-8

1. All sonnets are poems. (a) No sonnets are nonpoems. (b) Equivalent.

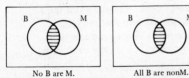

All S are P.   No S are nonP.

2. No butterflies are moths. (a) All butterflies are nonmoths. (b) Equivalent.

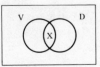

No B are M.   All B are nonM.

3. Some voters are Democrats. (a) Some voters are not nonDemocrats (b) Equivalent.

Some V are D.   Some V are not nonD.

4. Some minerals are not quartz. (a) Some minerals are nonquartz. (b) Equivalent.

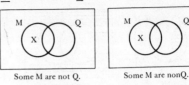

Some M are not Q.   Some M are nonQ.

Exercise 1-9

1. All amphoras are vases. (a) All vases are amphoras. (b) Not equivalent.

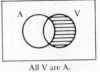

All A are V.   All V are A.

2. No wineskins are bottles. (a) No bottles are wineskins. (b) Equivalent.

No W are B.   No B are W.

3. Some towers are minarets. (a) Some minarets are towers. (b) Equivalent.

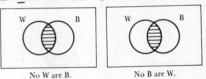

Some T are M.   Some M are T.

4. Some rulers are not emperors. (a) Some emperors are not rulers. (b) Not equivalent.

Some R are not E.   Some E are not R.

Exercise 1-10

1. All togas are garments. (a) All nongarments are nontogas. (b) Equivalent.

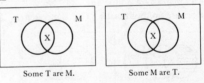

All T are G.   All nonG are nonT.

2. No essays are novels. (a) No non-novels are nonessays. (b) Not equivalent.

No E are N.

No nonN are nonE.

3. Some bats are vampires. (a) Some nonvampires are nonbats. (b) Not equivalent.

Some B are V.

Some nonV are nonB.

4. Some knives are not daggers. (a) Some nondaggers are not nonknives. (b) Equivalent.

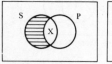

Some K are not D.

Some nonD are not nonK.

Exercise 1-11

1. All senators are politicians. (a) No senators are nonpoliticians. (b) Equivalent.

All S are P.

No S are nonP.

2. No biscuits are muffins. (a) All biscuits are nonmuffins. (b) Equivalent.

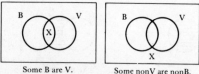

No B are M.   All B are nonM.

3. Some vampire bats are dangerous animals. (a) Some vampire bats are not nondangerous animals. (b) Equivalent.

Some V are D.

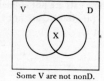

Some V are not nonD.

4. Some members are not lawyers. (a) Some members are nonlawyers. (b) Equivalent.

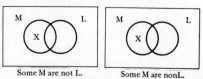

Some M are not L.   Some M are nonL.

Exercise 1-12

1. All asps are vipers. (a) All vipers are asps. (b) Not equivalent.

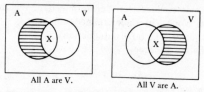

All A are V.   All V are A.

(Note: The original *implies* the converse by limitations: Some vipers are asps.)

2. No women are four-star generals. (a) No four-star generals are women. (b) Not equivalent.

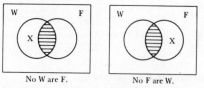

No W are F.   No F are W.

(c) The original statement and its converse become logically equivalent if the additional requirement that the class of things referred to by the predicate term must also contain at least one member is satisfied.

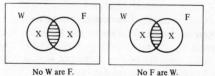

No W are F.   No F are W.

3. Some tables are marble things.
(a) Some marble things are tables. (b) Not equivalent. Strictly speaking the converse of the original I statement cannot be represented in a Venn diagram, since the class of marble things (the predicate term of the original statement) may be empty according to the Aristotelian interpretation. Consequently, we cannot deal with the obverse whose subject term is the class of marble things. (c) If the additional requirement that the class of things referred to by the predicate term must also contain at least one member is satisfied, then the original statement and its obverse are logically equivalent.

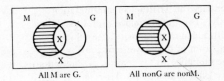

All M are G.   All nonG are nonM.

2. No elephants are carnivores. (a) No noncarnivores are nonelephants. (b) Not equivalent.

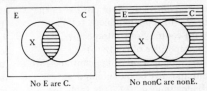

No E are C.   No nonC are nonE.

(Note: The original statement implies the contrapositive by limitation: Some noncarnivores are not nonelephants.
3. Some bicycles are valuable objects
(a) Some nonvaluable objects are nonbicycles. (b) Not equivalent.

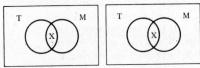

Some T are M.   Some M are T.

4. Some representatives are not elected persons. (a) Some elected persons are not representatives. (b) Not equivalent.

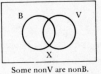

Some B are V.   Some nonV are nonB.

4. Some kettles are not deep things.
(a) Some nondeep things are not nonkettles. (b) Equivalent.

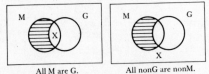

Some R are not E.   Some E are not R.

Exercise 1-13
1. All members are graduates of Harvard.
(a) All nongraduates of Harvard are nonmembers. (b) Not equivalent.

Some K are not D.   Some nonD are not nonK.

All M are G.   All nonG are nonM.

(c) If the additional requirements that the predicate class and the complementary classes of every term of the original statement must contain at least one member are satisfied, then the original statement and its contrapositive are logically equivalent.

Exercise 1-14
1. (a) Contradictory. (b) False. (c) False.
2. (a) Contrary (on Aristotelian interpretation only). (b) Undetermined. (c) False.
3. (a) Subimplicant. (b) Undetermined.
(c) True. 4. (a) Obverse (b) True
(c) True. 5. (a) Converse. (b) Undetermined. (c) Undetermined. 6. (a) Contrary of the converse or converse of the

contrary (on Aristotelian interpretation
only), (b) Undetermined. (c) False (only
with added restrictions). 7. (a) Subimplicant of the converse or converse of
the subimplicant (or converse by limitation).
(b) Undetermined. (c) True. 8. (a) Contradictory of the converse or converse of
the contradictory. (b) Undetermined.
(c) Undetermined. 9. (a) Contrapositive.
(b) True. (c) True. 10. (a) Contrary of
the contrapositive or contrapositive of the
contrary. (b) Undetermined. (c) False
(only for contrary of contrapositive, *not*
for contrapositive of contrary).
11. (a) Subimplicant of the contrapositive
or contrapositive of the subimplicant.
(b) Undetermined. (c) True (only for
subimplicant of the contrapositive).
12. (a) Contradictory of the contrapositive or contrapositive of the contradictory. (b) False. (c) False.

Exercise 1-15

1. (a) Contradictory. (b) False. (c) False.
2. (a) Subcontrary (on Aristotelian interpretation only). (b) Undetermined.
(c) Undetermined. 3. (a) Superimplicant.
(b) Undetermined. (c) Undetermined.
4. (a) Obverse. (b) True. (c) True.
5. (a) Contradictory of the obverse or
obverse of the contradictory. (b) False.
(c) False. 6. (a) Superimplicant of the
obverse or obverse of the superimplicant.
(b) Undetermined. (c) Undetermined.
7. (a) Converse. (b) Undetermined.
(c) Undetermined. 8. (a) Contrapositive.
(b) True. (c) True. 9. Subcontrary of
the contrapositive or contrapositive of the
subcontrary (on Aristotelian interpretation
only). (b) Undetermined. (c) Undetermined. 10. (a) Contradictory of the
contrapositive or contrapositive of the
contradictory. (b) False. (c) False.

Answers to Chapter 2

Exercise 2-1

1. (a) No, it only has one premise.
2. (a) Yes, (b) Yes, 3. (a) No, although it is a mediate inference, it has three premises. 4. (a) Yes. (b) No.
(c) No squares are conic sections.
All hyperbolas are conic sections.
Therefore, no hyperbolas are squares.
5. (a) Yes. (b) No.
(c) All drunkards are alcoholics.
Some drinkers are drunkards.
Therefore, some drinkers are alcoholics.
6. (a) Yes. (b) No.
(c) All documentaries are educational things.
Some films are documentaries.
Therefore, some films are educational things.
7. No, the term 'incandescent lights' appears three times and 'flourescent lights' only once. 8. (a) No, the first premise cannot be put in standard form. 9. (a) No, it is an immediate inference (conversion).
10. (a) No, it has four different terms.

Exercise 2-2

1. No Frenchmen are Germans.
Some composers are Frenchmen.
Therefore, some composers are not Germans.
(a) No F are G.
Some C are F.
∴Some C are not G.
(b) No M are P.
Some S are M.
∴Some S are not P.
(c) EIO-1
2. No Frenchmen are Germans.
Some Frenchmen are composers.
Therefore, some composers are not Germans.
(a) No F are G.
Some F are C.
∴Some C are not G.
(b) No M are P.
Some M are S.
∴Some S are not P.
(c) EIO-3

3. No rulers are paupers.
All kings are rulers.
Therefore, no kings are paupers.
(a) No R are P.
All K are R.
∴No K are P.
(b) No M are P.
All S are M.
∴No S are P.
(c) EAE-1
4. All kings are rulers.
No rulers are paupers.
Therefore, no paupers are kings.
(a) All K are R.
No R are P.
∴No P are K.
(b) All P are M.
No M are S.
∴No S are P.
(c) AEE-4
5. All novels are works of fiction.
No autobiographies are works of fiction.
Therefore, no autobiographies are novels.
(a) All N are F.
No A are F.
∴No A are N.
(b) All P are M.
No S are M.
∴No S are P.
(c) AEE-2
6. All novels are works of fiction.
Some autobiographies are not works of fiction.
Therefore, some autobiographies are not novels.
(a) All N are F.
Some A are not F.
∴Some A are not N.
(b) All P are M.
Some S are not M.
∴Some S are not P.
(c) AOO-2
7. All college professors are well-educated persons.
No well-educated persons are persons easily fooled.

Therefore, some persons easily fooled are not college professors.

(a) All P are E.
No E are F.
∴Some F are not P.

(b) All P are M
No M are S.
∴Some S are not P.

(c) **AEO-4**

8. All writers are creative persons.
All creative persons are intelligent persons.
Therefore, some intelligent persons are writers.

(a) All W are C.
All C are I.
∴Some I are W.

(b) All P are M.
All M are S.
∴Some S are P.

(c) **AII-4**

9. No friends are enemies.
No relatives are enemies.
Therefore, some relatives are not friends.

(a) No F are E.
No R are E.
∴Some R are not F.

(b) No P are M
No S are M.
∴Some S are not P.

(c) **EEO-2**

10. All interesting things to read are detective stories.
No interesting things to read are boring things.
Therefore, no boring things are detective stories.

(a) All I are D.
No I are B.
∴No B are D.

(b) All M are P.
No M are S.
∴No S are P.

(c) **AEE-3**

Exercise 2-3

Note: Each of the following is only one out of many possible correct answers.

1. Some animals are dogs.
No dogs are cats.
Therefore, some cats are not animals.

2. No horses are flowers.
No flowers are animals.

Therefore, no horses are animals.

3. Some reptiles are not extinct species.
All dinosaurs are reptiles.
Therefore, some dinosaurs are not extinct species.

4. No pines are oaks.
All pines are trees.
Therefore, no trees are oaks.

5. All Chinese are orientals.
Some Indians are orientals.
Therefore, some Indians are Chinese.

6. All basketball players are human beings.
Some men are not basketball players.
Therefore, some men are not human beings.

7. All roses are plants.
No roses are trees.
Therefore, no trees are plants.

8. All primates are mammals.
Some mammals are aquatic animals.
Therefore, some aquatic animals are primates.

Exercise 2-4

1. (b)

I = insects
B = butterflies
M = moths

(c) Invalid, because the conclusion requires that the entire area common to B and I be shaded.

2. (b)

S = swallowtails
M = moths
B = butterflies

(c) Valid, because the area common to S and M is shaded.

3. (b)

P = powerful men
R = reactionaries
D = dictators

(c) Valid, because there is an 'X' in the area common to P and R.

4. (b)

 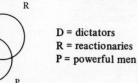

D = dictators
R = reactionaries
P = powerful men

(c) Invalid, because there is no 'X' *entirely* inside the area common to D and R.

5. (a) All roses are flowers.
All American Beauties are roses.
Therefore, all American Beauties are flowers.

(b)

(c) Valid, because the area outside F and inside A is entirely shaded.

6. (a) All roses are flowers.
All zinnias are flowers.
Therefore, all zinnias are roses.

(b)

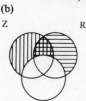

(c) Invalid, because one section inside Z and outside R is not shaded.

7. (a) No cats are canines.
No cats are wolves.
Therefore, some wolves are canines.

(b)

(c) Invalid, because there is no 'X' in the area common to W and Ca.

8. (a) Some actors are egoists.
Some actors are rich persons.
Therefore, some rich persons are egoists.

(b)

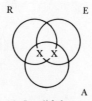

(c) Invalid, because there is no 'X' entirely inside the area common to R and E.

9. (a) No oak trees are pines.
All pines are conifers.
Therefore, no conifers are oak trees.

(b)

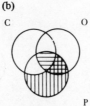

(c) Invalid, because one section common to C and O is not shaded.

10. (a) All boring persons are persons to be avoided.
All lawyers are boring persons.
Therefore, some lawyers are persons to be avoided.

(b)

(c) Invalid, because there is no 'X' in the area common to L and A.

Exercise 2-5

1. (a) No M are P.
Some M are S.
∴ Some S are not P.

(b)

(c) Valid, because there is an 'X' outside P and inside S.

2. (a) Some M are P.
No M are S.
∴ Some S are not P.

(b)

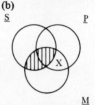

(c) Invalid, because there is no 'X' inside S and outside P.

3. (a) No P are M.
All S are M.
∴ Some S are not P.

(b)

(c) Invalid, because there is no 'X' inside S and outside P.

4. (a) All M are P.
Some S are M.
∴ Some S are P.

(b)

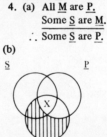

(c) Valid, because there is an 'X' in the area common to S and P.

5. (a) All P̄ are M.
Some M are not S.
∴ Some S are not P.

(b)

(c) Invalid, because there is no 'X' inside S and outside P.

6. (a) Some M are P.
All S are M.
∴ Some S are P.

(b)

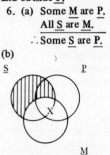

(c) Invalid, because there is no 'X' entirely inside the area common to S and P.

7. (a) Some P are M.
Some S are M.
∴ Some S are P.

(b)

(c) Invalid, because there is no 'X' entirely inside the area common to S and P.

8. (a) All P are M.
No M are S.
∴ No S are P.

(b)

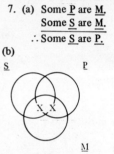

(c) Valid, because the area common to S and P is entirely shaded.

Exercise 2-6

1. (b) Rule 2: Illicit minor. (c) Invalid.
2. (b) No rules violated. (c) Valid.
3. (b) Rule 1: Undistributed middle.
(c) Invalid. 4. (b) Rule 5: Existential fallacy. (c) Invalid. 5. (b) Rule 2: Illicit major. (c) Invalid. 6. This is not a syllogism since the term 'kings' appears three times and the term 'monarchs' appears only once.

7. (a) No tigers are cheetahs.
   No lions are tigers.
   Therefore, no lions are cheetahs.
   (b) Rule 3: Negative premises. (c) Invalid
8. (a) Some politicians are not gangsters.
   All mayors are politicians.
   Therefore, some mayors are gangsters.
   (b) Rule 1: Undustributed middle; Rule 4: Affirmative conclusion from negative premises. (c) Invalid. 9. (b) Rule 5: Existential fallacy. (c) Invalid.
10. (b) Rule 1: Undistributed middle; Rule 2: Illicit minor. (c) Invalid.

Exercise 2-7

1. (a) No $\underline{M}$ are $\underline{P}$.
   Some $\underline{S}$ are $\underline{M}$.
   ∴Some $\underline{S}$ are $\underline{P}$.
   (b) Rule 4: Affirmative conclusion from negative premises. (c) Invalid.
2. (a) All $\underline{P}$ are $\underline{M}$.
   No $\underline{S}$ are $\underline{M}$.
   ∴No $\underline{S}$ are $\underline{P}$.
   (b) No rules violated. (c) Valid.
3. (a) All $\underline{M}$ are $\underline{P}$.
   No $\underline{M}$ are $\underline{S}$.
   ∴Some $\underline{S}$ are not $\underline{P}$.
   (b) Rule 2: Illicit major; Rule 5: Existential fallacy. (c) Invalid.
4. (a) All $\underline{P}$ are $\underline{M}$.
   Some $\underline{M}$ are $\underline{S}$.
   ∴Some $\underline{S}$ are $\underline{P}$.
   (b) Rule 1: Undistributed middle.
   (c) Invalid.
5. (a) No $\underline{M}$ are $\underline{P}$.
   Some $\underline{M}$ are $\underline{S}$.
   ∴Some $\underline{S}$ are not $\underline{P}$.
   (b) No rules violated. (c) Valid.
6. (a) Some $\underline{P}$ are not $\underline{M}$.
   Some $\underline{S}$ are not $\underline{M}$.
   ∴Some $\underline{S}$ are not $\underline{P}$.
   (b) Rule 2: Illicit major; Rule 3: Negative premises. (c) Invalid.

Exercise 2-8

1. (b) Rule 2: Illicit major. (c) Invalid.
2. (b) No rules violated. (c) Valid.
3. (b) Rule 5A: Negative conclusion without a negative premise. (c) Invalid.
4. (b) No rules violated. (c) Valid.
5. (b) Rule 1: Undistributed middle.
   (c) Invalid.

6. (a) No trees are things having gangrenous limbs.
   All maples are trees.
   Therefore, no maples are things having gangrenous limbs.
   (b) No rules violated. (c) Valid.
7. (a) No primates are unicellular organisms.
   All amoebae are unicellular organisms.
   Some amoebae are not primates.
   (b) No rules violated. (c) Valid.
8. (b) Rule 2: Illicit major. (c) Invalid.

Exercise 2-9

1. All mushrooms are fungi.
   [All toadstools are mushrooms.]
   Therefore, all toadstools are fungi.
2. [No elected officials are appointed officials.]
   Some judges are appointed officials.
   Therefore, some judges are not elected officials.
   OR
   [No appointed officials are elected officials.]
   Some judges are appointed officials.
   Therefore, some judges are not elected officials.
3. [No poisonous things are edible things.]
   Some mushrooms are poisonous things.
   Therefore, some mushrooms are not edible things.
   OR
   [No edible things are poisonous things.]
   Some mushrooms are poisonous things.
   Therefore, some mushrooms are not edible things.
4. All people who jog five miles every day are people who are in good physical condition.
   Some people are people who jog five miles every day.
   [Therefore, some people are people who are in good physical condition.]
5. No soaps are detergents.
   All detergents are cleansing agents.
   [Therefore, some cleansing agents are not soaps.]
6. [No things written in foreign languages are understandable things.]
   All operas are things written in foreign languages.
   Therefore, no operas are understandable things.

OR

[No understandable things are things written in foreign languages.]
All operas are things written in foreign languages.
Therefore, no operas are understandable things.

7. No reference books are books that can be taken out of the library.
All foreign language dictionaries are reference books.
[Therefore, no foreign language dictionaries are books that can be taken out of the library.]

OR

All foreign language dictionaries are reference books.
No reference books are books that can be taken out of the library.
[Therefore, no books that can be taken out of the library are foreign language dictionaries.]

8. [All liquors are bourbons.]
All whiskey are liquors.
Therefore, some whiskeys are bourbons.
This is valid on the restricted Aristotelian interpretation (**AAI-1**), but it is not sound, since the major premise is not true.

9. [All persons who can practice law are persons who have passed the bar examination.]
No members of the class of which Jack is the only member are persons who passed the bar examination.
No members of the class of which Jack is the only member are persons who can practice law.

10. [All persons who are members of Phi Beta Kappa are intelligent persons.]
All members of the class of which Mary is the only member is a member of Phi Beta Kappa.
Therefore, all members of the class of which Mary is the only member is an intelligent person.

Exercise 2-10

1. (a) All woodwinds are musical instruments.
All oboes are woodwinds.
[All oboes are musical instruments.]
Some drums are not musical instruments.

[Some drums are not oboes.]
All drums are cylindrical objects.
Therefore, some cylindrical objects are not oboes.

(b)

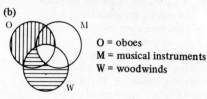

O = oboes
M = musical instruments
W = woodwinds

Valid.

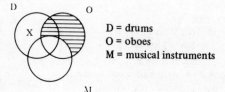

D = drums
O = oboes
M = musical instruments

Valid.

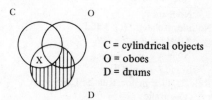

C = cylindrical objects
O = oboes
D = drums

The sorites is valid; no rule is violated.

2. (a) All zoologists are biologists.
All entomologists are zoologists.
[Therefore, all entomologists are biologists.]
No biologists are butterflies.
(Therefore, no butterflies are entomologists.)
All lepidopterists are entomologists.
[Therefore, no lepidopterists are butterflies.]
All swallowtails are butterflies.
Therefore, no swallow tails are lepidopterists.
[This is one of several possible correct answers.]

(b)

E = entomologists
Bi = biologists
Z = zoologists

Valid.

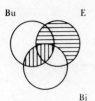

Bu = butterflies
E = entomologists
Bi = biologists

Valid.

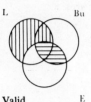

L = lepidopterists
Bu = butterflies
E = entomologists

Valid.

S = swallowtails
L = lepidopterists
E = entomologists

Valid.
No rule is broken.
The sorites as a whole is valid.

3. (a) Some Americans are Westerners.
All New Yorkers are Americans.
[Therefore, all New Yorkers are Westerners.]
No Tibetans are Westerners.
[Therefore, no Tibetans are New Yorkers.]
Some New Yorkers are pretzel vendors.
Therefore, some pretzel vendors are not Tibetans.
[This is one of several possible solutions in which only the first syllogism is invalid.]

(b)

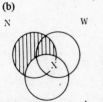

N = New Yorkers
W = Westerners
A = Americans

Invalid; Rule 1 is violated (Fallacy of Undistributed Middle).

4. (a) Some things that can be had for a song are things that are rubbish.
All things that are rubbish are things sold in the street.
[Therefore, some things that can be had for a song are things sold in the street.]
No things sold in the street are valuable materials.
[No valuable material are things that can be had for a song.]
All eggs of the Great Auk are valuable material.
Therefore, no eggs of the Great Auk are things that can be had for a song.

(b)

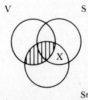

S = things that can be had for a song
St = things sold in the street
R = things that are rubbish

Valid.

V = valuable material
S = things that can be had for a song
St = things sold in the street

Invalid; Rule 2 is violated (Fallacy of Illicit Major).

5. (a) No intelligent persons are persons who are always talking.
All members of the class of which Paula is the only member are persons who are always talking.
[Therefore, all persons of the class of which Paula is the only member are not intelligent persons.]
All college graduates are intelligent persons.
Therefore, all persons of the class of which Paula is the only member are not college graduates.

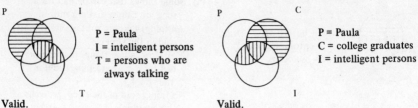

P = Paula
I = intelligent persons
T = persons who are
always talking

Valid.

P = Paula
C = college graduates
I = intelligent persons

Valid.
The sorites is valid; no rule is broken.

Answers to Chapter 3

Exercise 3-1

1. (a) Yes. (b) Pines are evergreens. Oaks are hardwoods. (c) And. (d) Yes.
2. (a) Yes. (b) Oaks are evergreens. Pines are hardwoods. (c) And. (d) Yes.
3. (a) Yes. (b) The earth is flat. (c) It is not true that. (d) Yes. 4. (a) Yes. (b) The earth is not flat. (c) You ought to know that. (d) No. 5. (a) Yes (b) The Flanagans did not come. Their car broke down. (c) Because. (d) No.
6. (a) Yes. (b) The Flanagans did not come. Their car broke down. (c) And. (d) Yes. 7. (a) No. 8. (a) Yes. (b) Joseph came out. He helped me shovel snow. (c) And. (d) Yes.
9. (a) No. 10. (a) Yes. (b) Maureen is not coming to dinner. She has to stay home and study. (c) Because. (d) No.

Exercise 3-2

1. (a) No. 2. (a) Yes. (b) A · D
(c) A= The Oakland Athletics is a baseball team. D= The Los Angeles Dodgers is a baseball team. (d) No 3. (a) Yes
(b) R · G (c) R= The gunmen robbed the bank. G= The gunmen made their getaway. (d) Sense of temporal sequence lost. 4. (a) Yes. (b) M · G (c) M= The gunmen covered their faces with masks. G= The gunmen wore gloves. (d) No.
5. (a) No. 6. (a) Yes. (b) S · M
(c) S= The band played Stardust. M= The band played Moon River. (d) Possible loss of temporal sequence, but this is not clear without more contextual information.
7. (a) Yes. (b) S · P (c) S= Kareem Abdul-Jabbar scored 20 points. P= Karrem Abdul-Jabbar played only half the game.
(d) Loss of suggestion that it is an accomplishment to score 20 points in only one half of a game. 8. (a) No.

Exercise 3-3

1. (a) S ∨ W (b) S= It is snowing in Detroit. W= The weather report is inaccurate. (c) None 2. (a) K · C (b) K= Joyce needs a kitchen table for her apartment. C= Joyce needs some chairs for her apart-

ment. (c) None. 3. (a) J ⊃ V (b) J= An American president's last name was Johnson V = He (the American president) was vice president before he was president.
(c) None. 4. (a) ~P (b) P = Sugar is a protein. (c) None. 5. (a) E ≡ S
(b) E = A geometrical figure is an equilateral. S = All its (the geometrical figures) sides have the same length. (c) None.
6. (a) Not adequately translatable
7. (a) A · S (b) A = Athens was a city-state in ancient Greece. S = Sparta was a city-state in ancient Greece. (c) None.
8. (a) D · ~S (b) D= His battery went dead. S = His car would start. (c) Sense of temporal sequence is lost. 9. (a) B ∨ S
(b) B = Carl drinks bourbon. S = Carl drinks scotch. (c) None. 10. (a) P ⊃ T
(b) P = It (the job) pays well. T = I will take the job. (c) None (causal overtones insofar as reason for action given).
11. (a) T ⊃ P (b) T = I will take the job. P = It (the job) pays well. (c) None.
12. (a) T ≡ P (b) T = I will take the job. P = It (the job) pays well. (c) None.
13. (a) ~R (b) R = All triangles are right triangles. (c) None. 14. (a) T ∨ B
(b) T = Candles can be made of tallow. B = Candles can be made of beeswax.
(c) None. 15. (a) M ≡ E (b) M = Oil and water will mix. E = Oil and water are emulsified. (c) Loss of suggestion of causal sequence. 16. (a) W · G (b) W = Most swans are white. G = Some swans are gray.
(c) 'Although' connotes an exception to the rule. 17. (a) E ⊃ D (b) E = A total eclipse of the sun occurs. D = The sky darkens. (c) Causal implications of the original are lost. 18. (a) E≡P (b) E = A total eclipse of the sun occurs. P = The moon is positioned directly between the earth and the sun. (c) Suggestion of causal connection is lost.

Exercise 3-4

1. (S · R) ∨ D 2. S · (R ∨ D)
3. S ∨ (R · D) 4. (S ∨ R) · D
5. S · (R · D) 6. (S · R) · D
7. (S · R) · D or S · (R · D) 8. ~(C · M)
9. C · ~M 10. ~C · M 11. ~C · ~M

12. $\simeq(\sim C \cdot \sim M)$ 13. $\simeq(C \cdot \sim M)$
14. $\simeq(\sim C \cdot M)$ 15. $(S \cdot H) \supseteq \sim C$
16. $S \supseteq (H \cdot \sim C)$ 17. $S \supseteq (\sim H \vee \sim C)$
18. $S \supseteq (H \vee C)$ 19. $S \supseteq (H \supset \sim C)$
20. $(S \vee H) \supseteq \sim C$

Exercise 3-5

1.

p	q	p	$\supset$	$\sim$	q
T	T		F	F	
F	T		T	F	
T	F		T	T	
F	F		T	T	
			(2)	(1)	

2.

p	q	p	$\vee$	$\sim$	q
T	T		T	F	
F	T		F	F	
T	F		T	T	
F	F		T	T	
			(2)	(1)	

3.

p	q	p	$\cdot$	$\sim$	q
T	T		F	F	
F	T		F	F	
T	F		T	T	
F	F		F	T	
			(2)	(1)	

4.

p	q	$\sim$	p	$\cdot$	$\sim$	q
T	T	F		F	F	
F	T	T		F	F	
T	F	F		F	T	
F	F	T		T	T	
		(1)		(2)	(1)	

5.

p	q	$\sim$	$(p$	$\cdot$	$q)$
T	T	F		T	
F	T	T		F	
T	F	T		F	
F	F	T		F	
		(2)		(1)	

6.

p	q	$\sim$	$(p$	$\cdot$	$\sim$	$q)$
T	T	T		F	F	
F	T	T		F	F	
T	F	F		T	T	
F	F	T		F	T	
		(3)		(2)	(1)	

7.

p	q	$(p \cdot q)$	$\supset$	p
T	T	T	T	
F	T	F	T	
T	F	F	T	
F	F	F	T	
		(1)	(2)	

8.

p	q	$(p \cdot q)$	$\supset$	q
T	T	T	T	
F	T	F	T	
T	F	F	T	
F	F	F	T	
		(1)	(2)	

9.

p	q	r	$(p \cdot q)$	$\supset$	r
T	T	T	T	T	
F	T	T	F	T	
T	F	T	F	T	
F	F	T	F	T	
T	T	F	T	F	
F	T	F	F	T	
T	F	F	F	T	
F	F	F	F	T	
			(1)	(2)	

10.

p	q	r	$(p \vee q)$	$\supset$	r
T	T	T	T	T	
F	T	T	T	T	
T	F	T	T	T	
F	F	T	F	T	
T	T	F	T	F	
F	T	F	T	F	
T	F	F	T	F	
F	F	F	F	T	
			(1)	(2)	

11.

p	q	r	$(p \supset q)$	$\supset$	r
T	T	T	T	T	
F	T	T	T	T	
T	F	T	F	T	
F	F	T	T	T	
T	T	F	T	F	
F	T	F	T	F	
T	F	F	F	T	
F	F	F	T	F	
			(1)	(2)	

12.

p	q	((p ⊃ q) · p) ⊃ q		
T	T	T	T	T
F	T	T	F	T
T	F	F	F	T
F	F	T	F	T
		(1)	*(2)*	*(3)*

2. (a) Equivalent.

(b)

p	q	p · ~q		~(~p ∨ q)		
T	T	F	F	F	F	T
F	T	F	F	F	T	T
T	F	T	T	T	F	F
F	F	F	T	F	T	T
		(2)	*(1)*	*(3)*	*(1)*	*(2)*

13.

p	q	((p ⊃ q) · ~q) ⊃ ~p				
T	T	T	F	F	T	F
F	T	T	F	F	T	T
T	F	F	F	T	T	F
F	F	T	T	T	T	T
		(2)	*(3)*	*(1)*	*(4)*	*(1)*

3. (a) Equivalent.

(b)

p	q	~ p · q		~(p ∨ ~q)		
T	T	F	F	F	T	F
F	T	T	T	T	F	F
T	F	F	F	F	T	T
F	F	T	F	F	T	T
		(1)	*(2)*	*(3)*	*(2)*	*(1)*

14.

p	q	(p ⊃ q) ≡ (~q ⊃ ~p)				
T	T	T	T	F	T	F
F	T	T	T	F	T	T
T	F	F	T	T	F	F
F	F	T	T	T	T	T
		(2)	*(3)*	*(1)*	*(2)*	*(1)*

4. (a) Not equivalent.

(b)

p	q	~ (p ∨ q)		~ p ∨ q	
T	T	F	T	F	T
F	T	F	T	T	T
T	F	F	T	F	F
F	F	T	F	T	T
		(3)	*(2)*	*(1)*	*(2)*

15.

p	q	~(p · q) ≡ (~ p ∨ ~ q)					
T	T	F	T	T	F	F	F
F	T	T	F	T	T	T	F
T	F	T	F	T	F	T	T
F	F	T	F	T	T	T	T
		(3)	*(2)*	*(4)*	*(1)*	*(2)*	*(1)*

16.

p	q	~(p · q) ≡ (~p · q)				
T	T	F	T	T	F	F
F	T	T	F	T	T	T
T	F	T	F	F	F	F
F	F	T	F	F	T	F
		(3)	*(2)*	*(4)*	*(1)*	*(2)*

5. (a) Equivalent.

(b)

p	q	p ⊃ q	~ p ∨ q	
T	T	T	F	T
F	T	T	T	T
T	F	F	F	F
F	F	T	T	T
			(1)	*(2)*

6. (a) Not equivalent.

(b)

p	q	~ (p ⊃ q)	p ∨ ~ q	
T	T	F	T	T	F
F	T	F	T	F	F
T	F	T	F	T	T
F	F	F	T	T	T
		(3)	*(2)*	*(2)*	*(1)*

Exercise 3-6

1. (a) Equivalent.

p	q	p · q ~ (~p ∨ ~q)			
T	T	T	T	F	F	F
F	T	F	F	T	T	F
T	F	F	F	F	T	T
F	F	F	F	T	T	T
		(3)	*(1)*	*(2)*	*(1)*

7. (a) Not equivalent.

(b)
p	q		p · q	p ≡ q
T	T		T	T
F	T		F	F
T	F		F	F
F	F		F	T

8. (a) Equivalent.

(b)
p	q	~	(p ·	~ q)	·	~	(q ·	~p)	p ≡ q
T	T	T	F	F	T	T	F	F	T
F	T	T	F	F	F	F	T	T	F
T	F	F	T	T	F	T	F	F	F
F	F	T	F	T	T	T	F	T	T
		(3)	(2)(1)		(4)(3)		(2)(1)		

Exercise 3.7

1. (a) Contingent statement.

(b)
p	q		p ⊃ q
T	T		T
F	T		T
T	F		F
F	F		T

2. (a) Tautology.

(b)
p		p ⊃ p
T		T
F		T

3. (a) Contingent statement.

(b)
p		p ⊃ ~ p
T		F F
F		T T
		(2) (1)

4. (a) Contradiction.

(b)
p	q	((p ⊃ q)	·	~ q)	· p
T	T	T	F	F	F
F	T	T	F	F	F
T	F	F	F	T	F
F	F	T	T	T	F
		(2)	(3) (1)		(4)

5. (a) Contingent statement.

(b)
p	q	((p ⊃ q)	·	~q) ∨ p
T	T	T	F	F T
F	T	T	F	F F
T	F	F	F	T T
F	F	T	T	T T
		(2)	(3) (1)	(4)

6. (a) Contradiction.

(b)
p		(p ∨ ~p)	⊃	(p · ~ p)
T		T F	F	F F
F		T T	F	F T
		(2) (1)	(3)	(2) (1)

7. (a) Contingent statement.

(b)
p	q	(p ∨ ~p)	⊃	(p · ~ q)
T	T	T F	F	F F
F	T	T T	F	F F
T	F	T F	T	T T
F	F	T T	F	F T
		(2) (1)	(3)	(2) (1)

8. (a) Contradiction.

(b)
p	q	~ (p ⊃ q)	≡	(~p ∨ q)
T	T	F T	F	F T
F	T	F T	F	T T
T	F	T F	F	F F
F	F	F T	F	T T
		(3) (2)	(4)	(1) (2)

9. (a) Tautology.

(b)
p	q	(~ p ⊃ q)	≡ (p ∨ q)
T	T	F T T	T T
F	T	T T T	T T
T	F	F T F	T T
F	F	T F F	T F
		(1) (2) (3)	(2)

10. (a) Contingent statement.

(b)
p	q	(~ p ⊃ q) ≡	(~ p ∨ q)
T	T	F T T T	F T
F	T	T T T T	T T
T	F	F T F F	F F
F	F	T F F T	T T
		(1) (2) (3)	(1) (2)

Answers to Chapter 4

Exercise 4-1

1. B = Fido is in the basement.
   Y = Fido is in the backyard.

   (a) B ∨ Y (b) ̄p ∨ q
   ~ B   ~ p
   ∴ Y   ∴ q

2. Using the same propositional constants as in 1:

   (a) B ∨ Y (b) p ∨ q
   ~ Y   ~ q
   ∴ B   ∴ p

3. D = All dogs are carnivores.
   F = Fido is a carnivore.

   (a) D ⊃ F (b) p ⊃ q
   D   p
   ∴ F   ∴ q

4. Using the same propositional constants as in 3:

   (a) D ⊃ F (b) p ⊃ q
   ~ F   ~ q
   ∴ ~ D   ∴ ~ p

5. I = The law of noncontradiction holds.
   T = Logical thought is possible.

   (a) ~ L ⊃ ~ T (b) ~ p ⊃ ~ q
   T   q
   ∴ L   ∴ p

6. W = This chair is made of Walnut.
   M = This chair is made of Mahogany.
   T = This chair is made of Teakwood.

   (a) (W ∨ M) ∨ T (b) (p ∨ q) ∨ r
   ~ W   ~ p
   ∴ M ∨ T   ∴ q ∨ r

7. S = We are going to the state park for a picnic.
   J = We will take Johnny along.
   B = We will take Billy along.

   (a) S ⊃ (J ∨ B) (b) p ⊃ (q ∨ r)
   S   p
   ∴ J ∨ B   ∴ q ∨ r

8. Using the same propositional constants as in 7:

   (a) S ⊃ (J · B) (b) p ⊃ (q · r)
   S   p
   ∴ J · B   ∴ q · r

9. Using the same propositional constants as in 7:

   (a) (S · J) ⊃ B (b) (p · q) ⊃ r
   S · J   p · q
   ∴ B   ∴ r

10. Using the same propositional constants as in 7:

   (a) (S ∨ J) ⊃ B (b) (p ∨ q) ⊃ r
   S   p
   ∴ B   ∴ r

11. Using the same propositional constants as in 7:

   (a) (S ∨ J) ⊃ P (b) (p ∨ q) ⊃ r
   J   q
   ∴ P   ∴ r

12. R = It is raining.
   W = The wind is blowing.
   T = Water will get in the tent.

   (a) (R · W) ⊃ T (b) (p · q) ⊃ r
   R   p
   W   q
   ∴ T   ∴ r

13. R = It is raining.
   C = It is getting cold.
   S = My car will start.

   (a) R ⊃ (C ⊃ ~ S) (b) p ⊃ (q ⊃ ~ r)
   R · C   p · q
   ∴ ~ S   ∴ ~ r

14. F = Snow is falling.
   C = It is getting cold.
   S = My car will start.

   (a) F ⊃ C (b) p ⊃ q
   C ⊃ ~ S   q ⊃ ~ r
   F   p
   ∴ ~ S   ∴ ~ r

15. E = The statement under discussion is an equivalence.
   I = The statement under discussion contains an implication.
   D = The statement under discussion is a disjunction.

   (a) E ⊃ I (b) p ⊃ q
   D ∨ E   r ∨ p
   ~ D   ~ r
   ∴ I   ∴ q

16. Using the same propositional constants as in 15:

(a)   D ∨ E   (b)   r ∨ p
        E ⊃ I   p ⊃ q
        ~ I   ~ q
   ∴ D   ∴ r

17.   C = The statement under discussion is a conjunction.
       D = The statement under discussion is a disjunction.
       I = The statement under discussion is an implication.

(a)   C ∨ D   (b)   p ∨ q
        C ∨ I   p ∨ r
        D ⊃ ~ I   q ⊃ ~ r
   ∴ C   ∴ p

18.   T = The statement under discussion is a truth-functional proposition.
       C = The statement under discussion is a command.
       P = The statement under discussion is a compound proposition.
       I = The statement under discussion contains a logical operator.

(a)   T ∨ C   (b)   p ∨ q
        T ⊃ P   p ⊃ r
        P ⊃ L   r ⊃ s
        ~ L   ~ s
   ∴ C   ∴ q

19.   Using the same propositional constants as in 18:

(a)   T ∨ C   (b)   p ∨ q
        T ⊃ P   p ⊃ r
        P ⊃ L   r ⊃ s
        ~ C   ~ q
   ∴ L   ∴ s

20.   A = This solution is an acid.
       R = Litmus paper placed in it (this solution) will turn red.
       B = This solution is a base.
       P = Litmus paper placed in it (this solution) will turn blue.

(a)   (A ⊃ R) · (B ⊃ P)   (b)   (p ⊃ q) · (r ⊃ s)
        A ∨ B   p ∨ r
   ∴ R ∨ P   ∴ q ∨ s

21.   Using the same propositional constants as in 20:

(a)   (A ⊃ R) · (B ⊃ P)   (b)   (p ⊃ q) · (r ⊃ s)
        ~ R · ~ P   ~ q · ~ s
   ∴ ~ A · ~ B   ∴ ~ p · ~ r

22.   H = Herb is a Hoosier.
       B = Herb is a Buckeye.
       I   = Herb is from Indiana.
       O = Herb is from Ohio.
       A = Herb is an American.

(a)   H ⊃ I   (b)   p ⊃ q
        B ⊃ O   r ⊃ s
        (I ∨ O) ⊃ A   (q ∨ s) ⊃ t
        H ∨ B   p ∨ r
   ∴ A   ∴ t

23.   P = Pete can come tonight.
       G = Gary can come tonight.
       R = Ralph can come tonight.
       S = Sam can come tonight.
       T = Ted can come tonight.

(a)   P ⊃ (G ∨ R)   (b)   p ⊃ (q ∨ r)
        G ⊃ S   q ⊃ s
        S ⊃ T   s ⊃ t
        P ⊃ ~ T   p ⊃ ~ t
        P   p
   ∴ R   ∴ r

24.   Using the same propositional constants as in 23:

(a)   (P ∨ G) ⊃   (b)   (p ∨ q) ⊃
          (~ R ∨ ~ S)   (~ r ∨ ~ s)
        ~ R ⊃ ~ T   ~ r ⊃ ~ t
        G · T   q · t
   ∴ ~ S   ∴ ~ s

Exercise 4-2

1. (b) Valid.

(a)	p	q	(Premise) q	(Conclusion) p ⊃ (p · q)	
	T	T	T	T	T
	F	T	T	T	F
	T	F	F	F	F
	F	F	F	T	F

2. (b) Valid.

			(Premise)	(Conclusion)	
(a)	p	q	$p \supset q$	$p \supset (p \cdot q)$	
	T	T	T	T	T
	F	T	T	T	F
	T	F	F	F	F
	F	F	T	T	F

3. (b) Invalid.

			(Premise)	(Conclusion)	
(a)	p	q	$q \supset p$	$p \supset (p \cdot q)$	
	T	T	T	T	T
	F	T	F	T	F
	T	F	T	F	F
	F	F	T	T	F

4. (b) Valid.

			(Premise 1)	(Premise 2)	(Conclusion)
(a)	p	q	$p \lor q$	$\sim p$	q
	T	T	T	F	T
	F	T	T	T	T
	T	F	T	F	F
	F	F	F	T	F

5. (b) Invalid.

			(Premise)	(Premise)	(Conclusion)
(a)	p	q	$p \lor q$	p	$\sim q$
	T	T	T	T	F
	F	T	T	F	F
	T	F	T	T	T
	F	F	F	F	T

6. (b) Invalid.

			(Premise)	(Premise)	(Conclusion)
(a)	p	q	$p \supset q$	q	p
	T	T	T	T	T
	F	T	T	T	F
	T	F	F	F	T
	F	F	T	F	F

7. (b) Invalid.

			(Premise)	(Premise)	(Conclusion)
(a)	p	q	$p \supset q$	$\sim p$	$\sim q$
	T	T	T	F	F
	F	T	T	T	F
	T	F	F	F	T
	F	F	T	T	T

8. (b) Valid.

(a)

p	q	r	p ⊃ q	q ⊃ r	p ⊃ r
T	T	T	T	T	T
F	T	T	T	T	T
T	F	T	F	T	T
F	F	T	T	T	T
T	T	F	T	F	F
F	T	F	T	F	T
T	F	F	F	T	F
F	F	F	T	T	T

9. (b) Valid.

(a) p	q	r	(Premise) p ⊃ q	(Premise) p ∨ r	(Premise) ~ r	(Conclusion) q
T	T	T	T	T	F	T
F	T	T	T	T	F	T
T	F	T	F	T	F	F
F	F	T	T	T	F	F
T	T	F	T	T	T	T
F	T	F	T	F	T	T
T	F	F	F	T	T	F
F	F	F	T	F	T	F

10. (b) Valid.

(a) p	q	r	(Premise) p ⊃ q	(Premise) q ⊃ r	(Premise) ~ r	(Conclusion) ~ p
T	T	T	T	T	F	F
F	T	T	T	T	F	T
T	F	T	F	T	F	F
F	F	T	T	T	F	T
T	T	F	T	F	T	F
F	T	F	T	F	T	T
T	F	F	F	T	T	F
F	F	F	T	T	T	T

11. (b) Invalid.

(a) p	q	r	(Premise) p ⊃ q	(Premise) p ⊃ r	(Premise) ~ r	(Conclusion) ~ q
T	T	T	T	T	F	F
F	T	T	T	T	F	F
T	F	T	F	T	F	T
F	F	T	T	T	F	T
T	T	F	T	F	T	F
F	T	F	T	T	T	F
T	F	F	F	F	T	T
F	F	F	T	T	T	T

12. (b) Invalid.

	p	q	r	(Premise) p ⊃ q	(Premise) p ∨ r	(Premise) ~p	(Conclusion) q
(a)							
	T	T	T	T	T	F	T
	F	T	T	T	T	T	T
	T	F	T	F	T	F	F
	F	F	T	T	T	T	F
	T	T	F	T	T	F	T
	F	T	F	T	F	T	T
	T	F	F	F	T	F	F
	F	F	F	T	F	T	F

13. (b) Valid.

	p	q	r	(Premise) p ⊃ q	(Premise) p ∨ r	(Premise) ~q	(Conclusion) r
(a)							
	T	T	T	T	T	F	T
	F	T	T	T	T	F	T
	T	F	T	F	T	T	T
	F	F	T	T	T	T	T
	T	T	F	T	T	F	F
	F	T	F	T	F	F	F
	T	F	F	F	T	T	F
	F	F	F	T	F	T	F

14. (b) Invalid.

	p	q	r	(Premise) p ⊃ (q ⊃ r)		(Premise) p ⊃ q	(Conclusion) r
(a)							
	T	T	T	T	T	T	T
	F	T	T	T	T	T	T
	T	F	T	T	T	F	T
	F	F	T	T	T	T	T
	T	T	F	F	F	T	F
	F	T	F	T	F	T	F
	T	F	F	T	T	F	F
	F	F	F	T	T	T	F

15. (b) Invalid.

	p	q	r	(Premise) p ⊃ (q ⊃ r)		(Premise) p ⊃ q	(Conclusion) p ⊃ r
(a)							
	T	T	T	T	T	T	T
	F	T	T	T	T	T	T
	T	F	T	T	T	F	T
	F	F	T	T	T	T	T
	T	T	F	F	F	T	F
	F	T	F	T	F	T	F
	T	F	F	T	T	F	T
	F	F	F	T	T	T	T

16. (b) Valid.

(a) p	q	r	(Premise) $p \supset (q \supset r)$		(Premise) $p \supset q$	(Conclusion) $p \supset r$
T	T	T	T	T	T	T
F	T	T	T	T	T	T
T	F	T	T	T	F	T
F	F	T	T	T	T	T
T	T	F	F	F	T	F
F	T	F	T	F	T	T
T	F	F	T	T	F	F
F	F	F	T	T	T	T

Exercise 4-3

Any one row with all true permises and a false conclusion is sufficient to prove the invalidity of the argument.

1.

p	q	r	(Premise) p q		(Premise) $p \lor r$			(Conclusion) r
T	T	F	T	T	T	T	F	F

2.

p	q	r	(Premise) $p \supset q$			(Premise) $p \lor r$			(Conclusion) q
F	F	T	F	T	F	F	T	T	F

3.

p	q	r	(Premise) $p \supset q$			(Premise) $p \lor r$			(Conclusion) $q \supset \sim r$			
T	T	T	T	T	T	T	T	T	T	F	F	T
F	T	T	F	T	T	F	T	T	T	F	F	T

4.

p	q	r	(Premise) $p \supset q$			(Premise) $p \lor r$			(Conclusion) $q \lor \sim r$			
F	F	T	F	T	F	F	T	T	F	F	F	T

5.

p	q	r	(Premise) $p \supset (q \supset r)$					(Premise) p	(Conclusion) r
T	F	F	T	T	F	T	F	T	F

6.

p	q	r	(Premise) $p \supset q$			(Premise) $q \supset r$			(Conclusion) $p \cdot r$		
F	F	T	F	T	F	F	T	T	F	F	T
F	F	F	F	T	F	F	T	F	F	F	F
F	T	T	F	T	T	T	T	T	F	F	T

7.

p	r	s	t	(p ⊃ r) · (s ⊃ t)	r V t	p V s
				(Premise)	*(Premise)*	*(Conclusion)*
F	T	F	T	F T T T F T T	T T T	F F F
F	T	F	F	F T T T F T F	T T F	F F F
F	F	F	T	F T F T F T T	F T T	F F F

8.

p	q	r	(p ⊃ q) V (q ⊃ r)	p V q	q · r
			(Premise)	*(Premise)*	*(Conclusion)*
T	F	F	T F F T F T F	T T F	F F F
T	F	T	T F F T F T T	T T F	F F T
T	T	F	T T T T T F F	T T T	T F F
F	T	F	F T T T T F F	F T T	T F F

Exercise 4-4

Note: Each answer below is only one of many possible proofs.

1. 1. p ⊃ (q · r)   Premise
   2. p / ∴ r   Premise / Conclusion
   3. q · r   M.P.,1,2
   4. r   Simp.,3
2. 1. p ⊃ ~ r   Premise
   2. q ⊃ r   Premise
   3. p / ∴ ~ q   Premise / Conclusion
   4. ~ r   M.P.,1,3
   5. ~ q   M.T.,2,4
3. 1. p ⊃ ~ r   Premise
   2. q V r   Premise
   3. p / ∴ q   Premise / Conclusion
   4. ~ r   M.P.,1,3
   5. q   D.S.,2,4
4. 1. (p · q) ⊃ (r · s)   Premise
   2. (r · s) ⊃ (t · u) / ∴ (p · q) ⊃ (t · u)   Premise / Conclusion
   3. (p · q) ⊃ (t · u)   H.Syll.,1,2
5. 1. (p · q) ⊃ (r · s)   Premise
   2. (r · s) ⊃ (t · u)   Premise
   3. p · q / ∴ t · u   Premise / Conclusion
   4. (p · q) ⊃ (t · u)   H.Syll.,1,2
   5. t · u   M.P.,3,4
6. 1. (p · q) ⊃ (r · s)   Premise
   2. (r · s) ⊃ (t · u)   Premise

3. p · q / ∴ u   Premise / Conclusion
4. (p · q) ⊃ (t · u)   H.Syll.,1,2
5. t · u   M.P.,3,4
6. u   Simp.,5
7. 1. p ⊃ q   Premise
   2. q ⊃ r   Premise
   3. p / ∴ p · r   Premise / Conclusion
   4. p ⊃ r   H.Syll.,1,2
   5. r   M.P.,3,4
   6. p · r   Conj.,3,5
8. 1. p ⊃ q   Premise
   2. q ⊃ r   Premise
   3. ~ r / ∴ ~ r · ~ p   Premise / Conclusion
   4. p ⊃ r   H.Syll.,1,2
   5. ~ p   M.T.,3,4
   6. ~ r · ~ p   Conj.,3,5
9. 1. (p ⊃ q) · (r ⊃ s)   Premise
   2. (q ⊃ t) · (s ⊃ u)   Premise
   3. p V r / ∴ t V u   Premise / Conclusion
   4. q V s   Dil.,1,3
   5. t V u   Dil.,2,4
10. 1. p   Premise
    2. p ⊃ q   Premise
    3. (p · q) ⊃ (r · s) / ∴ r · s   Premise / Conclusion
    4. q   M.P.,1,2
    5. p · q   Conj.,1,4
    6. r · s   M.P.,3,5
11. 1. p   Premise
    2. p ⊃ q   Premise
    3. (p · q) ⊃ (r · s) / ∴ s

		Premise / Conclusion	
	4.	q	M.P.,1,2
	5.	p · q	Conj.,1,4
	6.	r · s	M.P.,3,5
	7.	s	Simp.,6
12.	1.	p	Premise
	2.	p ⊃ q	Premise
	3.	(p·q) ⊃ (r·s) / ∴ s V t	
			Premise / Conclusion
	4.	q	M.P.,1,2
	5.	p · q	Conj.,1,4
	6.	r · s	M.P.,3,5
	7.	s	Simp.,6
	8.	s V t	Add.,7
13.	1.	p	Premise
	2.	(p V q) ⊃ (r · s)	
			Premise
	3.	s ⊃ t / ∴ t	Premise / Conclusion
	4.	p V q	Add.,1
	5.	r · s	M.P.,2,4
	6.	s	Simp.,5
	7.	t	M.P.,3,6
14.	1.	p	Premise
	2.	(p V q) ⊃ (r · s)	
			Premise
	3.	s ⊃ t / ∴ t V u	
			Premise / Conclusion
	4.	p V q	Add.,1
	5.	r · s	M.P.,2,4
	6.	s	Simp.,5
	7.	t	M.P.,3,6
	8.	t V u	Add.,7
15.	1.	p ⊃ q	Premise
	2.	q ⊃ r	Premise
	3.	r ⊃ s	Premise
	4.	∼ s / ∴ ∼ p	Premise / Conclusion
	5.	∼ r	M.T.,3,4
	6.	∼ q	M.T.,2,5
	7.	∼ p	M.T.,1,6
16.	1.	(p V q) ⊃ (r V s)	
			Premise
	2.	(r V s) ⊃ (t V u)	
			Premise
	3.	(t V u) ⊃ (v V w)	
			Premise
	4.	∼(v V w) / ∴ ∼ (p V q)	
			Premise / Conclusion
	5.	∼(t V u)	M.T.,3,4
	6.	∼(r V s)	M.T.,2,5
	7.	∼(p V q)	M.T.,1,6
17.	1.	(p V q) ⊃ (r ⊃ s)	
			Premise

	2.	p ⊃ r	Premise
	3.	p / ∴ s	Premise / Conclusion
	4.	r	M.P.,2,3
	5.	p V q	Add.,3
	6.	r ⊃ s	M.P.,1,5
	7.	s	M.P.,4,6
18.	1.	∼ (p · q)	Premise
	2.	(p · q) V (r ⊃ s)	
			Premise
	3.	∼ (p · q) ⊃ ∼ s / ∴ ∼ r	
			Premise / Conclusion
	4.	r ⊃ s	D.Syll.,1,2
	5.	∼ s	M.P.,1,3
	6.	∼ r	M.T.,4,5
19.	1.	∼ (p · q)	Premise
	2.	(p · q) V ((r · s) ⊃ (t V u))	
			Premise
	3.	∼(p · q) ⊃ ∼ (t V u) / ∴ ∼ (r · s)	
			Premise / Conclusion
	4.	(r · s) ⊃ (t V u)	
			D.Syll.,1,2
	5.	∼(t V u)	M.P.,1,3
	6.	∼ (r · s)	M.T.,4,5
20.	1.	(p V q) V (r V s)	
			Premise
	2.	(r V s) ⊃ t	Premise
	3.	t ⊃ p	Premise
	4.	∼ p / ∴ q	Premise / Conclusion
	5.	∼ t	M.T.,3,4
	6.	∼(r V s)	M.T.,2,5
	7.	p V q	D.Syll.,1,6
	8.	q	D.Syll.,4,7

Exercise 4-5

1.	1.	p ⊃ q	Premise
	2.	∼ p ⊃ r / ∴ r V q	
			Premise / Conclusion
	3.	∼ q ⊃ ∼ p	Trans.,1
	4.	∼ q ⊃ r	H.Syll.,3,2
	5.	∼∼ q V r	Impl.,4
	6.	q V r	D.N.,5
	7.	r V q	Comm.,6
2.	1.	(p V q) ⊃ r	Premise
	2.	p / ∴ r	Premise / Conclusion
	3.	p V q	Add.,2
	4.	r	M.P.,3
3.	1.	p ⊃ (r ⊃ q)	Premise
	2.	p	Premise
	3.	r / ∴ q	Premise / Conclusion
	4.	r ⊃ q	M.P.,1,2
	5.	q	M.P.,3,4

4. 1. p ∨ q   Premise
    2. ~ q ∨ r   Premise
    3. ~ p · (r ⊃ s) / ∴ s
                       Premise / Conclusion
    4. ~ p   Simp.,3
    5. q   D.Syll.,1,4
    6. ~ ~ q   D.N.,5
    7. r   D.Syll.,2,6
    8. r ⊃ s   Simp.,3
    9. s   M.P.,7,8
5. 1. ~ (q ∨ ~ p)   Premise
    2. (p · ~ q) ⊃ (p ⊃ r)
                       Premise
    3. r ⊃ s / ∴ p ⊃ s
                       Premise / Conclusion
    4. ~ q · ~ ~ p   DeM.,1
    5. ~ q · p   D.N.,4
    6. p · ~ q   Comm.,5
    7. p ⊃ r   M.P.,2,6
    8. p ⊃ s   H.Syll.,3,7

Exercise 4-6

1. Incorrect use of DeMorgan's Theorem.
Line 4 should be ~ (p ∨ q). 2. Incorrect
use of Modus Ponens. All inference rules
can only be used on a whole line, not part
of a line. 3. Two rules cannot be applied
to a single step. 4. Incorrect use of Disjunctive Syllogism; line 6 should be p.
5. Incorrect use of Disjunctive Syllogism
in line 3. All inference rules can only be
used on a whole line, not part of a line.

Exercise 4-7

Note: Each answer below is only one of
many possible proofs.
1. 1. p ∨ q   Premise
    2. (q ∨ p) ⊃ (r ∨ s)
                       Premise
    3. (s ∨ r) ⊃ ~ q / ∴ p
                       Premise / Conclusion
    4. q ∨ p   Comm.,1
    5. r ∨ s   M.P.,2,4
    6. s ∨ r   Comm.,5
    7. ~ q   M.P.,3,6
    8. p   D.Syll.,1,7
2. 1. q ⊃ ~ p   Premise
    2. p / ∴ ~ q   Premise / Conclusion
    3. ~ ~ p   D.N.,2
    4. ~ q   M.T.,1,3
3. 1. p ∨ (q ∨ r)   Premise
    2. (p ∨ q) ⊃ ~ s
                       Premise

    3. ~ r / ∴ ~ s   Premise / Conclusion
    4. (p ∨ q) ∨ r   Assoc.,1
    5. p ∨ q   D.Syll.,3,4
    6. ~ s   M.P.,2,5
4. 1. ~ r · ~ s   Premise
    2. (p ∨ q) ⊃ (r ∨ s) / ∴ ~ (p ∨ q)
                       Premise / Conclusion
    3. ~ (r ∨ s)   DeM.,1
    4. ~ (p ∨ q)   M.T.,2,3
5. 1. ~ r · ~ s   Premise
    2. (p ∨ q) ⊃ (r ∨ s) / ∴ ~ p · ~ q
                       Premise / Conclusion
    3. ~ (r ∨ s)   DeM.,1
    4. ~ (p ∨ q)   M.T.,2,3
    5. ~ p · ~ q   DeM.,4
6. 1. ~ r · ~ s   Premise
    2. (p ∨ q) ⊃ (r ∨ s) / ∴ ~ q
                       Premise / Conclusion
    3. ~ (r ∨ s)   DeM.,1
    4. ~ (p ∨ q)   M.T.,2,3
    5. ~ p · ~ q   DeM.,4
    6. ~ q   Simp.,5
7. 1. ~ r · ~ s   Premise
    2. (p ∨ q) ⊃ (r ∨ s) / ∴ ~ q ∨ t
                       Premise / Conclusion
    3. ~ (r ∨ s)   DeM.,1
    4. ~ (p ∨ q)   M.T.,2,3
    5. ~ p · ~ q   DeM.,4
    6. ~ q   Simp.,5
    7. ~ q ∨ t   Add.,6
8. 1. ~ r · ~ s   Premise
    2. (p ∨ q) ⊃ (r ∨ s) / ∴ ~ q · ~ r
                       Premise / Conclusion
    3. ~ (r ∨ s)   DeM.,1
    4. ~ (p ∨ q)   M.T.,2,3
    5. ~ p · ~ q   DeM.,4
    6. ~ q   Simp.,5
    7. ~ r   Simp.,1
    8. ~ q · ~ r   Conj.,6,7
9. 1. ~ r · ~ s   Premise
    2. (p ∨ q) ⊃ (r ∨ s) / ∴ ~ (p · q)
                       Premise / Conclusion
    3. ~ (r ∨ s)   DeM.,1
    4. ~ (p ∨ q)   M.T.,2,3
    5. ~ p · ~ q   DeM.,4
    6. ~ p   Simp.,5
    7. ~ p ∨ ~ q   Add.,6
    8. ~ (p · q)   DeM.,7
10. 1. ~ r ∨ ~ s   Premise
    2. (r · s) ⊃ (p · q) / ∴ q ∨ t
                       Premise / Conclusion
    3. ~ (r · s)   DeM.,1
    4. p · q   M.P.,2,3

5. q   Simp.,4
6. q ∨ t   Add.,5

11.   1. ~ p ∨ q   Premise
     2. (p ⊃ q) ⊃ (p ⊃ r) / ∴ p ⊃ r
           Premise / Conclusion
     3. p ⊃ q   Impl.,1
     4. p ⊃ r   M.P.,2,3

12.   1. ~ p ∨ q   Premise
     2. (p ⊃ q) ⊃ (p ⊃ r)
           Premise
     3. p / ∴ r   Premise / Conclusion
     4. p ⊃ q   Impl.,1
     5. p ⊃ r   M.P.,2,4
     6. r   M.P.,3,5

13.   1. ~ p ∨ q   Premise
     2. (p ⊃ q) ⊃ (p ⊃ r)
           Premise
     3. p / ∴ q · r   Premise / Conclusion
     4. p ⊃ q   Impl.,1
     5. p ⊃ r   M.P.,2,4
     6. r   M.P.,3,5
     7. q   M.P.,3,4
     8. q · r   Conj.,6,7

14.   1. ~ (p · ~ q)   Premise
     2. (p ⊃ q) ⊃ (p ⊃ r) / ∴ p ⊃ r
           Premise / Conclusion
     3. p ⊃ q   Impl.,1
     4. p ⊃ r   M.P.,2,3

15.   1. p · ~ r   Premise
     2. (p ⊃ q) ⊃ (p ⊃ r) / ∴ p · ~ q
           Premise / Conclusion
     3. ~ ~ (p · ~ r)
           D.N.,1
     4. ~ (p ⊃ r)   Impl.,3
     5. ~ (p ⊃ q)   M.T.,2,4
     6. ~ ~ (p · ~ q)
           Impl.,5
     7. p · ~ q   D.N.,6

16.   1. p · (q ∨ r)   Premise
     2. ~ (p · r) / ∴ q
           Premise / Conclusion
     3. (p · q) ∨ (p · r)
           Dist.,1
     4. p · q   D.Syll.,2,3
     5. q   Simp.,4

17.   1. p · (q ∨ r)   Premise
     2. ~ p / ∴ q   Premise / Conclusion
     3. (p · q) ∨ (p · r)
           Dist.,1
     4. ~ p ∨ ~ r   Add.,2
     5. ~ (p · r)   DeM.,4
     6. p · q   D.Syll.,3,5
     7. q   Simp.,6

18.   1. (p · q) ⊃ r   Premise
     2. (p · r) ⊃ q   Premise
     3. p / ∴ r ≡ q   Premise / Conclusion
     4. p ⊃ (q ⊃ r)   Exp.,1
     5. p ⊃ (r ⊃ q)   Exp.,2
     6. q ⊃ r   M.P.,3,4
     7. r ⊃ q   M.P.,3,5
     8. (r ⊃ q) · (q ⊃ r)
           Conj.,6,7
     9. r ≡ q   Equiv.,8

19.   1. (p · q) ≡ (r ∨ s)
           Premise
     2. r / ∴ p · r   Premise / Conclusion
     3. ((p · q) ⊃ (r ∨ s)) · ((r ∨ s) ⊃ (p · q))
           Equiv.,1
     4. (r ∨ s) ⊃ (p · q)
           Simp.,3
     5. r ∨ s   Add.,2
     6. p · q   M.P.,4,5
     7. p   Simp.,6
     8. p · r   Conj.,2,7

20.   1. ~ p ∨ (q · r)
           Premise
     2. r ⊃ p / ∴ p ≡ r
           Premise / Conclusion
     3. (~ p ∨ q) · (~ p ∨ r)
           Dist.,1
     4. ~ p ∨ r   Simp.,3
     5. p ⊃ r   Impl.,4
     6. (p ⊃ r) · (r ⊃ p)
           Conj.,2,5
     7. p ≡ r   Equiv.,6

Exercise 4-8

Note: Each answer below is only one of many possible proofs.

1.   1. q / ∴ p ⊃ (p · q)
           Premise / Conclusion
     2. p   Assumption
     3. p · q   Conj.,1,2
     4. p ⊃ (p · q)   C.P.,2–3

2.   1. p ⊃ (q ⊃ r) / ∴ (p · q) ⊃ r
           Premise / Conclusion
     2. p · q   Assumption
     3. p   Simp.,2
     4. q ⊃ r   M.P.,1,3
     5. q   Simp.,2
     6. r   M.P.,4,5
     7. (p · q) ⊃ r   C.P.,2–6

3.   1. p ⊃ (q ⊃ r)   Premise
     2. p ⊃ q / ∴ p ⊃ r
           Premise / Conclusion

3. p   Assumption
4. q ⊃ r   M.P.,1,3
5. q   M.P.,2,3
6. r   M.P.,4,5
7. p ⊃ r   C.P.,3-6

4.   1. q ⊃ r / ∴ p ⊃ (q ⊃ (r ∨ s))
      Premise / Conclusion
   2. p   Assumption
   3. q   Assumption
   4. r   M.P.,1,3
   5. r ∨ s   Add.,4
   6. q ⊃ (r ∨ s)   C.P.,3-5
   7. p ⊃ (q ⊃ (r ∨ s))
      C.P.,2-6

5.   1. p ⊃ r / ∴ p ⊃ (q ⊃ (r ∨ s))
      Premise / Conclusion
   2. p   Assumption
   3. q   Assumption
   4. r   M.P.,1,2
   5. r ∨ s   Add.,4
   6. q ⊃ (r ∨ s)   C.P.,3-5
   7. p ⊃ (q ⊃ (r ∨ s)
      C.P.,2-6

6.   1. (p · q) ∨ (r · s) / ∴ ~ p ⊃ (r · s)
      Premise / Conclusion
   2. ~ p   Assumption
   3. ~ p ∨ ~ q   Add.,2
   4. ~ (p · q))   DeM.,3
   5. r · s   D.Syll.,1,4
   6. ~ p ⊃ (r · s)
      C.P.,2-5

7.   1. p · (q ∨ r) / ∴ ~ q ⊃ (p · r)
      Premise / Conclusion
   2. ~ q   Assumption
   3. q ∨ r   Simp.,1
   4. r   D.Syll.,2,3
   5. p   Simp.,1
   6. p · r   Conj.,4,5
   7. ~ q ⊃ (p · r)
      C.P.,2-6

8.   1. r ≡ s   Premise
   2. p ∨ r / ∴ ~ p ⊃ (r · s)
      Premise / Conclusion
   3. ~ p   Assumption
   4. r   D.Syll.,2,3
   5. (r ⊃ s) · (s ⊃ r)
      Equiv.,1
   6. r ⊃ s   Simp.,5
   7. s   M.P.,4,6
   8. r · s   Conj.,4,7
   9. ~ p ⊃ (r · s)
      C.P.,3-8

9.   1. s / ∴ p ⊃ (q ⊃ (r ⊃ s))
      Premise / Conclusion
   2. p   Assumption
   3. q   Assumption
   4. r   Assumption
   5. s   Premise 1
   6. r ⊃ s   C.P.,4-5
   7. q ⊃ (r ⊃ s)   C.P.,3-6
   8. p ⊃ (q ⊃ (r ⊃ s))
      C.P.,2-7

10.   1. r / ∴ p ⊃ (p ∨ q)
      Premise
   2. p   Assumption
   3. p ∨ q   Add.,1
   4. p ⊃ (p ∨ q)   C.P.,2-3

Exercise 4-9
Note: Each answer below is only one of
many possible proofs.

1.   1. ~ q ⊃ (~ p · r)
      Premise
   2. ~ r / ∴ q   Premise / Conclusion
   3. ~ q   Assumption
   4. ~ p · r   M.P.,1,3
   5. r   Simp.,4
   6. r · ~ r   Conj.,2,5
   7.   I.P.,3-6

2.   1. p ⊃ (q · r)   Premise
   2. ~ q / ∴ ~ p   Premise / Conclusion
   3. ~ ~ p   Assumption
   4. p   D.N.,3
   5. q · r   M.P.,1,4
   6. q   Simp.,5
   7. q · ~ q   Conj.,2,6
   8. ~ p   I.P.,3-7

3.   1. p ∨ (q · r)   Premise
   2. p ∨ t   Premise
   3. t ⊃ ~ (q · r) / ∴ p
      Premise / Conclusion
   4. ~ p   Assumption
   5. q · r   D.Syll.,1,4
   6. t   D.Syll.,2,4
   7. ~ (q · r)   M.P.,3,6
   8. (q · r) · ~ q · r
      Conj.,5,7
   9. p   I.P.,4-8

4.   1. (r ∨ q) ⊃ p   Premise
   2. p ⊃ (s · t)   Premise
   3. ~ s ∨ ~ t / ∴ ~ (r ∨ q)
      Premise / Conclusion

► 4.	~~(r ∨ q)	Assumption
5.	r ∨ q	D.N.,4
6.	p	M.P.,1,5
7.	s · t	M.P.,2,6
8.	~(s · t)	DeM.,3
9.	(s · t) · ~(s · t)	
		Conj.,7,8
10.	~(r ∨ q)	I.P.,4–9

5.
1.	~p ⊃ q	Premise
2.	~(~p · q) / ∴ p	
		Premise / Conclusion
► 3.	~p	Assumption
4.	q	M.P.,1,3
5.	~~p ∨ ~q	
		DeM.,2
6.	p ∨ ~q	D.N.,5
7.	~q	D.Syll.,3,6
8.	q · ~q	Conj.,4,7
9.	p	I.P.,3–8

6.
1.	(p · q) ⊃ r	Premise
2.	~p ⊃ r	Premise
3.	q / ∴ r	Premise / Conclusion
► 4.	~r	Assumption
5.	~(p · q)	M.T.,1,4
6.	~p ∨ ~q	DeM.,5
7.	~~q	D.N.,3
8.	~p	D.Syll.,6,7
9.	r	M.P.,2,8
10.	r · ~r	Conj.,4,9
11.	r	I.P.,4–10

7.
1.	p ≡ q	Premise
2.	~r ∨ p / ∴ r ⊃ q	
		Premise / Conclusion

► 3.	~(r ⊃ q)	Assumption
4.	~~(r · ~q)	
		Impl.,3
5.	r · ~q	D.N.,4
6.	r	Simp.,5
7.	~q	Simp.,5
8.	(p ⊃ q) · (q ⊃ p)	
		Equiv.,1
9.	p ⊃ q	Simp.,8
10.	~p	M.T.,7,9
11.	~r	D.Syll.,2,10
12.	r · ~r	Conj.,6,11
13.	r ⊃ q	I.P.,3–12

8.
1.	p · q	Premise
2.	~(p ⊃ q) / ∴ r ⊃ s	
		Premise / Conclusion
► 3.	~(r ⊃ s)	Assumption
4.	q	Simp.,1
5.	~~(p · ~q)	
		Impl.,3
6.	p · ~q	D.N.,5
7.	~q	Simp.,6
8.	q · ~q	Conj.,4,7
9.	r ⊃ s	I.P.,3–8

Exercise 4-10

1. Invalid. 2. Invalid. 3. Valid.
4. Valid. 5. Valid. 6. Invalid 7. Valid.
8. Valid. 9. Invalid. 10. Invalid.

Answers to Chapter 5

Exercise 5-1

1. 'x is a woman'; 'x is a college graduate'; and 'x is stupid' (*or* 'x is a woman'; 'y is a college graduate'; 'x is y'; and 'x is stupid').
2. 'x is a player of the first rank'; 'x entered the tournament'. 3. 'x is a five-legged creature' (*or* 'x is a creature' and 'x has five legs'); 'x is hideous'. 4. 'x is a piece of cheap goods in the store'; 'x is shoddily made'; and 'x is defective'. 5. 'x is a centipede'; 'x is a mammal'. 6. 'x is a human'; and 'x is alive' (*or* 'x is a human'; 'y is alive'; and 'x is y'). 7. 'x is a human'; 'x is an animal'. 8. 'x is a player in the tournament'; 'Emil cannot beat x'. 9. 'x is a member of the L family'; 'x greets y'; 'x remembers the name of y'. 10. 'x is an actor'; 'x is an award winner'; 'x is an Academy Award winner'.

Exercise 5-2

1. 'Bx' = 'x is a biology class'; 's' = 'Susan'; 'Asx' = 'Susan attends x'; 'Tsx' = 'Susan is on time for x': '(x) ((Bx · Asx) ⊃ Lsx)'.
2. 'Nx' = 'x is a new movie'; 'Bx' = 'x is the best movie': '~ (x) (Nx ⊃ Bx)' *or* '(∃x) (Nx · ~ Bx)'. 3. 'Dx' = 'x is a member of the Dean's List'; 'Sxg' = 'x is a student with good grades': '(x)(Dx ⊃ Sxg)'. 4. 'Dx' = 'x is a heavy drinker'; 'Sx = 'x prefers scotch': (∃x) (Dx · Mx)'. 5. 'Ax' = 'x is an atheist'; 'Gx' = 'x believes in god': '(x) (Ax ⊃ ~ Gx) *or* '~ (∃x) (Ax · Gx)'.
6. 'Tx' = 'x entered the tournament'; 'Fx' = 'x is a player of the first rank': (x) (Tx ⊃ Fx). 7. 'Cx' = 'x is a piece of cheap goods in the store'; 'Sx' = 'x is shoddily made'; 'Dx' = 'x is defective': '(x) (Cx ⊃ (Sx ∨ Dx))'. 8. 'Cx' = 'x is centipede'; 'Mx' = 'x is a mammal': '(x) (Cx ⊃ ~ Mx) ⊃ (x) (Mx ⊃ ~ Cx)'.
9. 'Te' = 'Emil is in the tournament'; 'Tx' = 'x is in the tournament'; 'Bex' = 'Emil can beat x': 'Te · (∃x) (~ Tx · ~ Bex)'. 10. 'Lx' = 'x is a member of the L family'; 'Rxy' = x remembers the name of y'; 'Gxy' = 'x greets y': '(x) (y)((Lx · Rxy) ⊃ Gxy)'.

Exercise 5-3

1. Nothing that is male is female. 2. If everything is finite, then something is dead. 3. Not everything that is a canine is a dog. 4. Some canines are dogs *or* Some things are both canines and dogs. 5. Everything is either a friend or an enemy. 6. If every applicant expected that the job demanded a college education, then some applicants were familiar with the writings of Homer. 7. Every member of the O family remembers the name of anyone who owes money to him or her. 8. No one who is not in the tournament has beaten anyone who is. 9. There is no music that all musicians like. 10. All members of the orchestra who know each other intimately like each other.

Exercise 5-4

1. (a) a. (∃x) (Ax · Rx)
   b. (∃x) (Rx · Ax)
   (b) 1. (∃x)(Ax · Rx)/∴ (∃x)(Rx · Ax)
   Premise / Conclusion
   2. Aa · Ra   E.I.,1
   3. Ra · Aa   Comm.,2
   4. (∃x) (Rx · Ax)
   E.G.,3
   Same strategy for deducing a from b.
2. (a) a. (∃x)(Ax · ~ Rx)
   b. (∃x) (~ Rx · Ax)
   (b) For both deductions, the same strategy as in 1 is used.
3. (a) a. (x) (Ax ⊃ Fx)
   b. (x) (~ Fx ⊃ ~ Ax)
   (b) 1. (x)(Ax ⊃ Fx)/∴(x) (~ Fx ⊃ ~ Ax)
   Premise / Conclusion
   2. Aa ⊃ Fa   U.I.,1
   3. ~ Fa ⊃ ~ Aa
   Trans.,3
   4. (x) (~ Fx ⊃ ~ Ax)
   U.G.,3
   Same strategy for deducing a from b.
   But if alternatively:
   (a) a. (x) (Ax ⊃ Fx)
   b. ~ (∃x) (~ Fx · Ax)
   (b) 1. (x)(Ax ⊃ Fx)/∴ ~ (∃x) (~ Fx · Ax)
   Premise / Conclusion

2. Aa ⊃ Fa   U.I.,1
3. ~ (Aa · ~ Fa)
         Impl.,2
4. ~ (~ Fa · Aa)
         Comm.,3
5. (x) ~ (~ Fx · Ax)
         U.G.,4
6. ~ (∃x) (~ Fx · Ax)
         Q.E.,5

For deducing a from b, use Q.E., U.I.,
Comm., Impl., and U.G. in that order.

4. (a) a. (x) (Ax ⊃ Fx)
       b. (x) (~ Fx ⊃ ~ Ax)
   (b) Same as 3.
5. (a) a. (x) (Ax ⊃ Fx)
       b. ~ (∃x) (Ax · ~ Fx)
   (b) Same as 3, variant.
6. (a) a. (x) (Ax ⊃ ~ Px)
       b. (x) (Px ⊃ ~ Ax)
   (b) Same as 3, with negation signs to
       be dealt with.

But if alternatively:

   (a) a. ~ (∃x) (Ax · Px)
       b. ~ (∃x) (Px · Ax)
   (b) 1. ~ (∃x) (Ax · Px)/∴~(∃x) (Px · Ax)
                Premise / Conclusion
       2. (x) ~ (Ax · Px)
                Q.E.,1
       3. ~ (Aa · Pa)   U.I.,2
       4. ~ (Pa · Aa)   Comm.,3
       5. (x) ~ (Px · Ax)
                U.G.,4
       6. ~ (∃x) (Px · Ax)
                Q.E.,5

Similarly for deducing a from b.

7. (a) a. ~ (x) (Fx ⊃ Ax)
       b. (∃x) (Fx · ~ Ax)
   (b) 1. ~(x)(Fx ⊃ Ax)/∴(∃x) (Fx · ~ Ax)
                Premise / Conclusion
       2. (∃x) ~ (Fx ⊃ Ax)
                Q.E.,1
       3. ~ (Fa ⊃ Aa)
                E.I.,2
       4. ~ ~ (Fa · ~ Aa)
                Impl.,3
       5. Fa · ~ Aa   D.N.,4
       6. (∃x) (Fx · ~ Ax)
                E.G.,5

For deducing a from b: E.I., D.N., Impl.,
E.G., and Q. E. in that order.

8. (a) a. (x) (Ax ⊃ Fx)
       b. ~ (∃x) (Ax ⊃ Fx)

(b) 1. (x) (Ax ⊃ Fx)/∴~(∃x)(Ax ⊃ Fx)
                Premise / Conclusion
    2. Aa ⊃ Fa   U.I.,1
    3. ~ (Aa · ~Fa)
                Impl.,2
    4. (x) ~ (Ax · ~ Fx)
                U.G.,3
    5. ~ (∃x) (Ax · ~ Fx)
                Q.E.,4

For deducing a from b: Q.E., U.I., Impl.,
U.G. in that order.

9. (a) a. (x) (Ax ⊃ ~ Px)
       b. ~ (∃x) (Ax · Px)
   (b) Same strategy as for 8, with need
       for a D.N. step in both deduc-
       tions.
10. (a) a. ~ (x) (Fx ⊃ ~ Ax)
        b. (∃x) (Fx · Ax)
    (b) Same strategies as for 7, with need
        for repeated D.N.

Exercise 5-5

1. (a) 'Gx' = 'x grows on trees'; 'Tx' = 'x
       is a tomato'; 'Sx' = 'x is a squash';
       'Ax' = 'x is an acorn'.
       1. (x) (Gx ⊃ ~ Tx)
                Premise
       2. (x) (Gx ⊃ ~ Sx)
                Premise
       3. (x)(Ax⊃Gx)/∴(x)(Ax⊃~(Tx∨Sx))
                Premise / Conclusion
   (b) 4. Ga ⊃ ~ Ta   U.I.,1
       5. Ga ⊃ ~ Sa   U.I.,2
       6. Aa ⊃ Ga   U.I.,3
       7. Aa   Assumption
       8. Ga   M.P.,6,7
       9. ~Ta   M.P.,4,8
      10. ~Sa   M.P.,5,8
      11. ~Ta · ~Sa   Conj.,9,10
      12. ~ (Ta ∨ Sa) DeM.,11
      13. Aa ⊃ ~ (Ta ∨ Sa)
                C.P.,7–12
      14. (x) (Ax ⊃ ~ (Tx ∨ Sx))
                U.G.,12

But if symbolized as:

    1. (x) (Gx ⊃ ~ (Tx∨Sx))
                Premise
    2. (x)(Ax⊃Gx)/∴(x)(Ax⊃~(Tx∨Sx))
                Premise / Conclusion

then deduction may be accomplished by
U.I. (repeated), H. Syll., and U.G.

2. (a) 'Tx' = 'x is a member of the T
family'; 'Rxy' = 'x remembers the
name of y'; 'Sxy' = 'x speaks to y';
'Gxy' = 'x gossips about y'.
1. (x) (y) (Tx ⊃ (Rxy ⊃ Sxy))
Premise
2. (x) (y) (Tx ⊃ (Sxy ⊃ Gxy))/
∴(x) (y) (Tx ⊃ (Rxy ⊃ Gxy))
Premise / Conclusion
(b) 3. (y) (Ta ⊃ (Ray ⊃ Say))
U.I.,1
4. Ta ⊃ (Rab ⊃ Sab)
U.I.,3
5. (y) (Ta ⊃ (Say ⊃ Gay))
U.I.,2
6. Ta ⊃ (Sab ⊃ Gab)
U.I.,5
┌─7. Ta   Assumption
│ 8. Rab ⊃ Sab   M.P.,4,7
│ 9. Sab ⊃ Gab   M.P.,6,7
│10. Rab ⊃ Gab   H.Syll.,8,9
11. Ta ⊃ (Rab ⊃ Gab)
C.P.,7–10
12. (y) (Ta ⊃ (Ray ⊃ Gay))
U.G.,11
13. (x) (y) (Tx ⊃ (Rxy ⊃ Gxy))
U.G.,12

3. (a) 'Jx' = 'x is injured on the job';
'Zx' = 'x is a member of group Z';
'Ax' = 'x is alerted automatically';
'f' = 'Felice'.
1. (∃x) Jx ⊃ (x) (Zx ⊃ Ax)
Premise
2. Zf · ~ Af/∴(x) Jx
Premise / Conclusion
(b) ┌─3. (∃x) Jx   Assumption
│ 4. (x) (Zx ⊃ Ax)
│   M.P.,1,3
│ 5. Zf ⊃ Af   U.I.,4
│ 6. ~ (Zf · ~ Af)
│   Impl.,5
7. ~ (∃x) Jx   I.P.,3–6
Alternatively:
3. ~~ (Zf · ~ Af)
D.N.,2
4. ~ (Zf ⊃ Af) Impl.,3
5. (∃x) ~ (Zx ⊃ Ax)
E.G.,4
6. ~ (x) (Zx ⊃ Ax)
Q.E.,5
7. ~ (∃x) Jx   M.T.,1,6
4. (a) 'Yx' = 'x is a three-year-old horse';
'Tx' = 'x is a thoroughbred';

'Sx' = 'x is a standardbred'; 'Bx' =
'x is eligible for the Belmont
Stakes'.
1. (∃x) (Yx · (~ Tx · ~ Sx))
Premise
2. (x)(Bx⊃(Yx·Tx))/∴(∃x)(Yx·~Bx)
Premise / Conclusion
(b) 3. Ya · (~ Ta · ~ Sa)
E.I.,1
4. ~ Ta · ~ Sa Simp.,3
5. ~ Ta   Simp.,4
6. ~ Ta ∨ ~ Ya
Add.,5
7. ~ Ya ∨ ~ Ta
Comm.,6
8. ~ (Ya · Ta) DeM.,7
9. Ba ⊃ (Ya · Ta)
U.I.,2
10. ~ Ba   M.T.,8,9
11. Ya   Simp.,3
12. Ya · ~ Ba   Conj.,10,11
13. (∃x) (Yx · ~ Bx)
E.G.,12
5. (a) 'Fx' = 'x finishes first'; 'Dx' = 'x is
disqualified'; 'Sy' = 'y finishes
second'; 'Py' = 'y is placed first'.
1. (∃x)(Fx·Dx) ⊃ (y)((Sy·~Dy) ⊃ Py)
Premise
2. Fb · Db   Premise
3. Sm · ~ Pm/∴Dm
Premise / Conclusion
(b) 4. (∃x) (Fx · Dx)
E.G.,2
5. (y) ((Sy · ~ Dy) ⊃ Py)
M.P.,1,4
6. (Sm · ~ Dm) ⊃ Pm
U.I.,5
7. ~ Pm   Simp.,3
8. ~ (Sm · ~ Dm)
M.T.,6,7
9. Sm ⊃ Dm   Impl.,8
10. Sm   Simp.,3
11. Dm   M.P.,9,10
On the alternative correct symbolization of
premise 1 as '(x) ((Fx · Dx) ⊃
(y) ((Sy · ~ Dy) ⊃ Py)),' U.I. would
immediately yield '(Fb · Db) ⊃
(y) ((Sy · ~ Dy) ⊃ Py)', with M.P. following
to arrive at line 5 in the deduction above.
6. (a) 'Feh' = 'Ellen runs faster than
Harry'; 'Fhj' = 'Harry runs faster
than Joanne'.
1. Feh · Fhj   Premise

2. $(x)(y)(z)((Fxy \cdot Fyz) \supset Fxz)/\therefore Fej$
      Premise / Conclusion
(b) 3. $(y)(z)((Fey \cdot Fyz) \supset Fez)$
      U.I.,2
  4. $(z)((Feh \cdot Fhz) \supset Fez)$
      U.I.,3
  5. $(Feh \cdot Fhj) \supset Fej$
      U.I.,4
  6. Fej   M.P.,1,5

7. (a) 'Hx' = 'x is a human being'; 'Rxy' = 'x is entitled to as much respect as y'.
  1. $(x)(y)((Hx \cdot Hy) \supset Rxy)$
      Premise
  2. $Hs \cdot Hj /\therefore Rsj$
      Premise / Conclusion
(b) 3. $(y)((Hs \cdot Hy) \supset Rsy)$
      U.I.,1
  4. $(Hs \cdot Hj) \supset Rsj$
      U.I.,2
  5. Rsj   M.P.,2,4

8. (a) 'Fx' = 'x is a farmer'; 'Ex' = 'x is an executive'; 'b' = 'Bill'.
  1. $(x)(Fx \supset \sim Ex)$
      Premise
  2. $Eb /\therefore \sim Fb$ Premise / Conclusion
(b) 3. $Fb \supset \sim Eb$ U.I.,1
  4. $\sim \sim Eb$ D.N.,2
  5. $\sim Fb$ M.T.,3,4

9. (a) 'Qx' = 'x is a beauty queen'; 'Bx' = 'x is beautiful'; 'Gx' = 'x is a college graduate'.
  1. $(x)(Qx \supset Bx)$
      Premise
  2. $(\exists x)(Gx \cdot Qx) /\therefore (\exists x)(Gx \cdot Bx)$
      Premise / Conclusion
(b) 3. $Ga \cdot Qa$ E.I.,2
  4. $Qa \supset Ba$ U.I.,1
  5. Ga   Simp.,3
  6. $Qa \cdot Ga$ Comm.,3
  7. Qa   Simp.,6
  8. Ba   M.P.,4,7
  9. $Ga \cdot Ba$ Conj.,5,8
  10. $(\exists x)(Gx \cdot Bx)$
      E.G.,9

10. (a) 'Px' = 'x is a politician'; 'Lx' = 'x is a liar'; 'Wx' = 'x is a woman'.
  1. $(x)(Px \supset Lx)$
      Premise
  2. $(\exists x)(Wx \cdot Px) /\therefore (\exists x)(Wx \cdot Lx)$
      Premise / Conclusion
(b) 3. $Wa \cdot Pa$ E.I.,2
  4. $Pa \supset La$ U.I.,1

5. $Pa \cdot Wa$ Comm.,3
6. Pa   Simp.,5
7. La   M.P.,4,6
8. Wa   Simp.,3
9. $Wa \cdot La$ Conj.,8,7
10. $(\exists x)(Wx \cdot Lx)$
      E.G.,9

11. (a) 'Tx' = 'x is a terrier'; 'Px' = 'x is a poodle'; 'Dx' = 'x is a dog'; 'Cx' = 'x is a Cairn'.
  1. $(x)((Tx \lor Px) \supset Dx$
      Premise
  2. $(x)(Cx \supset Tx) /\therefore (x)(Cx \supset Dx)$
      Premise / Conclusion
(b) 3. $(Ty \lor Py) \supset Dy$
      U.I.,1
  4. $Cy \supset Ty$ U.I.,2
  5. $\sim Cy \lor Ty$ Impl.,4
  6. $(\sim Cy \lor Ty) \lor Py$
      Add.,5
  7. $\sim Cy \lor (Ty \lor Py)$
      Assoc.,6
  8. $Cy \supset (Ty \lor Py)$
      Impl.,7
  9. $Cy \supset Dy$ H.S.,1,3
  10. $(x)(Cx \supset Dx)$
      U.G.,9

12. (a) 'Ux' = 'x is a university'; 'Tx' 'x is financially sound'; 'Bx' = 'x is bankrupt'.
  1. $(x)(Ux \supset (Tx \lor Bx))$
      Premise
  2. $(\exists x)(Ux \cdot \sim Bx) /\therefore (\exists x)(Tx \cdot Ux)$
      Premise / Conclusion
(b) 3. $Ua \cdot \sim Ba$ E.I.,2
  4. $Ua \supset (Ta \lor Ba)$
      U.I.,1
  5. Ua   Simp.,3
  6. $Ta \lor Ba$ M.P.,4,5
  7. $\sim Ba \cdot Ua$ Comm.,3
  8. $\sim Ba$ Simp.,7
  9. $Ba \lor Ta$ Comm.,6
  10. Ta   D.S.,9,8
  11. $Ta \cdot Ua$ Conj.,10,5
  12. $(\exists x)(Tx \cdot Ux)$
      E.G.,11

Exercise 5-6

1. (a) $(\exists x)(Cx \cdot \sim Hx)$
  (b) 1. $(x)(Cx \supset Hx) \supset (\exists x)Ux$
      Premise
  2. $(x) \sim Ux /\therefore (\exists x)(Cx \cdot \sim Hx)$
      Premise / Conclusion

3. ~ (∃x) Ux   Q.E.,2
4. ~ (x) (Cx ⊃ Hx)
            M.T.,1,3
5. (∃x) ~ (Cx ⊃ Hx)
            Q.E.,4
6. ~ (Ca ⊃ Ha)   E.I.,5
7. ~ ~ (Ca · ~ Ha)
            Impl.,6
8. Ca · ~ Ha   D.N.,7
9. (∃x) (Cx · ~ Hx)
            E.G.,8
2. (a) (x) Ux
  (b) 1. (∃x) (Cx · Hx)
             Premise
     2. (x) ~ Hx/∴ (x) Ux
             Premise / Conclusion
     3. ~ (x) Ux   Assumption
     4. Ca · Ha   E.I.,1
     5. ~ Ha   U.I.,2

6. Ha   Simp.,4
7. Ha · ~ Ha   Conj.,5,6
8. (x) Ux   I.P.,3-7
3. (a) (x) (Cx ⊃ ~ Hx)
  (b) 1. (∃x) (Cx · Hx) ⊃ (x) Ux
             Premise
     2. (∃x) ~ Ux/∴ (x) (Cx ⊃ ~ Hx)
             Premise / Conclusion
     3. ~ (x) Ux   Q.E.,2
     4. ~ (∃x) (Cx · Hx)
             M.T.,1,3
     5. (x) ~ (Cx · Hx)
             Q.E.,4
     6. ~ (Ca · Ha)   U.I.,5
     7. ~ (Ca · ~ ~ Ha)
             D.N.,6
     8. Ca ⊃ ~ Ha   Impl.,7
     9. (x) (Cx ⊃ ~ Hx)
             U.G.,8

Answers to Chapter 6

Exercise 6-1

1. Inductive generalization. 2. Induction by analogy. 3. Inductive generalization. 4. Induction by analogy. 5. Induction by analogy. 6. Induction by analogy. 7. Inductive generalization. 8. Inductive generalization. 9. Inductive generalization. 10. Induction by analogy.

Exercise 6-2

1. c, d, a, b, e 2. d, c, e, b, a 3. c, b, e, a, d 4. c, a, b, e, d

Exercise 6-3

1. e, b, a, d, c 2. a, b, e, c, d 3. d, a, e, b, c 4. d, e, b, a, c

Exercise 6-4

1. e, b, a, d, c 2. a, b, e, c, d 3. d, a, e, b, c 4. d, e, b, a, c

Exercise 6-5

1. c, d, a, b, e 2. d, c, e, b, a 3. c, b, e, a, d 4. c, a, b, e, d

Exercise 6-6

1. (a) Strengthens by increasing the number of observed cases and increasing the negative analogy among them. (b) Strengthens by increasing the number of observed cases and increasing the negative analogy among them. (c) Destroys the argument by providing a counterexample. (d) Destroys the argument by providing a counterexample. (e) Strengthens the argument by increasing the number of observed cases and increasing the negative analogy among them. (f) Destroys the argument by providing a counterexample. 2. (a) Weakens by increasing the negative analogy between observed and unobserved cases, if one considers the information about Mrs. Kelly's brother-in-law relevant. (b) Strengthens, if one considers party-registration relevant. (c) Strengthens, if one considers party involvement relevant. (d) Weakens by increasing negative analogy between observed and unobserved cases, if one considers the generational history of the families relevant. (e) Strengthens by increasing the number of observed cases and increasing the negative analogy among the observed cases. (f) Weakens, if one considers the information about Mrs. Kelly's brother-in-law and the generational histories of the families relevant. (g) Strengthens, if one considers party registration and political activity relevant. (h) Strengthens, if one considers political activity and the generational histories of the families relevant. 3. (a) Weakens by increasing the negative analogy between the observed and unobserved cases. (b) Weakens by increasing the negative analogy between the observed and unobserved cases, if one considers the type of soap powder used relevant. (c) Weakens by increasing the negative analogy between observed and unobserved cases, if one considers the type of bleach and fabric softener relevant. (d) Strengthens by increasing the number of observed cases. (e) Strengthens by increasing the positive analogy among observed cases and between observed and unobserved cases, if one considers the plant of manufacture, the inspector, and place of purchase relevant. (f) Weakens by increasing the negative analogy between observed and unobserved cases, if one considers the fact that the Corleone's washing machine was a floor model relevant. (g) Weakens by increasing the negative analogy between the observed and unobserved cases, if one considers the size of the machine, and the use use of a certain type of soap powder, bleach, and softener relevant. (h) Strengthens by increasing the positive analogy between observed and unobserved cases and increasing the number of observed cases. 4. (a) Strengthens by increasing the positive analogy between observed and unobserved cases. (b) Weakens by increasing the negative analogy between the observed and unobserved case, if one considers the special program relevant. (c) Weakens by increasing the negative analogy between observed and unobserved

cases, if one considers the colleges applied to relevant. (d) Strengthens by increasing negative analogy among observed cases. (e) Strengthens by increasing the positive analogy between observed and unobserved cases, if one interprets this information as 'all of them scored better than 600.' Otherwise, it would have to be viewed as weakening the argument because it would appear that the negative analogy between observed and unobserved cases is increased. (f) Strengthens by increasing positive analogy between observed and unobserved cases, if one considers grades, college board scores and advances courses relevant. (g) Weakens by increasing negative analogy between observed and unobserved cases.

Exercise 6-7
1. b, a, d, e, c 2. c, b, d, a

Exercise 6-8
1. c, e, d, a, b (Note that 'a' and 'd' are not deducible from one another, so deductive strength strictly cannot be determined. However, 'a' covers a range of 31 percentage points and 'd' only covers 15 percentage points points, so it seems reasonable to say that 'a' is weaker than 'd'.) 2. a, d, b, c

Exercise 6-9
1. (a) Weakens by increasing positive analogy among observed cases and increasing negative analogy between observed and unobserved cases. (b) Strengthens by increasing the negative analogy among observed cases. (c) Weakens by increasing positive analogy among observed cases and increasing negative analogy between observed and unobserved cases. (d) Weakens by increasing positive analogy among observed cases, if one considers the sex of the students relevant. 2. (a) Weakens by increasing the positive analogy among observed cases and increasing the negative analogy between observed and unobserved cases, if one considers watching the same station relevant. (b) Weakens by increasing the positive analogy among observed cases and increasing the negative analogy between observed and unobserved cases. (c) Weakens by increasing the positive analogy among observed cases and increasing the negative analogy between observed and unobserved cases, if one considers the location of the viewers in the sample relevant. (d) Weakens by increasing the positive analogy among observed cases and increasing the negative analogy between observed and unobserved cases, if one considers watching *The Mary Tyler Moore Show* relevant. (e) Strengthens by increasing negative analogy among observed cases and increasing positive analogy between observed and unobserved cases, if one consider the location of the viewers in the samples relevant. (f) Strengthens by increasing the negative analogy among observed cases and increasing positive analogy between observed and unobserved cases.

Exercise 7-1

1. (a) We had a big snow storm last year.
   We had a big snow storm two years ago.
   We had a big snow storm three years ago.
   We had a big snow storm four years ago.
   ∴ We will have a big snow storm this year.

   (b) We had a big snow storm last year.
   We had a big snow storm two years ago.
   We had a big snow storm three years ago.
   We had a big snow storm four years ago.
   ∴ We have big snow storms every year.

   This year is a year.
   ∴ We will have a big snow storm this year.

   (c) A is a little stronger than B.

2. (a) The Smiths own a Fisher receiver-amplifier and get excellent service.
   The Parkers own a Fisher receiver-amplifier and get excellent service.
   The Roberts own a Fisher receiver-amplifier and get excellent service.
   The Mitchells own a Fisher receiver-amplifier and get excellent service.
   The Conners own a Fisher receiver-amplifier and get excellent service.
   The Carters just bought a Fisher receiver-amplifier.
   ∴ The Carters will get excellent service.

   (b) The Smiths own a Fisher receiver-amplifier and get excellent service.
   The Parkers own a Fisher receiver-amplifier and get excellent service.
   The Roberts own a Fisher receiver-amplifier and get excellent service.
   The Mitchells own a Fisher receiver-amplifier and get excellent service.
   The Conners own a Fisher receiver-amplifier and get excellent service.
   ∴ All persons who own Fisher receiver-amplifiers always get excellent service.

   The Carters just bought a Fisher receiver-amplifier.
   ∴ The Carters will get excellent service.

   (c) A may be a little stronger than B.

3. (a) Chimp A engaged in grooming behavior.
   Chimp B engaged in grooming behavior.
   Chimp C engaged in grooming behavior.
   Chimp D engaged in grooming behavior.
   Chimp E engaged in grooming behavior.
   Chimp F engaged in grooming behavior.
   Many chimps in addition to A, B, C, D, E, and F exist.
   ∴ At least one chimp other than A, B, C, D, E, or F will engage in grooming behavior.

   (b) Chimp A engaged in grooming behavior.
   Chimp B engaged in grooming behavior.
   Chimp C engaged in grooming behavior.
   Chimp D engaged in grooming behavior.
   Chimp E engaged in grooming behavior.
   Chimp F engaged in grooming behavior.
   ∴ All chimps engage in grooming behavior.

Many chimps besides A, B, C, D, E, and F exist.
∴ Many chimps besides A, B, C, D, E, and F will engage in grooming behavior.

(c) A is much stronger than B.

4. (a) My grandfather went bald before he was thirty years old.
My father went bald before he was thirty years old.
My older brother went bald before he was thirty years old.
∴ I will go bald before I am thirty years old.

(b) My grandfather went bald before he was thirty years old.
My father went bald before he was thirty years old.
My older brother went bald before he was thirty years old.
∴ All males in my family go bald before they are thirty years old.

I am a male in my family.
∴ I will go bald before I am thirty years old.

(c) A may be a little stronger than B.

5. (a) *Swan Lake* was composed by Tchaikovsky and is a great ballet score.
The Nutcracker was composed by Tchaikovsky and is a great ballet score.
Sleeping Beauty is a ballet score composed by Tchaikovsky.
∴ *Sleeping Beauty* is a great ballet score.

(b) *Swan Lake* was composed by Tchaikovsky and is a great ballet score.
The Nutcracker was composed by Tchaikovsky and is a great ballet score.
∴ All ballet scores composed by Tchaikovsky are great ballet scores.

Sleeping Beauty is a ballet score composed by Tchaikovsky.
∴ *Sleeping Beauty* is a great ballet score.

(c) A may be a little stronger than B.

6. (a) The movie I saw on the *Late Show* yesterday was interesting.

The movie I saw on the *Late Show* the night before that was interesting.
I will see many more movies on the *Late Show* in the future.
∴ At least one movie I will see on the *Late Show* in the future will be interesting.

(b) The movie I saw on the *Late Show* yesterday was interesting.
The movie I saw on the *Late Show* the night before that was interesting.
∴ All movies I see on the *Late Show* are interesting.

I will see many movies on the *Late Show* in the future.
∴ At least one movie I will see on the *Late Show* in the future will be interesting.

(c) A is much stronger than B.

7. (a) Regina is an intelligent woman and reads *Ms.* magazine.
Barbara is an intelligent woman and reads *Ms.* magazine.
Johanna is an intelligent women and reads *Ms.* magazine.
Elizabeth is an intelligent woman.
∴ Elizabeth reads *Ms.* magazine.

(b) Regina is an intelligent woman and reads *Ms.* magazine.
Barbara is an intelligent woman and reads *Ms.* magazine.
Johanna is an intelligent woman and reads *Ms.* magazine.
∴ All women who are intelligent read *Ms.* magazine.

Elizabeth is an intelligent woman.
∴ Elizabeth reads *Ms.* magazine.

(c) A is at least as strong as B.

8. (a) Italy is a European country and has shown aggressive tendencies.
Germany is a European country and has shown aggressive tendencies.
Spain is a European country and has shown aggressive tendencies.
France is a European country and has shown aggressive tendencies.
∴ At least one other European country will show aggressive tendencies.

(b) Italy is a European country and has shown aggressive tendnecies.
Germany is a European country and has shown aggressive tendencies.
Spain is a European country and has shown aggressive tendencies.
France is a European country and has shown aggressive tendencies.
∴ All European countries show aggressive tendencies.

Several other European countries exist.
∴ At least one other European country will show aggressive tendencies.

(c) A is stronger than B.

9. (a) There were interesting people at Joe's last party.
There were interesting people at Joe's party before last.
There were interesting people at Joe's party before the last two.
Joe is having another party tonight.
∴ There will be interesting people at Joe's party tonight.

(b) There were interesting people at Joe's last party.
There were interesting people at Joe's party before last.
There were interesting people at Joe's party before the last two.
∴ There are interesting people at all of Joe's parties.

Joe is having another party tonight.
∴ There will be interesting people at Joe's party tonight.

(c) A is stronger than B.

10. (a) Juan attends Princeton and had combined college board scores over 1100.
Kim attends Princeton and had combined college board scores over 1100.
Pete attends Princeton and had combined college board scores over 1100.
Michel attends Princeton and had combined college board scores over 1100.

Five thousand other students attend Princeton.
∴ At least one other Princeton student had combined college board scores over 1100.

(b) Juan attends Princeton and had combined college board scores over 1100.
Kim attends Princeton and had combined college board scores over 1100.
Pete attends Princeton and had combined college board scores over 1100.
Michel attends Princeton and had combined college board scores over 1100.
∴ All students who attend Princeton have combined college board scores over 1100.

Tony attends Princeton.
∴ Tony had combined college board scores over 1100.

(c) A is much stronger than B.

Exercise 7-2
1. a, c, f   2. a, b, d, e   3. a, c

Exercise 7-3
1. *Inductive argument:*
(a) A bluebird observed in Canada had a beak.
A pigeon observed in New York had a beak.
A red robin observed in Kentucky had a beak.
A sparrow observed in England had a beak.
A raven observed in Russia had a beak.
∴ All birds have beaks.
Arguments b, c, d, and e take the same form as argument a. *Order of decreasing inductive strengths:* b, a, d, e, c.

2. *Inductive argument:*
(a) Frenchie, a miniature poodle, is a carnivore.
Natasha, a Russian wolfhound, is a carnivore.
Pierre, a standard poodle, is a carnivore.

King, a German shepard, is a
carnivore.
Lassie, a collie, is a carnivore.
∴ All dogs are carnivores.

Arguments b, c, d, and e take the same form
as argument a. *Order of decreasing
inductive strength:* c, a, d, b, e.

Answers to Chapter 8

Exercise 8-1

1. *Proximate cause:* v. *Remote causes:* a through u, except b, d, h, l, o, q.
2. *Proximate cause:* t. *Remote causes:* a through s, except b, c, i, k, n, p. Note that, in both examples, it might be possible to give a justification for considering one or more of the excluded events as remote causes.

Exercise 8-3

1. a. Necessary but not sufficient.
b. Neither necessary nor sufficient.
c. Sufficient but not necessary.
d. Sufficient but not necessary (hermaphrodites are neither men nor women).
e. Necessary but not sufficient. f. Neither necessary nor sufficient. g. Sufficient but not necessary (one could use more or less than 6 ounces of orange juice). 2. Probably an overall B average, family income under $5000, and recommendations by two professors are necessary conditions for the scholarship. The conjunction of these three necessary conditions cannot be taken to be the sufficient condition, since student 10 satisfied all three conditions but did not receive the scholarship.

Exercise 8-4

1. Method of agreement: the only structural flaw common to all the malfunctioning sets was the improperly soldered wire. Therefore the presence of this improperly soldered wire was probably a necessary condition for this particular type of malfunction. 2. Method of difference: the only differences between the two groups, as groups, were the presence or absence of fluorine in the drinking water, and the subsequent difference in number of cavities. Therefore the presence of fluorine was probably a sufficient condition for the reduction in numbers of cavities. 3. Method of concomitant variations: expenditure in dollars varies positively with total income, and expenditure as a percentage of income varies inversely (though not perfectly so) with total income. It would not be unreasonable to conclude from this evidence that an increase in income is a necessary condition for an increase in expenditure on recreation and entertainment. 4. Joint method: the suspicious error was present on all the papers of X Fraternity students, and absent from the paper of all students who were not members of X Fraternity. Therefore being a member of X Fraternity was probably a necessary condition for making this particular error on the exam, though it was probably not a sufficient condition. 5. Method of difference: the various groups of chicks differed only in the substance with which they were inoculated (or not innoculated), and their subsequent death rates from the virus. Therefore, since the death rate of group 3 was markedly lower than that of any other group, the vaccine given to this group was probably a sufficient condition of the lower death rate. Vaccines 1, 2, and 4 were also sufficient conditions for lowering the death rate, although they were less effective than vaccine 3. 6. Joint method: the only known factor common to all occasions on which the phone died was the presence of a heavy, driving rain from the east. Consequently, such a rain was probably a necessary condition of this particular pattern of telephone malfunction. Also, given that probably no other factor changed when it was not raining hard from the east, it was probably also a sufficient condition. A more immediate (or less remote) "cause" of the malfunction was the accumulation of moisture in the defective wire. 7. Joint method: the suspect brand of thermostat was present in every case in which the heating system malfunctioned, and absent in almost every case in which it failed to malfunction. Therefore this brand of thermostat was probably a necessary condition of the malfunction. Since at least one such thermostat, however, was not associated with a malfunction, the sufficient cause was possibly not the thermostat itself, but some flaw which was present in most if not all of the individual thermostats of this brand.

Exercise 8-5

1. (1) Method of difference: presumably

the sudden-death victims, as a group, did not differ in other significant respects from the cardiac patients who did not die.

(2) (a) The argument would be strengthened if studies of larger groups— say 1,000 or 10,000—of cardiac patients showed similar discrepancies between the smoking habits of those who did and those who did not suffer sudden cardiac death. (b) The argument would be weakened if it were shown that most of the cigarette smokers among the sudden-death victims had been heavy smokers for ten years or more. (This might, however, provide strong evidence that prolonged heavy smoking is a cause of sudden cardiac death.) (c) It is doubtful that there is any single piece of evidence that would completely falsify the conclusion—or completely prove the truth of it.

(3) 'Cause' is here being used to refer to a sufficient condition. The fact that some nonsmokers are also victims of sudden cardiac death is good evidence that there are other causes as well—that is, that smoking is not a necessary condition.

2. (1) Method of concomitant variations: since the number of rich people and the rate of crime have both increased during the same period, it is assumed that one of the changes is probably the cause of the other. In this instance, the concomitant variation is positive.

(2) (a) The argument would be strengthened if it could be shown that the two factors consistently varied, not only in the same direction, but also at similar rates: for instance, that a ten percent increase in the number of rich people was accompanied or soon followed by twice as large an increase in crime as a five percent increase in rich people. (b) The argument would be weakened if it were found that one or more other possibly significant factors also varied concomitantly with the crime rate—for example, that the

number of people on welfare also increased. It would also be weakened if the relative rates of increase in the two factors already considered were widely disproportionate (contrary to the situation proposed in answer 2a). (c) Again, assuming the truth of the basic data (that both wealth and crime have increased during the same period), it is difficult to suggest any one piece of evidence that would absolutely falsify the conclusion.

(3) 'Cause' is certainly not being used here to refer to a necessary condition, since there is no suggestion that crime occurs only in the presence of wealth. It may be intended to refer to a sufficient condition, but this seems somewhat doubtful, since Quick is at pains to point out an intermediate element in the evidence—namely, that, for the rich, crime pays. It might thus be argued that, for Quick, the sufficient condition of crime is not the existence of wealth but the conjunction of wealth with the existence of a society in which the wealthy can profit from crime.

3. (1) Probably joint method. In the high-polio group, there was a general pattern, or condition, of drinking-whiskey-but-not-beer. In the lower ranks, this condition was reversed. Since other conditions (quality of living quarters, type of duty, and so on) were probably not always the same for the two groups, the method of difference cannot be used in this case.

(2) (a) The argument would be strengthened if it were found that in *every* case of paralytic polio, the affected individual had drunk whiskey and had not drunk beer; or if studies among other population groups in other parts of the world showed a similar pattern. (b) The argument would be weakened if it were shown that certain other possibly relevant conditions were consistently different for the two groups: for instance, that all the officers, and

only the officers, had eaten food from a particular source, or had attended training sessions at a particular place. (c) The conclusion would be falsified if a high-polio group were discovered in which beer rather than whiskey was the usual drink.

(3) 'Cause' is here being used to refer to a necessary condition, which may also be a sufficient condition. However, the evidence does not permit a conclusion as to whether the significant condition is the drinking of whiskey, or the non-drinking of beer or both.

4. (1) This appears to be an application of the joint method. In all the low-MS populations, conditions are favorable for infection in early childhood; no other condition appears to be common to all these populations. This condition is absent in all high-MS populations.

(2) (a) The argument would be strengthened if studies of MS victims and nonvictims *within* any one of these countries or regions showed a similar pattern of early exposure for the nonvictim, early protection for the victim. (b) The argument would be weakened if it were shown that a region of high childhood exposure—such as China, where, as in Japan, human excrement has traditionally been used for fertilizer—had a high rate of MS. (c) The conclusion would be falsified if MS were shown to be caused by a hereditary genetic factor, or by a virus incapable of transmission by means of body wastes. But this can be done only at a relatively abstract theoretical level. It is not clear which, if any, observations would falsify the hypothesis.

(3) 'Cause' is here being used to refer to a necessary condition. Widespread exposure to infection at an early age is seen as probably a necessary condition of a low MS rate; widespread protection from infection at an early age is seen as

probably a necessary condition for a high MS rate; but neither is thereby shown to be a sufficient condition.

5. (1) Method of concomitant variations: the rate of mortality from these types of cancer varied in accordance with the per capita consumption of beer from one state to another.

(2) (a) The argument would be strengthened if records of the individuals who died of these types of cancer showed that a high percentage of the them were indeed beer drinkers. (b) The argument would be weakened if comparison of a group of the cancer victims with an otherwise similar group of nonvictims showed no significant difference in beer-drinking habits. (c) The conclusion that beer causes cancer would be falsified only if it could be shown that no beer drinker had ever had cancer.

(3) 'Cause' is here being used to refer to a sufficient condition.

6. (1) Possible method of agreement: the suggested condition was present in nearly all the cases studied, and it was apparently the only condition (or at least the only one thought likely to be significant) which was present in nearly all. It must be presumed that there is some more proximate cause of these deaths which is itself caused by conditions other than depression, since not all of the 26 victims had this common history.

(2) (a) The argument would be strengthened if all of the victims had undergone physical examinations shortly before suffering their heart attacks, and had shown no medical warning signs of impending heart trouble. (b) The argument would be weakened if all of the victims were shown to have been exposed to a particular and unusual industrial chemical or other possibly hazardous working condition shortly before death. (c) It is not likely, given accuracy of the initial data, that any

single item of evidence would completely falsify the conclusion.

(3) 'Cause' is here being used to refer to a necessary condition. Presumably, there were other employees who also experienced the sequence of depression and arousal, but did not suffer heart attacks; thus, the condition cannot be regarded as sufficient.

7. (1) Method of difference: as a group, the angina patients who received drug treatment apparently differed only in this respect from the angina patients who received surgery, yet the caused event—lowered death rate—was present in the first group and not in the second.

(2) (a) The argument would be strengthened if a larger study group, or one followed for a longer time, showed the same results; or if each drug patient were paired with a surgery patient essentially similar to him in all other respects, and the results still showed lower death rates for the drug patients. (b) The argument would be weakened if it were shown that the drug patients, as a group, suffered from less severe angina than the surgery patients, or from less advanced coronary obstruction. (c) There does not seem to be any one item that could completely falsify the conclusion, given accuracy of the research data.

(3) 'Cause' here is being used to refer to a sufficient condition: the drug treatment is presented as a sufficient condition for the lowered death rate.

8. (1) Method of difference, assuming that the two groups, as groups, differed only in respect to the use or nonuse of marijuana. The experimental conditions were the same for cells taken from both groups.

(2) (a) The argument would be strengthened if a follow-up study showed that the smokers did in fact suffer from a higher disease rate than the nonsmokers, or if studies of larger groups showed similar laboratory results. (b) The argument would be weakened if it were shown that the smokers, as a group, tended to eat less well, get less rest, or otherwise take poorer care of their general health than the nonsmokers. (c) The experiment could be invalidated if it were found that the cultural medium used for cells from the smokers had accidentally been contaminated with a substance inhibiting cell reproduction, but even this would not prove the conclusion to be false.

(3) 'Cause' is here being used to refer to a sufficient condition.

9. (1) Method of difference: the institution of screening was presumably the only change in significant conditions between 1972 and 1973.

(2) (a) The argument would be strengthened if the institution of similar procedures in several other countries were followed by a similar drop in hijackings, or if the procedures were eliminated here and hijackings did in fact increase significantly. (b) The argument would be weakened if it were found that at least some potential hijackers knew of an easy way to smuggle weapons past the screening equipment, but had not done so, or if it turned out that there had in reality been 30 or more attempted hijackings in 1973, but that the knowledge of these had been kept secret. (c) No observations could completely falsify the conclusion.

(3) 'Cause' is here being used to refer to a sufficient condition.

10. (1) Method of concomitant variations: a downturn in the economy is consistently accompanied, or followed at fairly predictable intervals, by rises in the incidence of certain other phenomena.

(2) (a) The argument would be strengthened if were found that all or most of the victims had lost their jobs or otherwise suffered loss of income during the recession. (b) The argument would be weak-

ened if it were found that stress did not, in general, contribute to the likelihood of a heart attack, stroke, or kidney failure. (c) It seems unlikely that any single piece of evidence would completely falsify the conclusion.

(3) 'Cause' is here being used to refer to a sufficient condition. Note, however, that a causal chain intervenes between the recession and the heart attack or other proximate cause of death. The recession itself is a fairly remote sufficient condition.

11. (1) Joint method: when the condition (capital punishment) is present, the supposed effect (low murder rate) is also present; when the supposed effect is absent, so also is the condition.

(2) (a) The argument would be strengthened if reinstitution of capital punishment were followed by a significant drop in the murder rate. (b) The argument would be weakened if it were shown that some other possibly significant condition had also changed during the time when capital punishment was suspended, or that the rise in numbers of murders was about in proportion to the rise in numbers of the general population, so that the murder rate had remained about the same. (c) The conclusion would be falsified if reinstitution of capital punishment were followed by an increase in the murder rate.

(3) 'Cause' is here probably being used to refer to a necessary condition and possibly also a sufficient one.

12. (1) Concomitant variations: the average age of malnutrition symptoms has declined concomitantly with the rise of the trend to bottle-feeding.

(2) (a) The argument would be strengthened if studies of two groups of children, known to be alike in all significant respects except that one group was breast-fed and the other bottle-fed, showed earlier or more

severe malnutrition in the bottle-fed group. (b) The argument would be weakened if it were shown that the bottle-fed children, as a group, and breast-fed children in the same societies showed no difference in malnutrition levels in the two groups. (c) The conclusion cannot be totally falsified.

(3) 'Cause' is here being used to refer to a sufficient condition.

13. (1) Concomitant variations: the degree of memory loss increased as the LSD dose became larger.

(2) (a) The argument would be strengthened if larger doses— say 150 and 200 micrograms—were followed by even greater memory losses. (b) The argument would be weakened if it were determined that none of the subjects had ever used LSD before, and that tests on regular users of LSD showed no significant differences. (c) Assuming accuracy of the data, it is unlikely that any one piece of evidence could absolutely falsify the conclusion.

(3) 'Cause' is here being used to refer to a sufficient condition.

14. (1) Method of difference: the swine, as groups, were presumably alike in all significant respects save the controlled difference in diet.

(2) (a) The argument would be strengthened if similar studies using other animals showed similar effects. (b) The argument would be weakened if the diet containing the "trans" fatty element were shown to contain as well some other possibly active element not present in the diet of the other groups. The conclusion also would be seriously weakened if a similar study using whole margarine, instead of the "trans" fatty element alone, showed no significantly higher degree of arterial damage in the margarine group than in the other groups. (c) The conclusion cannot be falsified in any absolute sense.

(3) 'Cause' is here being used to refer to a sufficient condition.

Answers to Chapter 9

Exercise 9-1

1. Nearer to 0. 2. Nearer to 1. 3. Nearer to 0. 4. Nearer to .5. 5. 0 or at least very near to 0. 6. 1. 7. Nearer to 1. 8. Nearer to .5. 9. Nearer to 1. 10. 1 or at least very near to 1.

Exercise 9-2

1. No—logically inconsistent. 2. Yes— logically consistent. (John may take the course two different semesters, failing the first and passing the second.) 3. No— logically inconsistent. 4. Yes—logically consistent (she could have had a multiple birth—twins, triplets, etc.) 5. Yes— logically consistent. (Both Republican and Democratic candidates may lose, and an Independent may win.)

Exercise 9-3

1. (a) 2/525,000 or 1/262,500.
(b) 10/525,000 or 1/52,500.
2. 156/342,576 or 1/2196 assuming that it is permissible to apply the relative frequency definition to single cases.
3. (a) $\frac{5}{1+5} = \frac{5}{6} = .83$. (b) Assuming that there is no probability of a tie, the odds of losing are .17 or 1 to 5.
4. (a) 4/52 or 1/13. (b) 40/52 or 10/13.
(c) 6/52 or 3/26. (d) 20/52 or 5/13.
(e) 1/52. 5. (a) $\frac{5}{4+5} = \frac{5}{9}$ = about .55.
(b) $\frac{3}{3+1} = \frac{3}{4}$ = about .75.
6. (a) 99,200/100,000 = .992.
(b) 800/100,000 = 8/1000 = .008 assuming that probabilities can be computed for single cases. 7. (a) 15/50 = 3/10 = .3 assuming that probabilities can be computed for single cases. (b) 1/2 = .5. 8. (a) 45/75 = 3/5 = .6.
(b) 30/75 = 2/5 = .4 assuming that probabilities can be computed for single cases. 9. 20/50 = 2/5 = .4.

Exercise 9-4

1. (a) Independent. (b) Restricted conjunction rule. (c) Initial probability of each simple event is 1/6. (d) 1/36.
(e) $P(x \text{ and } y) = P(x) \times P(y) = \frac{1}{6} \times \frac{1}{6} = \frac{1}{36}$
2. (a) Dependent. (b) Restricted conjunction rule. (c) Initial probability of each simple event is 1/52. (d) 1/311,875,200.
(e) P(v and w and x and y and z) =
P(v) × P(w given v) ×
P(x given w and v) ×
P(y given x and w and v) ×
P(z given y and x and w and v) =
$\frac{1}{52} \times \frac{1}{51} \times \frac{1}{50} \times \frac{1}{49} \times \frac{1}{48} = \frac{1}{311,875,200}$
3. (a) Independent. (b) Restricted conjunction rule. (c) Initial probability of each simple event is 1/52. (d) 1/133,225.
(e) P(x and y) = P(x) × P(y) =
$\frac{1}{365} \times \frac{1}{365} = \frac{1}{133,225}$
4. (a) Independent. (b) Restricted conjunction rule. (c) Initial probability of selecting a black ball from Urn 1 is 1/3; from Urns 2 and 3 the initial probability is 1/6. (d) 1/108.
(e) P(x and y and z) = P(x) × P(y) × P(z) =
$\frac{1}{3} \times \frac{1}{6} \times \frac{1}{6} = \frac{1}{108}$
5. (a) Independent. (b) Restricted conjunction rule. (c) Initial probability of drawing a red ball from Urn 1 is 1/3, of drawing a white ball from Urn 2 is 1/2, and of drawing a black ball from Urn 3 is 1/6.
(d) 1/36.
(e) P(x and y and z) = P(x) × P(y) × P(z) =
$\frac{1}{3} \times \frac{1}{2} \times \frac{1}{6} = \frac{1}{36}$
6. (a) Dependent. (b) General conjunction rule. (c) Initial probability of drawing a red ball is 1/3, of drawing a white ball after a red ball is 10/29, and of drawing a blue ball after a red ball and then a white ball is 10/28. (d) 100/2436 or about .04.
(e) P(x and y and z) =
P(x) × P(y given x) × P(z given y and x) =
$\frac{10}{30} \times \frac{10}{29} \times \frac{10}{28} = \frac{1000}{24,360} = \frac{100}{2436}$

7. (a) Independent. (b) Restricted conjunction rule. (c) Initial probability for each person is 1/4. (d) 1/1024.
(e) P(v and w and x and y and z) =
P(v) × P(w) × P(x) × P(y) × P(z) =
$\frac{1}{4} \times \frac{1}{4} \times \frac{1}{4} \times \frac{1}{4} \times \frac{1}{4} = \frac{1}{1029}$

8. (a) Independent. (b) Restricted conjunction rule. (c) Initial probability of each simple event is 1/2. (d) 1/16.
(e) P(w and x and y and z) =
P(w) × P(x) × P(y) × P(z) =
$\frac{1}{2} \times \frac{1}{2} \times \frac{1}{2} \times \frac{1}{2} = \frac{1}{16}$

9. (a) Independent. (b) Restricted conjunction rule. (c) Initial probability of each simple event is 1/4. (d) 1/16.
(e) P(x and y) = P(x) × P(y) =
$\frac{1}{4} \times \frac{1}{4} = \frac{1}{16}$

10. (a) Dependent. (b) General conjunction rule. (c) Initial probability of drawing the first ace is 1/12, of drawing the second ace is 3/51. (d) 1/211.
(e) P(x and y) = P(x) × P(y) =
$\frac{1}{13} \times \frac{3}{51} = \frac{3}{663} = \frac{1}{221}$

Exercise 9-5
1. (a) Mutually exclusive events.
(b) Restricted disjunction rule. (c) Initial probability of drawing a white ball is 5/30, of drawing a blue ball is 6/30. (d) Not relevant. (e) 11/30.
(f) P(x or y) = P(x) + P(y) =
$\frac{5}{30} + \frac{6}{30} = \frac{11}{30}$

2. (a) Not mutually exclusive. (b) Restricted disjunction rule. (c) Initial probability of both coming up heads (by restricted conjunction rule) is 1/2 × 1/2 or 1/4. (d) Not relevant. (e) 3/4 or .75.
(f) P(x or y) = P(x) + P(y) − P(x and y) =
$\frac{1}{2} + \frac{1}{2} - \frac{1}{4} = \frac{3}{4}$

3. (a) Not mutually exclusive.
(b) General disjunction rule. (c) Initial probability of boy living to his twentieth birthday is 9/10, of girl living to her twentieth birthday is 8/10. (d) P(x and y) = P(x) × P(y) = 9/10 × 8/10 = 72/100.
(e) 98/100 or .98.

(f) P(x or y) = P(x) + P(y) − P(x and y) =
$\frac{9}{10} + \frac{8}{10} - \frac{72}{100} = \frac{170}{100} - \frac{72}{100} = \frac{98}{100} = .98$

4. (a) Mutually exclusive. (b) Restricted disjunction rule. (c) Initial probability of each simple event is 4/52 or 1/13.
(d) Not relevant. (e) 4/13 or about .31.
(f) P(w or x or y or z) =
P(w) + P(x) + P(y) + P(z) =
$\frac{1}{13} + \frac{1}{13} + \frac{1}{13} + \frac{1}{13} = \frac{4}{13}$

5. (a) Mutually exclusive. (b) Restricted disjunction rule. (c) Initial probability of each simple event is 1/52. (d) Not relevant. (e) 1/13.
(f) P(w or x or y or z) =
P(w) + P(x) + P(y) + P(z) =
$\frac{1}{52} + \frac{1}{52} + \frac{1}{52} + \frac{1}{52} = \frac{4}{52} = \frac{1}{13}$

6. (a) Not mutually exclusive.
(b) General disjunction rule. (c) Initial probability of drawing black ball from Urn 1 is 1/3, from Urn 2 is 1/6.
(d) P(x or y) = P(x) × P(y) = 1/3 × 1/6 = 1/18. (e) 4/9.
(f) P(x or y) = P(x) + P(y) − P(x and y) =
$\frac{1}{3} + \frac{1}{6} - \frac{1}{18} = \frac{3}{6} - \frac{1}{18} = \frac{8}{18} = \frac{4}{9}$

7. (a) Not mutually exclusive.
(b) General disjunction rule. (c) Initial probability of selecting a red ball from Urn 1 is 1/3, from Urn 2 is 1/3. (d)
(d) P(x and y) = P(x) × P(y) = 1/3 × 1/3 = 1/9. (e) 5/9.
(f) P(x or y) = P(x) + P(y) − P(x and y) =
$\frac{1}{3} + \frac{1}{3} - \frac{1}{9} = \frac{2}{3} - \frac{1}{9} = \frac{5}{9}$

8a. (a) Mutually exclusive events. (b) Restricted disjunction rule. (c) Initial probability of selecting a white ball is 5/50 or 1/10, of selecting a black ball is 15/50 or 3/10. (d) Not relevant. (e) 4/10 or .40.
(f) P(x or y) = P(x) + P(y) = $\frac{1}{10} + \frac{3}{10} = \frac{4}{10}$

8b. (a) Mutually exclusive events. (b) Restricted disjunction rule. (c) Initial probability of selecting a red ball is 20/50 or 2/5, of selecting a yellow ball is 10/50 or 1/5. (d) Not relevant. (e) 3/5 or .60.
(f) P(x or y) = P(x) + P(y) = $\frac{2}{5} + \frac{1}{5} = \frac{3}{5}$

8c. (a) Mutually exclusive. (b) Restricted disjunction rule. (c) Initial probability of selecting a black ball is 3/10, of selecting a yellow ball is 1/5. (d) Not relevant. (e) 1/2 or .5.
(f) P(x or y) = P(x) + P(y) =
$$\frac{3}{10} + \frac{1}{5} = \frac{5}{10} = \frac{1}{2}$$
9. (a) Mutually exclusive events. (b) Restricted conjunction rule. (c) Initial probability of selecting a box with dishes, pots and other kitchen equipment is 2/10, of selecting a box with canned and boxed food is 2/10. (d) Not relevant. (e) 2/5 or .40.

(f) P(x or y) = P(x) + P(y) = $\frac{2}{10} + \frac{2}{10} =$
$$\frac{4}{10} = \frac{2}{5}$$
10. (a) Not mutually exclusive events. (b) General disjunction rule. (c) Initial probability of one adult member in the family is 1/2, of three school-aged children in the family is 3/5. (d) P(x and y) = P(x) × P(y) = 1/2 × 3/5 = 3/10. (e) 4/5 or .80.
(f) P(x or y) = P(x) + P(y) − P(x and y) =
$$\frac{1}{2} + \frac{3}{5} - \frac{3}{10} = \frac{11}{10} - \frac{3}{10} = \frac{8}{10} = \frac{4}{5}$$

Answers to Chapter 10

Exercise 10-1
1. Probably mixed. (It would certainly evoke emotions in others, and it would probably express a feeling.) 2. Noncognitive. 3. Mixed. 4. Mixed. 5. Cognitive. 6. Noncognitive. 7. Mixed. 8. Probably mixed. 9. Noncognitive. 10. Mixed.

Exercise 10-4
1. Apparent. 2. Apparent. 3. Apparent/Verbal. 4. Apparent/Verbal. 5. Real. 6. Apparent/Verbal, or possibly real. 7. Apparent. 8. Apparent/Verbal. 9. Real. 10. Apparent. 11. Real.

12. Real. 13. Apparent/Verbal. 14. Real. 15. Apparent. 16. Real. 17. Apparent/Verbal. 18. Apparent/Verbal. 19. Apparent. 20. Apparent.

Exercise 10-5
1. Apparent. 2. Real. 3. Apparent. 4. Apparent. 5. Real, or possibly apparent. 6. Apparent. 7. Apparent. 8. Apparent. 9. Apparent. 10. Real. 11. Apparent. 12. Apparent. 13. Apparent. 14. Real. 15. Real. 16. Apparent. 17. Apparent. 18. Real. 19. Real. 20. Apparent.

Answers to Chapter 11

Exercise 11-1

1. c 2. c 3. a 4. a 5. a 6. b 7. a
8. a 9. b 10. c

Exercise 11-2

1. The definition 'Man is a rational animal' was originally formulated by the Greeks. 2. The definition ' "Expire" means "die" ' is a synonymous definition. 3. The so-called "domino theory" was used by the administrations of several American presidents in the 1950s and 1960s to justify American involvement in Vietnam.
4. "Law school," says Millard Rund, executive director of the Association of American Law Schools, "is a place where society's generalists are educated."
5. 'Quasar' = df. 'any of various very distant celestial objects that resemble stars but emit unusually bright blue and ultraviolet light and radio waves.' 6. Then Attorney General Elliot Richardson resigned from the Nixon Administration during the "Saturday night massacre" [or simply "massacre"] rather than fire former special Watergate prosecutor Archibald Cox when President Nixon ordered him to do so.
7. All of Descartes' philosophical system follows from the initial argument 'I think, therefore I am.' 8. Henry Ford II suggested a 10-cent-per-gallon tax on gasoline to finance aid to the people most seriously hurt by the recession. "I realize it may have a short-term adverse impact on auto sales," said Ford, "but we will never get a full-fledged recovery in the auto industry if we don't give the nation some elbow room to fight its way out of the recession."

Exercise 11-3

1. Connotative. 2. Synonymous. 3. Enumerative, denotative (unless one believes that numbers are nothing more than numerals, in which case it would be an ostensive definition). 4. Enumerative, ostensive. 5. Connotative, by genus and difference (genus = 'polyhedron'). 6. Operational. 7. Connotative. 8. Connotative, by genus and difference (genus = 'letter of the Hebrew alphabet'). 9. Connotative, by genus and difference (genus = oak). 10. Synonymous. 11. Enumerative, denotative. 12. Operational. 13. Synonymous. 14. Connotative, by genus and difference (genus = 'lizard'). 15. Connotative. 16. Synonymous. 17. Operational. 18. Enumerative, ostensive. 19. Enumerative, denotative. 20. Connotative.

Exercise 11-4

Note: Each answer below is only one of many possible answers.
1. (a) City. (b) New York, Chicago, Dallas, San Francisco. (denotative definition) (c) An inhabited place having a large size and population 2. (a) Film. (b) *Casablanca, 2001: A Space Odyssey, Last Tango in Paris, Play it again Sam* (denotative definition). (c) A representation of a story or series of events by means of a series of pictures projected on a screen in rapid succession, usually with accompanying sound. 3. (a) Meteor (b) At night: Pointing at streaks of light coming from the direction of the constellation Perseus (ostensive definition). (c) A streak of light in the night sky produced by a small particle of matter from the solar system which falls through the earth's atmosphere and burns. 4. (a) Cloth. (b) Cotton, wool, silk, nylon, orlon acrylic (denotative definition). (c) A pliable material made usually by weaving, felting, or knitting natural or synthetic fibers and filaments.
5. (a) Human (noun). (b) Clare Boothe Luce, King Faisal, Queen Elizabeth, James Baldwin (denotative definition). (c) A species of primate which has evolved from the great apes; it is characterized by a highly developed brain and erect carriage; it has developed speech, hands with opposing thumbs which can grasp objects, toolmaking ability and a high degree of social organization. 6. (a) Talkative. (b) That lady over there, Daisy Miller's mother, is very loquacious (ostensive definition). (c) Tending to talk excessively.

7. (a) Trachea. (b) Difficult, if not impossible, to define denotatively. A doctor might give an ostensive definition by pointing to the windpipe of a dissected cadaver. (c) The main tube of a system of tubes through which air passes in and out of the lungs in vertebrates. 8. (a) Backbone. (b) Teacher pointing to the spine of a skeleton in a museum (ostensive definition). (c) A flexible series of connected bones called vertebrae which encloses the spinal cord and provides the central basis of support for the truck of the body of a vertebrate. 9. (a) Jewel. (b) Diamond, emerald, ruby, sapphire (denotative definition). (c) A precious stone, often cut and polished as an ornament 10. (a) Wealthy (b) The following persons are rich: Nelson Rockefeller, John Paul Getty, and the Shah of Iran. (c) Having abundant possessions and especially material wealth.

Exercise 11-5

1. If you place an object in water, and it does not sink to the bottom it is buoyant. 2. If you hold your finger on the side of an object opposite to your eyes and can still see it clearly, the object is transparent. 3. If you place a person with a disease in close and prolonged contact with a group of people, and many persons in the group catch the same disease shortly thereafter, the disease is contagious. 4. If you feed a substance to an organism, and the organism dies, the substance is a poison for that organism. 5. If you divide a number by two and the quotient is a whole number, the original number is an even number.

Exercise 11-6

1. Limited reportive, theoretical. 2. Precising. 3. Stipulative. 4. Persuasive. 5. Limited reportive, theoretical. 6. Reportive. 7. Stipulative and limited reportive, theoretical. 8. Stipulative. 9. Reportive, legal. (This is not a limited reportive definition since the legal meaning of the word 'escrow' is its only meaning.)

Exercise 11-7

Note: Each answer below is only one of many possible answers.
1. A forecast is a prediction. 2. A closed shop is any establishment having only union labor. 3. A politician is an elected official whose primary concern is to stay in power rather than to exercise his power for the good of the people. 4. Context: general definition: Any "work of art" is pornographic which has as its only goal sexual stimulation as an end in itself, without any further educational or cultural purpose or attempt at social commentary. 5. Context: science fiction: Z-rays are electromagnetic waves similar to x-rays, but more powerful, capable of penetrating any known object; as a result they can be deflected only by a strong magnetic field. 6. Context: physics: Acceleration is the rate of change of velocity. 7. Context: Current economic crisis: Any event is 'recent' which has occurred since the beginning of the Arab oil embargo in the fall of 1973. 8. A coup d'etat is the sudden and successful use of political or military power to change or overthrow and existing government. 9. Socialism is that form of government in which the state controls most aspects of the individual's life and personal freedom is severely hampered. 10. Bail: Security given against the future appearance of a prisoner at a specific time and place in order to obtain his release from jail.

Exercise 11-8

Note: Each answer in part (b) below is only one of many possible answers.
1. (a) Noncircularity. (b) A potter's wheel is a horizontal disk which can be made to revolve and on which is placed the clay being shaped by a craftsman.
2. (a) Clarity. (b) 'Bread' means 'Brot'; or point out some loaves or slices of bread.
3. (a) Accuracy (too broad). (b) Perjury is lying under oath or failing to do what has been promised under oath.
4. (a) Accuracy (too narrow). (b) An antenna is a device, usually metallic, for transmitting or receiving radio waves.
5. (a) Affirmativeness. (b) A fresco is a painting made of fresh plaster which is still moist. 6. (a) Clarity. (b) Saccharin is a white powder that tastes sweet like sugar.
7. (a) Clarity (too vague) and accuracy (too broad). (b) Saccharin is a white crystaline solid, used as an artificial sweetener, whose formula is $C_7H_5O_3NS$.
8. (a) Noncircularity. (b) A tuning fork

is a U-shaped piece of metal which always gives off the same tone when struck and is used for setting the pitch of musical instruments. 9. (a) Accuracy (too broad). (b) A novel is a fictional prose narrative, usually long and having a complex plot. 10. (a) Noncircularity (b) An invertebrate is any animal not having a spinal cord.

Exercise 11-9

1. Semantically analytic; true. 2. Syntactically analytic; true. 3. Contingent; undetermined. 4. Syntactically analytic; false. 5. Contingent; false. 6. Syntactically analytic; true. 7. Semantically analytic; true. 8. Contingent; true. 9. Contingent; true. 10. Semantically analytic; false. 11. Contingent; true. 12. Syntactically analytic; true. 13. Semantically analytic; true. 14. Syntactically analytic; true. 15. Contingent; undetermined.

Answers to Chapter 12

1. Begging the question. 2. Straw person.
3. Hasty generalizations 4. Argument
against the person (abusive). 5. False
cause. 6. Argument from ignorance.
7. Argument against the person (tu quoque).
8. Appeal to the people. 9. Argument
against the person (tu quoque). 10. Appeal
to pity. 11. Hasty generalization.
12. Accident. 13. Appeal to force.
14. Appeal to authority. 15. Accident.
16. Appeal to force. 17. False dilemma.
18. Equivocation (or possibly accident).
19. Equivocation. 20. Division.
21. Accent. 22. Amphiboly (or equivocation on 'students'). 23. Irrelevant conclusion. 24. Begging the question.
25. Argument from ignorance. 26. Appeal
to force. 27. Argument against the person
(circumstantial); (possibly accident, or
equivocation on 'kill'). 28. False cause.
29. Appeal to authority. 30. Appeal to
force. 31. Argument against the person
(abusive). 32. Appeal to pity. 33. Argument against the person (circumstantial).
34. Argument against the person (circumstantial). 35. Division. 36. Composition.
37. False dilemma 38. Amphiboly.
39. Equivocation (or accident). 40. Irrelevant conclusion (or possibly hasty generalizations). 41. Argument against the person
(circumstantial, or possibly tu quoque).
42. False cause (or hasty generalization).
43. Complex question. 44. Argument
from ignorance; also ad hominem and
appeal to force. 45. False dilemma
46. Division. 47. Equivocation.
48. Hasty generalization. 49. Irrelevant
conclusion (or false cause). 50. Accent.